MW00489929

STECK-VAUGHN

GATEWAYS TO CORRECT
SPELLING

Fred C. Ayer

STECK-VAUGHN
C O M P A N Y
A Subsidiary of National Education Corporation

Victor Muntean

Acknowledgments

Supervising Editor
Diane Sharpe

Project Editor
Teresa Turner

Design Manager
Sharon Golden

Designer
Priscilla Vogt

Credits
Cover photography © David Muench

Dictionary sample, P. 151: © 1988 by Houghton Mifflin Company.
Reprinted by permission from WEBSTER'S II NEW RIVERSIDE UNIVERSITY DICTIONARY.

ISBN 0-8114-4780-4

Copyright © 1991 Steck-Vaughn Company

All rights reserved. No part of the material protected by this copyright may be reproduced or utilized in any form or by any means, electronic or mechanical, including photocopying, recording, or by any information storage and retrieval system, without permission in writing from the copyright owner. Requests for permission to make copies of any part of this work should be mailed to: Copyright Permissions, Steck-Vaughn Company, P.O. Box 26015, Austin, TX 78755. Printed in the United States of America.

3 4 5 6 7 8 9 10 11 12 13 14 15 POH 00 99 98 97 96 95 94 93

Contents

Contents

Part 2: The Technical Gateway

Practical Group of Spelling Words

To the Teacher

To develop any speller for students beyond elementary school age, two main things must be considered. The first is the selection and organization of a group of words students really need to study and use. The second is the development of activities to help students master and retain the correct spellings of these words.

Word lists and their mastery, however, are not enough. Students must also learn how to correct their spelling errors. This is best accomplished by use of a dictionary. For this reason, students must be taught basic techniques in the correct use of the dictionary.

Gateways to Correct Spelling has been developed with the above concerns in mind. How well it addresses these concerns is indicated by the fact that the sales of this book make it one of the leading advanced spellers in the United States.

It is common knowledge that many students can often correctly spell words on tests but misspell the same words in other written work. This problem of transfer from word-list testing to correct spelling in written work can best be solved by means of written exercises. These exercises must require not only that students have the opportunity to spell a word correctly in context, but also that they develop a technique of proofreading to discover their own mistakes. This latter skill can be acquired by means of exercises in which misspelled words are identified and corrected. *Gateways to Correct Spelling* provides such exercises, necessary not only for immediate recall and reinforcement of useful and frequently misspelled words, but also for solving the problem of transfer from word lists to written work.

FOUNDATIONS OF AN ADVANCED SPELLER

The major facts of organization and the general principle of learning to spell at the upper school levels are so different in this book from those used in other spellers that it seems desirable to discuss them at this point. The details of the methods can be found by carefully studying each lesson.

THE VOCABULARY

Gateways to Correct Spelling includes two sets of carefully selected spelling words: (1) The Basic Group; and (2) The Practical Group.

1. The Basic Group of Spelling Words

The basic group of 720 spelling words constitutes the basic group of spelling words that are attacked vigorously by direct spelling methods in Part 1 of this book. It is the more important of the two sets for poor and average spellers and should be studied by all students as an approach to the more advanced aspects of spelling treated in Part 2. These 720 words cause four-fifths of the spelling errors made by persons beyond elementary school age. Students who master this group of words will, at the same time, develop a method of examining words which will greatly increase their general spelling vocabulary.

2. The Practical Group of Spelling Words

This group reflects two chief principles of selection: (1) commonly used words, in addition to the 720 in the basic list, which are known to give spelling difficulty; and (2) words pertinent to business, literature, and general correspondence which reflect significant principles and techniques of correct spelling and pronunciation. All of these words are arranged in groups to demonstrate practical spelling techniques and best ways of using a dictionary.

THE BEST METHODS

This book, instead of stamping in the old mistakes by use of the same old letter-by-letter drill methods, utilizes the *whole-word, hard-spot* study method. Studies have shown that good spellers do not use the letter-by-letter repetition method. They first see the whole word; then analyze it, or large parts of it, to detect difficult or unusual spots; then with rhythmic sweeps of the eye from left to right, quickly *fuse* the several parts of the word into a *unified whole*. To spell a word correctly, students must look at its parts with sufficient care and detail so that afterward they will be able to see or recall the whole word as a unified group of letters.

Merely printing hard spots is not enough. The learner's attention must be directed to the hard spots and a definite method provided for their speedy fusion into a unified view of the whole word. Good visualization is greatly aided by careful word scrutiny and analysis.

This spelling program anticipates most of the hard spots in spelling and provides additional exercises to remedy difficulties which may be peculiar to individual students. The exercises which accompany each word help the student make an aggressive attack upon the special spelling difficulties in the word. They also aid the student in developing a method of attack for the mastery of all spelling words.

In addition to the dictionary practice afforded by the routine procedure in Part 1, a large share of Part 2 is devoted directly to the more technical aspects of correct dictionary usage. Every spelling and pronunciation presented in this book is based upon one or more leading authorities. Where authorities disagree the spelling or pronunciation best adapted to correct recall has been selected.

To the Student

Experts say that the best way to succeed in learning to spell is to take on responsibility for your own progress. Convince yourself, first of all, that good spelling is a necessity in your education. The knowledge of words is the key to all learning. To study spelling as directed in this book will improve your knowledge of words and ability in writing, in reading, and in speaking. Poor spelling is taken everywhere to be a sign of carelessness and the mark of poor education. It defeats your best efforts in school, and later on in the business world. Good spelling, on the other hand, speeds up your education, makes writing a pleasure, and is an aid to success in social and business life.

The lessons ahead offer you the best set of words and the easiest ways to learn to spell, as determined through thousands of hours of study and experimentation. All you have to do is study with zeal and keep track of your own progress. That is *your* responsibility. How far you go is strictly up to you.

Part One
The Main Gateway

Short Cuts to Basic Spelling

Part 1 presents a series of short cuts to quick mastery of the words which cause four-fifths of all mistakes made in spelling. All users of this book should carefully study the directions which follow.

HOW TO STUDY

Learning to spell a word successfully consists of four phases: (1) you see the word clearly; (2) you identify the meaning and pronunciation of the word; (3) you drill to memorize the word; and (4) you drill to recall the word.

1. How to See a Word Clearly

Most words which appear in Parts 1 and 2 of this book are familiar but "tricky" words. *Gateways to Correct Spelling* presents these words in the best way possible for you to see them clearly. Note, for example, the word *financial* which appears in the first line of Lesson 1 as follows:

financial A budget is a fi nan′ cial plan. Look at the whole word *financial* first. How many letters are there? Spell the word slowly one time. Note the first and last letters. Try to see all of the letters at one glance. If the word is too long, try to see all of the letters in each syllable; *fi, nan,* and *cial.*

Pronounce the word correctly as you look at it in the illustrative sentence, *A budget is a fi nan′ cial plan.* Examine any hard spots printed in italics, such as *cia.* Then pronounce *fi nan′ cial* to yourself by syllables. At the same time, try to see all of the letters in each syllable. Repeat this until you can see *financial* as one word with all the letters in proper order. Now cover the word, and see if you can visualize it correctly. Spell the word to yourself, and check it with the text. If you cannot spell it correctly, study the word as before.

2. How to Identify a Word

Many mistakes in spelling are made because certain words look or sound a good deal like others. For example, students frequently confuse *there* with *their, to* with *too,* and *except* with *accept.*

Gateways to Correct Spelling is arranged to help you identify the word. Each new word is followed by a sentence which illustrates a proper meaning of the word. If you do not recognize the word or are not sure you can pronounce it correctly after looking at it in the illustrative sentence, look it up in the dictionary.

3. How to Memorize a Word

Gateways to Correct Spelling presents special memory aids for most words. Your attention is called to peculiarities in the word, such as the *cia* in *financial*.

The sentences which appear in the text preceded by the heading *MEMO* will also help you remember the spelling. For example, "MEMO: A good vocation has a good vacation."

4. How to Recall a Word

The three phases of studying a spelling word—seeing clearly, identifying, and memorizing—are essential in learning to recall a word later on. Your ability to recall a word accurately will be quickened and strengthened by doing the drills which accompany each lesson. After the preliminary study of each word separately as directed up to this point, take three words at a time for additional practice.

As an illustration of this practice, take the first three words, *financial, owing,* and *vacation*, in Lesson 1 on page 10. After these three words, you will find a special drill in the form of the sentence, *O __ ing to their fi __ an __ __ al situation, they couldn't take a va __ a __ ion.* As you read this sentence to yourself, try to visualize the correct missing letters. If you have any difficulty, look at the complete word in the lesson above. When you can fill in the missing letters mentally without any delay, write them in the sentence containing the three words. Check the spelling at once. If you have made any mistakes, study the hard parts, and test yourself again.

When you have studied all of the twelve words in Lesson 1, work all the exercises that follow. Test yourself by doing the same exercises a week later on a separate sheet of paper.

5. Pretest, Reviews, and Posttest

Before studying Lesson 1, take the Pretest on page 6. This test is not to be graded. The purpose of the Pretest is to help you to spot some spelling weaknesses you may have before study begins.

Each group of six lessons is followed by a Review. When you are sure you have mastered the words in the preceding six lessons, take the Review. Take extra care to study any words you may have missed.

When you have finished all the lessons in *Gateways to Correct Spelling*, take the Posttest on page 234. Your score on the Posttest will indicate what sections of the book you should target for further study.

Answers to the Pretest, Reviews, and Posttest can be found in the Answer Key beginning on page 245.

A. In each sentence, find the misspelled words. Write each word correctly in the blank. If there are no misspelled words, write a *C* in the blank.

_____ 1. Always keep first aid supplies where they are easily acessable.

_____ 2. Mike's teacher said that his school atendence record for this year is poor.

_____ 3. They adopted a cat for their daughter beccause they thought the responsibility would be good for her.

_____ 4. Belinda's favorite flavor of ice cream is choclate.

_____ 5. Ms. Ruiz makes homemade Christmas decerations.

_____ 6. Do you dissagree with the candidate's statement?

_____ 7. Have you foregoten Uncle Kyle's birthday?

_____ 8. Alicia is jelus of her sister's good grades.

_____ 9. The thunderstorm began at midnight.

_____ 10. Is this an orijinal work of art?

_____ 11. It takes great persevereance to learn a new language.

_____ 12. The silk dress is beautiful, but not practicle.

_____ 13. A large cuantity of barbecue was served at the picnic.

_____ 14. His children are eight and ten years of age, respektivly.

_____ 15. The first step in the recipe was to seperate two eggs.

_____ 16. The doctor says his loss of memory is temperary.

_____ 17. The tution charged by state universities is usually quite reasonable.

_____ 18. Wuld you help me?

_____ 19. Drive strait ahead for one mile, and then turn left.

_____ 20. Mario always makes a good first impresion.

Each correct answer is worth 1 point.	Total score: 20 points

B. In each sentence, cross out the incorrect word in parentheses. Then write the correct word in the blank.

1. Adam often asks his friends to (advise, advize) him. _____

2. The president of the company will (autherise, authorize) her to bargain with the labor union. _____

3. I (can't, cant) go to the party tomorrow. _____

4. The seminar improved Jennifer's (communication, comunication) skills.

   _____

5. Is 20 evenly (divisable, divisible) by 4? _____

6. His friends often try to (embarras, embarrass) him. _____

7. Janet will serve (eclairs, ecleres) at the party. _____

8. What time is the (facilty, faculty) meeting tomorrow? _____

9. The attorney's (examination, examanation) of the witness brought many new facts to light. _____

10. Most Americans share many (fundimental, fundamental) beliefs.

    _____

11. Did you hear about the (horrible, horable) train wreck? _____

12. Do you know which words are most often (mispeled, misspelled)?

    _____

13. The photographer went out in the storm to try to get pictures of the (lightening, lightning). _____

14. Mei read a (pamphlet, pamplet) on aging. _____

15. Is it company (policy, pollicy) to provide maternity leave? _____

16. The judge will (pronounce, pernounce) sentence on the convicted men tomorrow.

    _____

17. Do you (recal, recall) who gave us this punch bowl? _____

18. She made a complete (recovery, recovry). _____

Each correct answer is worth 1 point.   Total score: 18 points

C. Each sentence contains one or more spelling errors. Cross out each misspelled word, then write the word correctly above it.

1. I don't know wether the situation would warent legal action.

2. This year Earth Day will coinside with our city's bienial clean-up day.

3. There has been some confuzion over the company's new pollicy on work hours.

4. Does this company have an oficial pollicy against discrimination?

5. The preperation of Indian food requires great pacience.

6. The mayor was ignerint of the agency's corruption.

7. When we all yelled "suprise," Heather shreiked.

8. He claims to be a desendent of George Washington.

9. Can you devize a plan to raise funds for the new jymnasium?

10. Religus freedom is one of the privliges we enjoy in this country.

11. That song has a very unusial rithm.

12. Vilence is never a good solution to a problem.

13. One of the main aceivments of this adminestracion is the reduction of taxes for those in the middle and lower income brackets.

14. Do you like suger in your coffee?

15. The new chiarperson plans to standerdise membership requirements across the nation within the month.

16. David has always been good at fixing machinary.

17. Mebbe the workers will be able to lay the asfalt on the new road this Sunday, so that the traffic flow won't be disturbed during the work week.

18. Preperations for the bufet took two days.

19. The feiry blaze moved straight tward the houses.

20. The existance of rare plant species in that area makes it a prime candidate for federal protection.

Each correct answer is worth 1 point.   Total score: 20 points

D. The following letter contains many spelling errors. Cross out each misspelled word. Then write the word correctly above the misspelled word.

Dear Sirs,

I've discovered that some of your products contain larger quanttities of a hazardous chemical than is alowable. As the cherperson of Consumors for the Environment, I'm especialy concerned about the effect large ammounts of this chemical will have on the environment.

Our contry's citizens must use their influance as consummers to stop pollution before ireperable harm is done. Many customors now use their nolege of environmental concerns to choose products.

I am asking for your co-operacion in changing your products to eliminate hazardous chemicals. I apreciate innything you can do towarrd making your products safer.

Sincerely yers,

Each correct answer is worth 1 point.	Total score: 17 points

E. In each group of words, cross out any misspelled words. Then write each word correctly in the blank. If there are no misspelled words, write a _C_ in the blank.

1. sachel	ignorant	decoration	_____
2. advise	bachaler	misspell	_____
3. policy	fiery	viel	_____
4. nevertheless	sissors	grammar	_____
5. carying	horrible	coincide	_____
6. interprise	knowledge	would	_____
7. warrant	rhythm	hieght	_____
8. yours	desendant	faculty	_____
9. anything	impression	drownned	_____
10. leger	practical	violence	_____

Each correct answer is worth 1 point.	Total score: 10 points

LESSON 1

Budgets

It is important that you study each word as directed in the "How to Study" section on page 4. The heading *Memo*, as used below and elsewhere, introduces a catchy saying to help you remember a spelling. In sentences with missing letters, visualize the whole word, and write in the missing letters.

1. financial A budget is a fi nan′ *cia*l plan.
Note the *cia* in *financial*. Compare *special, commercial*.

2. owing I ended the month ow′ing $45.00 on my credit card.
Omit the *e* in *owing*. Compare *owe, owing; make, making*.

3. vacation The Salazars needed to try to figure a va ca′ *tio*n into their budget.
MEMO: A good vocation has a good vacation.

■ O __ ing to their fi __ an __ __ al situation, they couldn't afford to take a family va __ a __ ion last year.

4. balance He tried his best to bal′*ance* his checkbook.
Note the *ance* in *balance*. Compare *attendance, resistance*.

5. paid When all their bills were pa*i*d, the Yamamotos only had $20.00 left.
Compare *pay, paid; lay, laid.* MEMO: Paid off and laid off

6. account Eva Robles tried to balance her checking a*c* count′.
Note the *cc* in *account*. MEMO: An accurate account

■ Maria p __ __ d the b __ __ __ __ ce on our telephone a __ c __ __ nt.

7. knew Christopher *k*new that he couldn't afford a vacation this year.
Distinguish *knew* from *new*. MEMO: He knew his new knife.

8. just If she could just save a little more money, they might be able to afford a vacation.
Do not pronounce *just "jest."* MEMO: Just a junior in June

9. always Emilio al′*ways* tried to pay his bills in total each month.

■ Erin __ __ ew she should al __ __ ys spend j __ st what she could afford.

10. against The tight budget made him decide a ga*i*nst′ buying the new car.
Study the *ai* sounds in *against (e), certain (i), pain (a)*.

11. develop Sarah decided to de vel′op a budget for her family.

12. decision Their de ci′ *sio*n was to save more money from their paycheck each month so they could afford a vacation next year.
Note the one *c* and one *s* in *decision*. Compare *precision, vision*.

■ After the new budget was d __ v __ lo __ ed, the committee made a de __ i __ ion ag __ __ nst buying new office furniture.

☐ EXERCISE I

Write each italicized word correctly in the first blank. In the second blank, write the word or phrase in dark type that most nearly means the opposite of the word.

1. *against:* **withdrawn, for, secondary** _____ _____

2. *decision:* **response, indecision, relevant** _____ _____

3. *owing:* **debt, money, paying** _____ _____

4. *vacation:* **work, travel, leisure** _____ _____

5. *always:* **nothing, nowhere, never** _____ _____

6. *balance:* **to make equal, to make uneven,** _____ _____
to make balloons

7. *develop:* **to begin, to destroy, to figure** _____ _____

☐ EXERCISE II

In each sentence, find any misspelled words. Write each word correctly in the blank. If there are no misspelled words, write a *C* in the blank.

_____ 1. According to my ledger, this acountt has been paid in full.

_____ 2. Jest do as I say!

_____ 3. Kristen new what she must do.

_____ 4. I doubt that the balance of Mr. Ratto's debt will ever be paid in full.

_____ 5. Just remember that whatever decicion you make, you must stick to it.

_____ 6. When Marta went on vacation, she left oweing a month's rent on her apartment.

_____ 7. One must fight for or against the issues in this political campaign.

_____ 8. She is an excellent finantial manager.

_____ 9. He enjoyed his vacacion so much that he decided not to come home.

_____ 10. All ways pay your bills on time.

Dieting

Study each word carefully. In the sentences with missing letters, visualize the whole word, and write in the missing letters.

1. **busy**
Amy was often too b*us'*y to plan nutritious meals.
Spell *busy* with one *s*. Compare *business, busily*.

2. **buy**
It was faster to b*uy* junk food.
It is *buy*, not *by*. MEMO: She was too busy to buy the blouse.

3. **copy**
She got a cop*'y* of a diet plan at her doctor's office.
Note the single *p* in *copy*. Compare *copying*; contrast *poppy*.

■ Abdul tries to b _u_ y healthful food even when he is b _u_ s _y_ because he knows his younger brother will co _p_ _y_ him.

4. **losing**
Los*'ing* fifteen pounds before his vacation was his goal.
Lose loses an *e* in *losing*. See also *owing, mowing, having*.

5. **coming**
Isabel's relatives are com*'ing*, and it will be hard for her to diet.
Note the omitted *e* in *coming*. Compare *come, coming; ride, riding*.

6. **Saturday**
On Sat*'ur* day, Michael bought a calorie chart at the mall.
Saturday is always capitalized. Note the *ur* in *Saturday*.

■ She is co _m_ _i_ ng on Sat _u_ _r_ day for the first time since lo _s_ _i_ ng 30 pounds.

7. **handful**
He was only allowed a hand*'ful* of nuts.
Note that *full* changes to *ful* in *handful*. Compare *useful, grateful*.

8. **bury**
She decided to b*ur'*y the candy in the pantry so her husband wouldn't be tempted to cheat on his diet.
Note the one *r* in *bury*. See also *busy, copy, duly*.

9. **having**
Hav*'ing* to go on a diet is not fun.

■ He felt so guilty after ha _v_ _i_ ng a handf _u_ _l_ of candy that he decided to b _u_ r _y_ the rest of the box in the garbage can.

10. **half**
Please give me ha*l*f of the orange.
Focus attention on the *l* in *half*. Compare *calf, halfback*.

11. **duly**
Having gained two pounds, she felt du*'ly* frustrated.
There is only one *l* in *duly*. Compare *truly, unruly*.

12. **truly**
He tru*'ly* wanted to lose the weight.
Compare *true, truly; due, duly; blue, bluing*.

■ He tr _u_ _l_ _y_ stuck to his diet, and he du _l_ _y_ lost ha _l_ f of his extra weight.

☐ EXERCISE I

In each sentence, cross out the incorrect word in parentheses. Then write the correct word in the blank.

1. (Half—Halve) a loaf is often much better than none.

_____

2. Are you (comeing—coming) to the luncheon?

_____

3. Lupe was much too (bussy—busy) to take a break this morning.

_____

4. (Loseing—Losing) the tennis match was a blow to Susan's ego.

_____

5. The concert on (Saterday—Saturday) night has been sold out for months.

_____

6. He sprinkled a (handfull—handful) of walnuts over the chocolate ice cream.

_____

7. Could I borrow a (coppy—copy) of the morning newspaper?

_____

8. (Haveing—Having) to work late is never fun.

_____

9. He (truely—truly) believed that it would turn out for the best.

_____

10. The employees will be (duely—duly) rewarded.

_____

☐ EXERCISE II

Write the correct word in each blank. Choose from the words below.

| half | duly | bury | copy | losing | handful |
| having | truly | buy | busy | coming | Saturday |

1. Receiving the prize is only _____half_____ the fun of _____ won.

2. She was too _____busy_____ to _____coming_____ the contract.

3. He was afraid of _____losing_____ the _____handful_____ of change.

4. Melissa was _____coming_____ to visit on _____Saturday_____.

5. They _____duly_____ arranged to _____bury_____ the body.

6. The sweater she found on sale was _____truly_____ a good _____buy_____.

13

Grocery Shopping

The words in this lesson are very often confused with one another. In the sentences with missing letters, visualize the whole word, and write in the missing letters.

1. to   Elena went to the grocery store every Friday.
MEMO: To go to town to give to the needy

2. two   Lettuce was two for the price of one.
Two is the correct spelling of the numeral *2*.

3. too   The asparagus was much too expensive to buy that day.
Too also means *also*. Emily cried, *too*. MEMO: Too much to do

■ **The ice cream wasn't t __ __ expensive, so they decided t __ buy t __ __ gallons.**

4. there   There, on aisle eight, were her favorite crackers.
Note the *here* in *there*. Do not confuse *there* with *they're*.

5. their   Their grocery prices were generally low.
The *heir* in *their* suggests possession. It's *their* business.

6. therefore   The spinach was on sale; there'fore he bought two packages.
Always put three *e*'s in *therefore*. Compare *wherefore*.

■ **The grocery store near th __ i __ house has high prices; th __ __ ef __ r __, they don't shop th __ __ __.**

7. its   The jar had lost its label.
The word *its* is the possessive case of *it*.

8. it's   It's almost time for the grocery store to close.
The word *it's* is a contraction of *it is*.

9. itself   It wasn't the ice cream it self' that made their bill high, but the fudge topping and nuts they bought to go with it.
The word *itself* combines *it* and *self*. Compare *himself, herself*.

■ **I __ __ not the potato it __ e __ __ which is high in calories, but the butter and sour cream you use to improve it __ taste.**

10. write   It helps to write out a grocery list.
Center attention on the *wr* beginning of *write*. Compare *wrist*.

11. right   The toothpaste is on the aisle to your right.
Consult your dictionary on this puzzler: "Write *rite* right."

12. written   His grocery list was not writ'ten neatly.
Note the two *t*'s in *written*. Compare *bite, bitten; smite, smitten*.

■ **Wr __ __ __ the check r __ g __ t, so she can read what you've wr __ __ __ __ __.**

☐ EXERCISE I

Each sentence contains one or more spelling errors. Cross out each misspelled word, then write the word correctly above it.

1. Its to bad that their were no writen instructions for us to follow.

2. Only too of the students got the write answer.

3. Chiang and Mei forgot there tickets; therfore, they couldn't go too the concert.

4. Its lovely to watch the kitten bathing itselff in the sunlight.

5. Their are letters to right and packages to mail before we can finish this project.

6. Too bluebirds flew away, but one had broken it's wing.

7. Too get their, turn write at the second stop sign.

☐ EXERCISE II

In each sentence, cross out the incorrect word in parentheses. Then write the correct word in the blank.

1. Did you find the (written—writen) message difficult to understand?

_____

2. Whichever of the (too—two) answers is correct, write it carefully.

_____

3. (Too—To) know oneself is to discover the meaning of life.

_____

4. Jacob wanted us all (there—their) for the beginning of the performance.

_____

5. (Two—Too) many crooks never learn that crime does not pay.

_____

6. Each pen comes in a package with (it's—its) matching pencil.

_____

7. Fortunately, the damage to the engine (it's self, itself) was minimal.

_____

Dress for Success

You will not learn to spell these words merely by reading the exercises. Study each word carefully. In the sentences with missing letters, visualize the whole word, and write in the missing letters.

1. **style**   Makoto dresses in the latest styl*e*.
Put a *y* in your *style*. Compare *stylish*; contrast *while*.

2. **stretch**   The elastic allowed the material to stre*t*ch.
Note the *tch* in *stretch*. Compare *scratch, itch.*

3. **waist**   The wa*i*st of the old pair of pants was quite small.

■ This st __ l __ of dress will str __ __ __ h at the w __ __ st.

4. **flies**   The buyer fli*e*s to New York for many of the fashion shows.
Compare *fly, flies; cry, cries; supply, supplies.*

5. **except**   They had the shirt in every size ex *cept'* his.
Distinguish *except* from *accept*. STUDY: No one would *accept* a bribe *except* a person who is willing to break the law.

6. **which**   *Wh*ich scarf looks best with this blouse?
Focus on the *wh* in *which*. Compare *where, when, what.*

■ She wears her uniform, w __ ich is flattering, when she fl __ __ s, e __ __ __ __ pt when she's off duty.

7. **whom**   To *w*hom do these gloves belong?
Use the correct forms: *to whom, for whom, by whom.*

8. **whose**   *Wh*ose earrings are these?
Do not confuse *whose* with the contraction *who's.*

9. **led**   The salesperson led the customer to the sale rack.
You *lead* a horse now; you *led* the horse yesterday.

■ W __ ose dress l __ d the fashion show, and by __ __ om was it bought?

10. **either**   I wear *ei'* ther the red or the blue tie with that suit.
STUDY: I can see an *i* in *either* with either eye.

11. **until**   The store is open un til' 9:00 this evening.
Note carefully the one *l* in *until*. Contrast *still, till.*

12. **maybe**   Ma*y'* be I should buy both dresses.
Observe that *maybe* is a combination of *may* and *be.*

■ I can wear e __ __ her jeans or a suit on my new job, but m __ __ be I should wear a suit unt __ __ I find out what is appropriate.

16

☐ EXERCISE I

Write the correct word in each blank. Choose from the words below.

| maybe | except | led | whose | stretch | which |
| until | either | waist | whom | flies | style |

1. An acrobat _____ through the air with the grace of a swooping bird.

2. Juan could hardly wait _____ the packages had arrived.

3. _____ one book or the other will win first prize in the contest.

4. Did you see the old movie based on Hemingway's novel, *For _____ the Bell Tolls*?

5. I often read fashion magazines to keep up with what is in _____ .

6. There was no solution to our problem _____ the one Ling suggested.

7. If you _____ a rubber band too far, it will break.

8. Bend from the _____ to do the exercise properly.

9. There is no doubt in my mind who _____ us to safety.

10. _____ of the two problems did you find easier?

11. _____ the child's dog will return when it gets dark.

12. Jessica could not find the man _____ leather jacket was found in the gymnasium last night.

☐ EXERCISE II

Arrange the following words in correct alphabetical order. Check the spelling of each word as you write it.

| waist | whom | where | which |
| want | when | went | whose |

1. _____

2. _____

3. _____

4. _____

5. _____

6. _____

7. _____

8. _____

Health Care

Consult a dictionary for the correct pronunciation of each word that follows. Study each word carefully. In the sentences with missing letters, visualize the whole word, and write in the missing letters.

1. **severe**   He had a se ver*e'* headache.
                   Note the *ever* in *severe*. Accent the last syllable.

2. **cough**   He went to the drugstore for co*ugh* medicine.
                   Focus on the *ough* in *cough*. MEMO: Enough of a rough cough

3. **ache**   Her tooth began to a*che* badly.
                   Note the *che* in *ache*. Contrast *aching*.

■ **The sick child had a se __ er __ c __ __ g __ and an __ c __ __ in her stomach.**

4. **hoarse**   The speaker was too ho*arse* to talk.
                   MEMO: A hoarse roar from the coarse boar

5. **stomach**   She felt a sharp pain in her stom'a*ch*.
                   Note the *tom* in *stomach*. Stress the *a* in *stomach*.

6. **accolade**   The nurse received an ac'co lade' for his caring attitude.
                   Note the double *c* in *accolade*. MEMO: Orangeade,
                   lemonade, accolade

■ **A h __ __ rs __ voice and an upset st __ ma __ __ kept him from receiving the ac __ o __ __ de.**

7. **hospital**   She was rushed to the hos'pit al.
                   Compare *vital*; contrast *pistol*.

8. **physician**   The *phy* si'*ci*an recognized the symptoms at once.
                   There is a *y* in *physician*. Compare *physical, musician*.

9. **once**   Take this vitamin *once* a day.

■ **The hosp __ t __ __ ph __ __ ic __ __ n treated him at on __ __.**

10. **benefited** The child ben'e fit'ed from the treatment.
                   Stress the three *e*'s in *benefited*. Note the single *n, f,* and *t*.

11. **medicine**   This med'*i* cine will usually relieve cold symptoms quickly.
                   Stress the two *i*'s in *medicine*. Focus attention on the *cine*.

12. **immediately** He dialed 911 i*m* me'di ate ly after the accident.
                   Note the two *m*'s and the final silent *e* in *immediately*.

■ **The patient ben __ fit __ __ from the med __ c __ __ __ almost i __ __ ediat __ __ __.**

☐ EXERCISE I

In each sentence, find any misspelled words. Write each word correctly in the blank. If there are no misspelled words, write a *C* in the blank.

_____ 1. Penicillin is one of the medicines which has greatly bennefited humanity in the last fifty years.

_____ 2. If your throat is sore and you are horse, you might be suffering from a virus.

_____ 3. The physican thought Matthew's aches and pains warranted putting him in the hospital.

_____ 4. Did you experience a sharp ache in the region of the stomech?

_____ 5. I knew imediately that there had been a terrible mistake.

_____ 6. The firefighter received an accolade for her prompt first aid.

_____ 7. Drive slowly through the hospitel zone.

_____ 8. Keep on taking the medcine until it's gone.

☐ EXERCISE II

Write the correct word in each blank. Choose from the words below.

immediately	benefited	hospital	stomach	ache	severe
medicine	physician	accolade	hoarse	cough	

1. Dr. Garcia thought that the _____ she prescribed should have

   _____ Alicia more quickly.

2. Once the hero was identified, the mayor gave him an _____.

3. A conscientious _____ will try to determine the symptoms of a

   _____ disease as quickly as possible.

4. "If your head should continue to _____, it would be wise to go to the

   _____ for a checkup," said the doctor.

5. If your throat is sore and you develop a _____, you should

   _____ gargle with warm salt water.

6. Although Tony had no temperature, he was _____ and had an

   upset _____.

Child Care

The different parts of each lesson reinforce each other. It is important to study the entire lesson. Study each word carefully. In the sentences with missing letters, visualize the whole word, and write in the missing letters.

1. **heard**   She he*ar*d the baby begin to cry.
                  Note the *ear* in *hear* and *heard*.

2. **here**   The babysitter should be her*e* at 6 P.M.
                  Do not confuse *here* with *hear*. *Here* and *there*

3. **friend**   She often got child care tips from her best fr*ie*nd.
                  Visualize the *ie* in *friend*. Note the two *i*'s in *friendship*.

■ My fr __ __ nd came her __ as soon as he he __ rd that I needed a babysitter.

4. **says**   The teacher s*ays* that my son is doing well.
                  Compare I *say*, he *says*. Note the past tense: she *said*.

5. **weigh**   The nurse will w*eigh* the baby now.
                  Compare *weigh*, *weight*. Remember the *eigh*t in *weight*.

6. **coarse**   We dismissed the babysitter because of her co*arse* language.
                  Do not confuse *coarse* with *course*. Think of coarse sand.

■ The doctor's co __ rs __ manners w __ __ __ h on my mind, but she s __ __ s she will be gentle with my daughter.

7. **wait**   They had to wa*i*t to see the doctor.
                  Center on the *ai* in *wait*. MEMO: Wait for the bait.

8. **awful**   The bruise on the child's forehead was aw'ful.
                  Awful is shortened from *awe* and *full*. Compare *handful*.

9. **because**   The mother kept her son indoors be c*ause*' he had a cold.
                  Note carefully the *au* in *because*. Compare *pause*.

■ The little girl had to wa __ t to go outside bec __ __ s __ of the aw __ u __ storm.

10. **usually**   The little boy u'*su al* ly looked forward to going to school.
                  Note the two *u*'s and two *l*'s in *usually*. Compare *awfully*.

11. **break**   Stop swinging on that branch, or it will br*eak*.
                  Distinguish *break* from *brake*.

12. **least**   At le*ast* the shot should keep him from getting the measles.
                  Note the *east* in *least*. MEMO: At least the beast could eat a feast.

■ The teacher us __ a __ ly gave the children a br __ __ k of at l __ __ st ten minutes.

20

☐ EXERCISE I

In each sentence, cross out the incorrect word in parentheses. Write the correct word in the blank.

1. That china is hard to replace, so be careful not to (break—brake) a piece of it.

_____

2. Why couldn't Amanda (weight—wait) long enough for the message to arrive?

_____

3. "Have you (herd—heard) any news from the hikers?" Enrique asked.

_____

4. "Nicole seldom finishes a job before she begins another," Mei (says—seys).

_____

5. I think that it would be better to (weigh—weight) the sand before it is dumped at the

construction site. _____

6. Tatsuo couldn't come to the meeting (becuse—because) he was waiting for an

important phone call. _____

7. He usually exercises for at (lest—least) an hour, but last night he only spent thirty

minutes at the gym. _____

☐ EXERCISE II

Write each italicized word correctly in the first blank. In the second blank, write the word or phrase in dark type that most nearly means the opposite of the word.

1. *friend:*   **buddy, relative, enemy**   _____   _____

2. *least:*   **best, worst, most**   _____   _____

3. *awful:*   **terrible, wonderful, bad**   _____   _____

4. *coarse:*   **fine, rough, pretty**   _____   _____

5. *here:*   **at home, there, nearly**   _____   _____

6. *usually:*   **frequently, hardly ever, often**   _____   _____

A. The following business letter contains many spelling errors. Cross out each misspelled word. Write the word correctly above the misspelled word.

Dear Mr. Gray:

I am writing two you in an attempt to correct the ballance in my bank acount. Their appears to be an awfull mistake. I am sending you a coppy of the financial statement that I received last Saterday. It could not be write baccause, accept for one check in the amount of $22.95, I have not writen any other checks this month.

I allways make sure I at leased know the total amount I have each month, no matter how busie I am. May be your computer jest made an error.

Please check to see if their is an erorr, and let me know your desision. I will be comming downtown next Monday. Would it help for me to see you in person?

Sincerely yours,

Each correct answer is worth 2 points.	Total score: 40 points.

B. In each sentence, find any misspelled words. Write each word correctly in the blank. If there are no misspelled words, write a *C* in the blank.

_____ **1.** The dog tried to berry its bone.

_____ **2.** Did she decide to by that sweater?

_____ **3.** The townspeople gave an accolade to the hero.

_____ **4.** The letter from her friend ended with the phrase "Yours trully."

_____ **5.** We were upset to learn that we were loseing our neighbors.

_____ **6.** Immediattely report any disturbances to the police.

_____ **7.** Wiegh each barrel carefully, and store it in the cellar.

_____ **8.** The guard lead the prisoner to his cell.

Each correct answer is worth 3 points.	Total score: 24 points.

C. In each sentence, cross out the incorrect word in parentheses. Then write the correct word in the blank.

1. (It's—Its) raining very hard.

_____

2. Where are you going on (vacacion—vacation)?

_____

3. He's coming, (two—too).

_____

4. Will the workers bring (there—their) tools?

_____

5. Be sure to take your (medicine—medcine).

_____

6. The volunteers will be arriving (hear—here) immediately.

_____

7. Does your head (ache—ake)?

_____

8. Did Tim (break—brake) his leg when he fell?

_____

9. The dog's fur was very (coarse—course).

_____

10. (Witch—Which) of the candidates will be elected?

_____

11. Tell me (onse—once) more.

_____

12. Is Dr. Smith your (physician—phisician)?

_____

Each correct answer is worth 2 points.	Total score: 24 points.

D. In each group of words, cross out any misspelled words. Then write each word correctly in the blank. If there are no misspelled words, write a _C_ in the blank.

1. whom	style	servere	_____
2. half	theirfore	hospital	_____
3. duly	caugh	either	_____
4. stommick	stretch	waist	_____
5. against	usualy	heard	_____
6. knew	weight	whose	_____

Each correct answer is worth 2 points.	Total score: 12 points.

Remodeling a House

It will help if you memorize the short sayings introduced by the word *MEMO*. Study each word carefully. In the sentences with missing letters, visualize the whole word, and write in the missing letters.

1. **steel**   Their new sink was made of stainless steel.
Distinguish *steel* from *steal*. MEMO: Feel the steel wheel.

2. **laid**   The workman laid the new kitchen floor.
The past tense of *lay* is *laid*. Compare *lay, laid; say, said*.

3. **straight**   Be sure to keep the tape measure straight.
Center on the *aigh* in *straight*. MEMO: Said to be laid straight

■ The workman l __ __ d the kitchen tiles stra __ __ __ t alongside the ste __ l sink.

4. **where**   Have you decided where you'll want the arched window?
Note the *here* in *where*. Compare *there*.

5. **lose**   Don't lose track of how many yards of carpet we'll need.
Distinguish *lose* from *loose*. MEMO: Lose whose loose goose?

6. **nickel**   He didn't want to spend a nick' el over $300 to build the deck.
Note the unusual *el* ending of *nickel*. Contrast *pickle* and *tickle*.

■ Wh __ r __ did the workman lo __ __ the ni __ k __ l?

7. **though**   Even though he liked the blue carpet, she selected the green.
Note the *thou* in *though*. Compare *through, dough*.

8. **steal**   Do you think anyone would steal the loose bricks from the yard?
Center on the *ea* in *steal*. MEMO: Don't steal the meal of real veal.

9. **many**   Man' y people prefer hardwood floors.
Pronounced *men' i*, but spelled *many*. Compare *any*.

■ Tho __ __ __ m __ n __ workmen were in and out of our house, they didn't see the thief ste __ l the television.

10. **believe**   Do you be lieve' that we bought enough paint?
Observe the *lie* in *believe*. Compare *relieve, belief*.

11. **theory**   Do you have a the' o ry about why the new paint peeled?
Note the three syllables. MEMO: Theodore's theory of geography

12. **parallel**   Try to keep the lines in the wallpaper pattern par' al lel.
Sound both *a*'s in *parallel*. Note the final *llel*.

■ They bel __ ev __ in the th __ __ ry of decorating that states that furniture should be arranged in par __ __ l __ l lines.

☐ EXERCISE I

Each sentence contains one or more spelling errors. Cross out each misspelled word. Then write the word correctly above it.

1. Draw two parrallel lines that bisect the vertical line of the triangle.

2. I could not understand the thory that was explained in the scientist's book.

3. Manny steal pipes were layd across the construction site.

4. I do not beleive that the newspaper carrier would steel the nickle from the box.

5. Did you loose your package where the highway curves and then goes strait?

6. Do you know wear he went?

7. Even thogh he was late, he stopped to buy the flowers.

8. Try to keep the ruler parellel with the edge of the paper.

9. He layed the money on the counter.

10. Is she generally a person you can beleave?

11. You must make sure the seams in the wallpaper are streight, or the pattern will be crooked.

☐ EXERCISE II

Write the correct word in each blank. Choose from the words below.

parallel	believe	steal	nickel	where	laid
theory	many	though	lose	straight	steel

1. _____ did Jonathan find that old Indian-head _____?

2. In _____, all _____ lines in the diagram should run to the horizon.

3. The _____ girders must be _____ in a square to form the structure of the ceiling.

4. _____ the night be long, the day will surely dawn.

5. Did the art dealer _____ the painting, or did someone _____ it?

6. _____ people _____ in life after death.

Choosing a Wardrobe

Take time to review the previous lessons. Frequent review is the key to recalling spellings correctly. Study each word carefully. In sentences with missing letters, visualize the whole word, and write in the missing letters.

1. **clothes** When are you planning to take the clo*thes* to the cleaners?
Put an *e* in *clothes*. Contrast *cloth, clothe, clothes,* and *clothing*.

2. **beauty** Dry cleaning will preserve the b*eau*' ty of that blouse.
Note the *beau* in *beauty*. Compare *beautiful*.

3. **women** The wom' en looked forward to the coat sale.
Compare *man, men; woman, women; gentleman, gentlemen*.

■ **Many men and w __ m __ n buy clo __ __ __ __ for their b __ __ uty.**

4. **choose** It was difficult for him to choo*se* between the two ties.
Keep the two *o*'s in *choose*. MEMO: Choose the loose goose.

5. **material** Cotton is a practical ma te'ri al for summer.
Note the *mate* in *material*. Compare *serial, financial*.

6. **wear** Do you think one material will w*ear* better than another?
Distinguish *wear* from *ware*. The bearskin will wear, not tear.

■ **When buying clothes, it's smart to cho __ s __ a ma __ __ __ __ al that will we __ r well.**

7. **occasionally** Oc ca' *si*on al*ly* she wore a sweater instead of a blouse.
Note the two *c*'s, one *s*, and two *l*'s in *occasionally*.

8. **satisfied** He was very sat' is fi*ed* with his purchase.
Center on the *fied* in *satisfied*. Compare *notified, justified*.

9. **woman** The dress was very flattering to the wom' an.
MEMO: Fan the Roman woman.

■ **There is oc __ a __ iona __ __ y a man or a w __ m __ n who is never satisf __ __ d with his or her clothes.**

10. **color** Which col' or scarf do you prefer?
Focus on *olo* in *color*. MEMO: A colony of colored colonnades.

11. **blue** Mary's dress was a light shade of blu*e*.
Distinguish *blue* from *blew*. MEMO: The best hue is true blue.

12. **prefer** Which do you pre fer', long or short sleeves?
Accent the *fer* in *prefer*. I *in fer'* you *pre fer'* to *de fer'*.

■ **Many men pref __ __ the c __ l __ r bl __ __.**

☐ EXERCISE I

Each sentence contains one or more spelling errors. Cross out each misspelled word. Then write the word correctly above it.

1. Some people feel that in order to be accepted, they must chose buetiful and expensive cloths.

2. However, each must chose cloths that ware well and are within a budget.

3. Occasionally, a woman or a man will preffer cloths of a bright coler, but blew is my favorite.

4. I hope that you will be satisffied with the materiel in the suit.

5. It is said that beautie is in the eye of the beholder.

6. She ocassionally shopped at that grocery store.

7. Is it true that wommen buy more cloathes than men?

8. Aunt Jenny is one womman who doesn't enjoy dressing up.

9. Make sure you are satisfyed with the cloathes you choose.

☐ EXERCISE II

Write the correct form in each blank without referring to the word list. When you have completed the exercise, check your answers with the dictionary.

1. Write the *ing* form of the word *clothes*. _____

2. Add the suffix *ful* to *beauty* to form an adjective. _____

3. Write the plural possessive form of *woman*. _____

4. Write the past tense of *choose*. _____

5. Write the *ing* form of *prefer*. _____

6. Add the suffix *ly* to *occasion* to form an adverb. _____

7. Add the suffix *ed* to form the past tense of *satisfy*. _____

8. Add the suffix *ed* to form the past tense of *color*. _____

The Seasons of the Year

Study each word carefully. In the sentences with missing letters, visualize the whole word, and write in the missing letters.

1. **autumn**   Another name for the *au'* tum*n* season is fall.
   Compare *autumn, autumnal; column, columnist; hymn, hymnal.*

2. **scenery**   The woodland sce*n'* er y was breathtaking.

3. **sight**   The red, yellow, and orange leaves were a beautiful si*gh*t.
   Distinguish *sight* from *site.* In *sight* of the building *site*

   ■ The a __ tu __ __ s __ __ nery was a pretty si __ __ t.

4. **benefit**   The autumn scenery is a ben*'* e fit of living in New England.
   Sound both *e*'s in *benefit.* Compare *benefited, benefiting.*

5. **regard**   Which season do you re gard*'* as most beautiful?
   Focus on *gard* in *regard.* Compare *reward, retard.*

6. **series**   The baseball World Se*'* r*ies* is held each year in the autumn.
   Focus on the *ie* in *series.* MEMO: Queries about the World Series

   ■ If our team were to win the World Ser __ __ s, I would reg __ __ d it as a ben __ fit to our city.

7. **authority**   An *au* thor*'* i ty says summer is the best time to catch trout.
   Sound the *i* in *authority.* Compare *authorize, majority.*

8. **been**   It has be*e*n a hard winter for the wild animals.
   Note the *bee* in *been,* but pronounce it *bin.*

9. **useful**   The map to the summer camp was very us*e'* ful.
   Use the *e* in *useful,* but not in *using.* Compare *useless.*

   ■ It has b __ __ n very us __ fu __ for Aunt Martha to consult an a __ th __ rity on when to plant her vegetables.

10. **quiet**   The world seems very qui*'* et on a snowy winter night.
    Distinguish *quiet* from *quite.* Note the two syllables in *qui' et.*

11. **sincerity**   The sin *cer'* ity of their wish to return next spring is evident.
    Note the *it* in *sincerity.* Compare *authority;* contrast *sincerely.*

12. **special**   For me, winter is a spe*'* cial time of year.
    Focus on the *cia* in *special.* Compare *social, commercial.*

   ■ I do not doubt his sinc __ __ __ ty when he says that a summer picnic in a q __ __ __ t place is a spe __ __ __ l treat.

⬜ EXERCISE I

Write the correct word in each blank. Choose from the words below.

special	quiet	been	series	benefit	scenery
sincerity	useful	authority	regard	sight	autumn

1. What is more beautiful than the _____ on a fine _____ day!

2. The representative's _____ over the committee has _____ granted by the chairperson.

3. Sharon's _____ has proven _____ in her role as counselor to children.

4. The _____ math courses you are taking will _____ you in the business world.

5. Does Dr. Berman _____ this _____ of math books as an improvement over the one used last year?

6. The painter captured the _____ of a sunset and the feeling of

_____ it conveys.

⬜ EXERCISE II

Match each word in Column A with its meaning in Column B. Place the letter of the meaning in the blank in front of the word it defines.

COLUMN A

1. _____ useful

2. _____ benefit

3. _____ special

4. _____ sincerity

5. _____ scenery

6. _____ quiet

7. _____ authority

8. _____ regard

9. _____ been

COLUMN B

a. power

b. unusual, a reduced price

c. able to be used

d. honesty, frankness

e. think of

f. past participle of *be*

g. tranquil, without noise

h. help, profit

i. a view, landscape

Ordering from Catalogs

Look carefully for the silent letters in the words which follow. Study each word carefully. In the sentences with missing letters, visualize the whole word, and write in the missing letters.

1. **catalog** The cat' *a* log advertised many articles.
   Note the middle *a* in *catalog*.

2. **manufacture** Does the Johnson Company man' u fac' *ture* any of the items in this catalog?
   Note the two *u*'s in *manufacture*. Compare *manual* labor.

3. **item** Be sure to include a description of the i' tem when ordering.
   Pronounce *item* carefully. Compare *system*.

■ **They man __ fact __ __ __ every it __ m listed in the cat __ l __ g.**

4. **absolutely** The blouse in the catalog would be ab' so lut*e'* ly perfect with her blue suit.
   Note the silent *e* in *absolutely*. Compare *completely, definitely*.

5. **certain** Be *cer'* t*a*in to add the shipping charges to your order.
   Note the *cer* in *certain*. Compare *certificate, captain*.

6. **neither** N*ei'* ther of the catalogs carried the seeds he wanted.
   Note the *e* before *i*.

■ **N __ __ ther of them could be abs __ lu __ __ ly __ ert __ __ n that the shoes they ordered would fit.**

7. **balloon** A ba*l* loon' flight for two is on page 8 of the catalog.
   A *balloon* is round and has two *l*'s.

8. **nineteen** If I order now, I can get two pairs for nine' teen dollars.
   Note that *nine, ninety,* and *nineteen* have an *e* after the *n*.

9. **height** It is important to consider your h*eight* when ordering proportioned slacks.
   Note the *eight* in *height*. MEMO: Height: eight feet

10. **debtor** The de*bt'* or refused to pay the bill for his catalog order.
    The word *debtor* is pronounced *det' er*. Compare *debt, doubt*.

11. **merchandise** What is the total cost of the mer' chan di*se*?
    Put a *hand* in *merchandise*. MEMO: A rise in merchandise

12. **junior** The shirt only came in jun' *ior* sizes.
    Compare *junior* with *senior*.

■ **Although she is only a j __ n __ __ r in high school, she has ordered so much merch __ n __ i __ __ that she is a d __ __ t __ r of the mail-order company.**

☐ EXERCISE I

Write each italicized word correctly in the first blank. In the second blank, write the word or phrase in dark print that most nearly means the opposite of the word.

1. *absolutely:*   **unruly, partially, entirely**   _____   _____

2. *certain:*   **unsure, likely, unqualified**   _____   _____

3. *debtor:*   **doctor, delirium, creditor**   _____   _____

4. *height:*   **altitude, surmount, depth**   _____   _____

5. *neither:*   **both, either, none**   _____   _____

☐ EXERCISE II

In each sentence, cross out each incorrect word in the parentheses. Then write the correct word in the blank.

1. Jevetta was in her (junier—junior) year in high school.

_____

2. Amber ordered several items of (merchandise—merchandice) from the store.

_____

3. The company found it was not practical to (manufacture—manufacter) toys.

_____

4. A helium (balloon—baloon) can soar high above the city for many hours.

_____

5. The governor had been in office for a total of (ninteen—nineteen) years.

_____

6. The company sent me a (catlog—catalog) for the coming year.

_____

7. Many of the small (items—itims) are very beautiful.

_____

8. Are you (absolutely—absolutly) sure you don't want to see the new horror movie?

_____

9. I (niether—neither) confirmed nor denied the rumor.

_____

Health Care

Study each word carefully. In the sentences with missing letters, visualize the whole word, and write in the missing letters.

1. tobacco   The nicotine in to bac' co is a very addictive drug.
Note the one *b* and two *c*'s in *tobacco*.

2. through   People can improve their health thr*ough* education.
Distinguish *through* from *threw*. He *threw* the box *through* the open door.

3. using   He has been u*s' ing* a new technique to stop smoking.
Omit the *e* in *using*. Compare *abuse, abusing; amuse, amusing*.

■ **The ex-smoker said he was thr ___ ___ ___ ___ u ___ ___ ng toba ___ ___ o.**

4. almost   It is al' most time for my annual physical exam.
There is only one *l* in *almost*. MEMO: Alfredo almost never laughs.

5. ready   Are you read' y to welcome your new baby?
Note the *a* in *ready*. MEMO: A steady tread and a ready head

6. separate   The outpatients were in a sep' a rate wing of the hospital.
Sound both *a*'s in *separate*. Think of preparation for separation.

■ **A sep ___ rate hospital for children was a ___ ___ ost re ___ dy to open.**

7. said   Not enough has been s*aid* about the importance of a good diet.
Compare *pay, paid; lay, laid*.

8. entitled   The book is en ti' tled *For a Healthy Heart*.
Note that *entitle* begins and ends with an *e*. Compare *encircle*.

9. salary   The nurse's sal' a ry should be higher.
Sound both *a*'s in *salary*. MEMO: A salary balance in Alabama

■ **Although she is ___ nti ___ ___ ed to a sa ___ ___ ry for her work with the seriously ill, she s ___ ___ d that she would rather work as a volunteer.**

10. anxious   The parents-to-be were extremely anx' ious.
Center on the *anx* in *anxious*. Compare *anxiety, gracious*.

11. absence   Good health is said to be the ab' sence of disease.
Note that *absence* ends in *ence*. Compare *presence, silence*.

12. affairs   The terminally ill man was anxious to put his af fairs' in order.
Include two *f*'s in *affairs*.

■ **He was an ___ ___ ___ us about how his ab ___ ___ ___ ___ ___ due to illness would affect his af ___ ___ irs.**

☐ EXERCISE I

In each sentence, find any misspelled words. Write each word correctly in the blank. If there are no misspelled words, write a *C* in the blank.

_____ 1. Each of you is entittled to a share in the profits.

_____ 2. When you tour France, be sure to travel through the tunnel under the Alps.

_____ 3. The ambassador was concerned over the state of afairs.

_____ 4. "Seperate the yolks of the eggs from the whites," Tammy said.

_____ 5. Mr. Stanley was anxous about his assistant's absence.

_____ 6. If you are a capable worker, you can demand more sallary.

_____ 7. I find it difficult to prepare meals without useing butter.

_____ 8. "Supper is almost ready!" he called.

☐ EXERCISE II

The following business letter contains many spelling errors. Cross out each misspelled word. Then write the word correctly above the misspelled word.

Dear Representative Bell:

I recently read about your bill to increase the tax on tobbacco products. I see

two benefits of such legislation. First, it might help discourage young people from

useing tobacco. Second, it would help pay for services threw raising revenue.

It is time we got readdy to seperate our knowledge about the dangers of smoking

from our dislike of government regulation. The Surgeon General has sayed that

smoking is one of the most serious health problems we face in this country. We

should all be anxius to help correct the situation.

I feel the American people are intitled to breathe clean air wherever they go.

This afair should be one of our top concerns. An absense of this priority among

our representatives in Congress does not make them worthy of earning their salery.

Sincerely yours,

Pet Care

Do not use contractions in business or formal letters. In most contractions, an apostrophe (') is used in place of one or more letters. In the sentences with missing letters, visualize the whole word, and write in the missing letters.

1. couldn't   He took his puppy because he coul*d'*n't find a boarding kennel.
The contraction *couldn't* is the shortened form of *could not.*

2. wouldn't   She woul*d'*n't think of leaving her dog in the hot car.
The contraction *wouldn't* is the shortened form of *would not.*

3. doesn't   Doe*s'*n't Fluffy need fresh water?
The contraction *doesn't* is the shortened form of *does not.*

■ **She do __ sn't really want another cat, but she co __ __ d __ 't find a home for the kitten, and she wo __ __ dn't take it to the animal shelter.**

4. can't   Can't Susan keep your hamster while you're on vacation?
The contraction *can't* is the shortened form of *cannot.*

5. isn't   I*s'*n't your dog vaccinated against rabies?
The contraction *isn't* is the shortened form of *is not.*

6. didn't   She took her cat to the vet because he di*d'*n't feel well.
The contraction *didn't* is the shortened form of *did not.*

■ **She is __ 't sure what age her dog is because she did __ 't ask the man from whom she bought him, and now she ca __ 't remember his name.**

7. don't   Don't you think your poodle needs grooming?
The contraction *don't* is the shortened form of *do not.*

8. possessive   The dog was very pos se*s'* sive of her home.
Note the four *s's* in *possessive.* Compare *possesses.*

9. yours   Which of the two kittens is yours?
Note the *u* in *yours.* Compare *ours, hour, courteous.*

■ **The cats are yo __ rs, but you do __ 't have to be so pos __ e __ __ ive of them.**

10. sure   Are you sur*e* that your dog has had all his shots?
Center on the *su* in *sure.* Compare *sugar, surely.*

11. etc.   She bought her new puppy a dish, brush, bone, bed, *etc.*
The abbreviation *etc.* is a contraction of *et cetera.*

12. period   I don't want the dog to track mud in this house, pe*'ri* od!
Pronounce the three syllables in *period* carefully.

■ **I'm s __ re I don't want the mess, bother, e __ c., of having a dog, per __ __ d!**

□ EXERCISE I

Write the word or words that each contraction stands for.

1. isn't _____

2. don't _____

3. couldn't _____

4. wouldn't _____

5. doesn't _____

6. can't _____

□ EXERCISE II

Write the contraction that may be used for each expression.

1. are not _____

2. could have _____

3. must not _____

4. you would _____

5. did not _____

6. should have _____

7. let us _____

8. were not _____

9. we would _____

10. you are _____

11. there is _____

12. will not _____

13. could not _____

14. would not _____

15. should not _____

16. do not _____

□ EXERCISE III

Each sentence contains one or more spelling errors. Cross out each misspelled word. Then write the word correctly above it. REMEMBER: If an apostrophe is left out of a word, the word is misspelled.

1. It doesnt matter if you can or cant complete the project.

2. You often form the posessive case by adding an apostrophe and an *s*.

3. Are you shur that you add a periud after *etc.*?

4. Wouldnt you think that he wouldve known the book was yours?

5. He couldnt remember where he put his keys.

A. In each sentence, cross out the incorrect word in parentheses. Then write the correct words in the blank.

1. (Chews,—Choose) the color you like best.

_____

2. Her (sincerety—sincerity) is evident.

_____

3. She went (strait—straight) home.

_____

4. Are those (close—clothes) new?

_____

5. He would never (steal—steel).

_____

6. The muddy little dog was quite a (site—sight) to behold.

_____

7. The (baloon—balloon) rose slowly into the sky.

_____

8. Did you (loose—lose) this jacket?

_____

9. I don't (believe—beleive) him.

_____

10. Which car do you (perfer—prefer)?

_____

Each correct answer is worth 2 points.	Total score: 20 points.

B. The following letter contains many spelling errors. Cross out each misspelled word. Write the word correctly above the misspelled word.

Dear Gloria,

Rob and I just returned from our trip threw New England. We are absolutely certan that the speciel beuty of the autum senery is without parallell. Occasionaly we would see a tree of such magnificent hieght and collor that we were sertin it couldnt be topped. I cann't think of a more queit, peaceful way to spend a vacation and hope you and Luis are able to go there next year. Dont miss it if you get the chance.

Sincerely,

Each correct answer is worth 2 points.	Total score: 32 points.

C. In each sentence, find any misspelled words. Write each word correctly in the blank. If there are no misspelled words, write a C in the blank.

_____ 1. Janet's boyfriend was too possesive of her time.

_____ 2. They packed their camera, knapsacks, ect., to go camping.

_____ 3. "I don't want to hear about it, period," she said.

_____ 4. Is that book your's?

_____ 5. Does'nt he look funny in that picture?

_____ 6. Cant you wait until we get to the next town?

_____ 7. Does that company manufactuer that item?

_____ 8. Is n't that Joe across the street?

_____ 9. It's difficult to beleive all the statements in the pamphlet.

_____ 10. Whom will the charity ball benifit?

_____ 11. Even through he didn't like liver, he ate it.

_____ 12. Is this materiel machine washable?

Each correct answer is worth 3 points.	Total score: 36 points.

D. In each group of words, cross out any misspelled words. Then write each word correctly in the blank. If there are no misspelled words, write a C in the blank.

1. debtor   niether   sure   _____

2. absence   affares   through   _____

3. tobaco   junior   been   _____

4. usefull   wear   regard   _____

5. series   authority   merchandice   _____

6. wouldn't   satisfied   therie   _____

7. steel   entitled   anxious   _____

8. using   almost   salery   _____

Each correct answer is worth 1½ points.	Total score: 12 points.

Applying for a Job

It will help your spelling and writing if you note the separate syllables in each word. Study each word carefully. In sentences with missing letters, visualize the whole word, and write in the missing letters.

1. **business**
He is looking for job openings in the oil drilling b*usi'* ness.
The word *business* (biz' ness) has only two syllables.

2. **president**
When she applied for the job, she met the pres*'* i dent of the company.

3. **executive**
Perhaps someday she will be an *ex ec'* u tive in the company.
Note the *cuti* in *executive*. Compare *execute, executing*.

■ **As pres __ d __ nt, she was chief ex __ __ utive of the bu __ __ ness.**

4. **capacity**
Her ca pac' i ty for hard work was very great.
Note the *city* in *capacity*. MEMO: His capacity for veracity

5. **commercial**
The interviewer asked if he had a co*m* mer' *ci*al driver's license.
Place two *m*'s in *commercial*. Compare *commence, commerce*.

6. **organization**
It seemed like a well-run or' gan i za' *ti*on.
Remember that *organization* is derived from *organize*.

■ **On his previous job, he showed an unusual c __ pa __ ity for the org __ n __ __ ation of small co __ __ erc __ __ l firms.**

7. **courteous**
The receptionist was very cour' te ous over the phone.
Keep the *court* in *courteous*. Compare *courtesy, courtly*.

8. **position**
For which po *si' ti*on are you applying?
Focus on the *si* in *position*. Compare *ambition, positive*.

9. **independent**
The job called for him to be an in' de pend' ent worker.

■ **The po __ __ tion required ind __ pend __ nt leadership and c __ __ rt __ __ __ s manners.**

10. **satisfactory**
The starting salary of the position was sat' is fac' to ry.
Note the three words: *sat, is,* and *factory,* in *satisfactory*.

11. **service**
The company's goal was to provide serv' ice to the community.
Note the *ice* in *service*. Contrast *serve, servant*.

12. **policy**
An insurance pol' i cy was part of the employee benefit package.
Center on the *icy* in *policy*. MEMO: The polite police policy

■ **Her last job taught her that sat __ __ fact __ __ y s __ rv __ __ __ is always the best pol __ __ y.**

☐ EXERCISE I

The following letter contains many spelling errors. Cross out each misspelled word. Then write the word correctly above the misspelled word.

Dear Ms. Yancy:

I am writing to apply for a posision in your organizeation. I just left a bussines where my job required me to act in a corteous, independant manner. The person serving in the capacity of presdent and chief exective officer of that servise-oriented company found my work to be very satisfactery.

I feel that having a commerrcial driver's license will also come in handy on this job. If it is your company's pollicy to grant interviews, I would like to schedule one as soon as possible.

Sincerely yours,

☐ EXERCISE II

In each sentence, cross out the incorrect word in parentheses. Then write the correct word in the blank.

1. The attitude of the staff is (satisfactry—satisfactory).

_____

2. The (service—servase) at that restaurant is excellent.

_____

3. That cab driver certainly was (curteous—courteous).

_____

4. The (president—precedent) is elected to a four-year term.

_____

5. His (capacity—capasity) for food was astounding.

_____

6. What (positon—position) does she play on the team?

_____

7. Which is your favorite television (commercial—comerical)?

_____

8. I'll check my new insurance (polisy—policy) carefully.

_____

9. She is extremely (indipendent—independent).

_____

10. The (organization—organisation) of that conference was good.

_____

The Weather

Refer to a dictionary if you are unsure of pronunciation. Study each word carefully. In the sentences with missing letters, visualize the whole word, and write in the missing letters.

1. bulletin
The noon weather bul' *le* tin predicted rain.
Note the *bullet* in *bulletin*. Compare *bull, bullet*.

2. official
The *of* fi' *cia*l rainfall for the month was two inches.
Note the two *f*'s in *official*. MEMO: I am off to offer the office to the official officer.

3. bureau
The weather bu' *reau* is forecasting a freeze for tonight.

■ An of __ ic __ __ l bul __ __ t __ n came from the weather bu __ __ __ __.

4. announcement
Because of the snow, he made an a*n* noun*ce'* ment that there would be no school the next day.
Note the four *n*'s in *announcement*. Compare *ounce*.

5. changeable
The weather was chang*e' a* ble from hour to hour.
Keep the *change* in *changeable*. MEMO: *Able* to *change*

6. weather
Fair we*a*th' er lasted the entire week.
MEMO: Heavy leather for wet weather.

■ The an __ __ __ n __ __ ment predicted chan __ __ __ ble w __ __ ther.

7. temporary
The fog posed only a tem' po ra' ry problem for air traffic.
Pronounce the *o* in *temporary*. Compare *honor, honorary*.

8. lightning
The l*i*ght' ning was followed by thunder.
Note carefully the *ning* in *lightning*.

9. Tuesday
The weather forecast for Tu*es'* day is more sunshine.
Center on the *ue* in *Tuesday*. MEMO: Dues on Tuesday

■ There was a tem __ __ r __ ry period of li __ __ t __ ing on T __ __ sday.

10. possibility
There was no pos' *s*i bil' i ty of rain in the forecast.
Focus on the *ossi* in *possibility*. Compare *possible*.

11. shining
The sun was shin' ing brightly.
Omit the *e* in *shining*. Compare: *pine, pining; dine, dining*.

12. Wednesday
We*dnes'* day should bring the first frost of the year.
Note the *ednes* in *Wednesday*.

■ There is a good po __ s __ b __ lity that the sun will be shi __ __ ng on W __ __ n __ __ day.

□ EXERCISE I

The following weather report contains many spelling errors. Cross out each misspelled word. Then write the word correctly above the misspelled word.

The offisial weathar bulettin from the New Orleans National Wether Service

forecasts the possibility of rain Tuseday. Temporery thunderstorms accompanied

by lighting are possible for the evening. The weather conditions will be changeble

early Wenesday. There is a posibility of the sun's shinning Wenesday about noon.

For further information, please listen to the next wether anouncement at four

o'clock this afternoon.

□ EXERCISE II

Match each word in Column A with its meaning in Column B. Place the letter of the meaning in the blank in front of the word it defines.

COLUMN A

1. _____ shining
2. _____ official
3. _____ changeable
4. _____ Wednesday
5. _____ bulletin
6. _____ possibility
7. _____ temporary
8. _____ weather
9. _____ bureau
10. _____ lightning
11. _____ announcement
12. _____ Tuesday

COLUMN B

a. climate

b. authorized

c. day before Thursday

d. something announced

e. news flash

f. department

g. gleaming

h. not permanent

i. electric flash

j. changing often

k. chance

l. day before Wednesday

Traveling

Study each word carefully. In the sentences with missing letters, visualize the whole word, and write in the missing letters.

1. scene   The scene from the train window was spectacular.
Note the silent letters.

2. appreciate   I ap pre' ci ate friendly hotel personnel.
Center on the two p's in appreciate. Compare *approve*.

3. description   He gave a detailed de scrip' tion of his lost luggage.
Pronounce the *des* in *description*. MEMO: Destroy the despised description.

■ I certainly ap __ re __ __ __ te the detailed d __ __ crip __ __ __ n of a typical Paris street s __ __ n __ .

4. error   There seems to be an er' ror in my flight schedule.
Count the three r's in *error*. Compare *terror, mirror*.

5. estimate   Can you es' ti mate our time of arrival?
Note the *i* in *estimate*. Compare *intimate, legitimate*.

6. length   What is the length of this flight?
Pronounce *length* carefully. Compare *strong, strength*.

■ An er __ __ r was made in the est __ m __ te of the l __ n __ __ __ of the flight, so we will land at 4:30 instead of 4:00.

7. traveler   You could tell she was not an experienced trav' el er.
Think of a *lone* traveler. There are no double letters.

8. journey   They were very tired after their long jour' ney.
Focus on the *ou* in *journey*. MEMO: A journal of our journey

9. tired   He was tired of trying to read the complicated map.
Note the *tire* in *tired*. MEMO: Too tired to be inspired

■ The trav __ l __ r was t __ __ __ d after the long j __ __ rn __ __ .

10. circumstances   Cir' cum stanc' es delayed their arrival by half an hour.
MEMO: A circle of circumstances at the circus

11. advise   I would not ad vise' you to travel in this storm.
MEMO: We advise you to take the doctor's advice.

12. proceed   Pro ceed' with caution on the icy roads.
MEMO: To succeed, you must proceed to exceed.

■ Under the __ __ rcumstan __ __ __ , would you advi __ e us to proc __ __ __ on our trip?

☐ EXERCISE I

In each sentence, cross out the incorrect word in parentheses. Then write the correct word in the blank.

1. Mr. Sanchez will (advice—advise) his employees of the changes.

_____

2. The weary (traveller—traveler) rested in a roadside park.

_____

3. He wanted us to repeat the (scean—scene) from the play.

_____

4. The pilgrims were resolved to finish the (journey—jorney) on foot.

_____

5. Check your letter to see if you have made an (error—eror).

_____

6. Could Cynthia walk the entire (lenth—length) of the tightrope?

_____

☐ EXERCISE II

In each sentence, find any misspelled words. Write each word correctly in the blank. If there are no misspelled words, write a C in the blank.

_____ 1. Your advice is something I sincerely appresiate.

_____ 2. After our journy, we should be tired.

_____ 3. Please advice me how to proceed.

_____ 4. What is your estimate of the damage?

_____ 5. The circumstanses defied description.

_____ 6. The crying little boy caused quite a sceen in the store.

_____ 7. The police asked for as detailed a describtion as she could give.

_____ 8. I feel that he made an ererr in judgment.

_____ 9. Is this jacket the proper lenth?

_____ 10. The student became tried of studying for the final exam.

_____ 11. The weary travaler stopped at the closest motel.

_____ 12. When you come to the fork in the road, procede to the right.

Hazardous Driving

Go through all of the exercises, but concentrate on the words which are the most difficult to recall. Study each word carefully. In sentences with missing letters, visualize the whole word, and write in the missing letters.

1. **naturally**   The driver was nat′u ral *ly* cautious when the roads were icy.
Note the *rally* in *naturally*. Compare *especially, generally*.

2. **rhyme**   During the trip, the children tried to think of words that *rhy*me with ice.
Center your attention on the *rhy* in *rhyme* and *rhythm*.

3. **rhythm**   The sleet kept up a steady *rhy*thm on the pavement.
MEMO: Neither rhyme, rhythm, nor rhetoric in rhubarb

■ **Nat __ r __ __ ly, the sounds of the tires on the icy road seemed to have r __ __ th __ , but not rh __ m __ .**

4. **icicle**   An i′ cic le had formed on the car door handle.
Focus on the *cicl* in *icicle*. Contrast *bicycle* and *tickle*.

5. **minute**   The wet road became more dangerous by the min′ ute.
Distinguish *minute* (min′ it) from *minute* (mi nut′).

6. **disappear**   The snow on the highway made the center line dis′ ap pe*ar*′.
Note the *pear* in *disappear*. Also note the one *s* and the two *p*'s.

■ **The melting ic __ __ le will completely dis __ p __ __ __ r within a min __ t __ or two.**

7. **early**   If you leave for work too e*ar*′ ly, the bridges won't be sanded.
Note the *ear* in *early*. Compare *earnest*.

8. **expect**   The forecasters *ex* pect′ the roads to thaw by this afternoon.
Focus on the *exp* in *expect*. Distinguish *expect* from *suspect*.

9. **hour**   Because the roads were wet, rush h*our* driving was slow.
Distinguish *hour* from *our*. MEMO: An hour in sour flour

■ **The drivers e __ __ ect to start on the long, cold journey at an e __ rly __ o __ r.**

10. **automobile**   Buy snow tires for your au′ to mo b*ile*′ before your trip north.
Note the *mobile* in *automobile*. Compare *automotive*.

11. **especially**   Be es pe′ ci*al ly* careful driving in the heavy rain today.
Note the *special* in *especially*. Compare *commercially*.

12. **equipped**   Many cars in the south are not e quipped′ for driving on ice.
Note the double *p* in *equipped*. MEMO: Equipped to be shipped

■ **The __ __ t __ mob __ __ __ __ is __ spec __ __ l __ y well equ __ p __ __ d for the icy drive.**

□ EXERCISE I

Write the correct word in each blank. Choose from the words below.

equipped   automobile   expect   disappear   icicle   rhyme
especially   hour   early   minute   rhythm   naturally

1. Mrs. Laval thought that five was too _____ in the morning to begin the trip.

2. Do you _____ many people at the family reunion?

3. She is a _____ gifted dancer.

4. James is _____ fond of this chocolate icebox pie.

5. A new _____ must have adequate safety features.

6. The silvery _____ dangled from the edge of the roof.

7. Most poems _____.

8. Wait a _____; we're coming!

9. Most rock music has a strong _____.

10. The magician made the rabbit _____ after it was pulled from a hat.

11. Which bicycle comes _____ with a headlight?

12. Each stroke of the clock heralded the _____ of midnight.

□ EXERCISE II

In each sentence, find any misspelled words. Write each word correctly in the blank. If there are no misspelled words, write a *C* in the blank.

_____ 1. Do those words rhyme?

_____ 2. That icicle looks as if it might fall from the roof at any minuite.

_____ 3. Did they dissappear early this morning?

_____ 4. We expect the automobile to be fully equiped.

_____ 5. The rhythm of that song is especially nice.

_____ 6. Each minute seemed to last at least an our.

Lessons in Life

Study each word carefully. In sentences with missing letters, visualize the whole word, and write in the missing letters.

1. **belief**   His be l*ief'* in her honesty is unshaken.
Distinguish *belief* from *believe*. Compare *relief, relieve*.

2. **religious**   She believed that her re li*'gio*us convictions helped her through the hard times.
Note the *ious* in *religious*. Compare *mysterious, superstitious*.

3. **soul**   It is said that confession is good for the so*ul*.
Distinguish *soul* (spirit) from *sole* (alone). STUDY: His sole purpose was saving souls.

■ One's rel __ g __ __ __ s bel __ __ __ about the s __ __ l is a personal matter.

4. **receipt**   Did you ask for a re *ceip*t*'* for that self-help book?
Focus on the *ceip* in *receipt*. Contrast *reception, deceit*.

5. **acknowledge**   People need to ac knowl*'* edge their mistakes.
Note the *know* and the *ledge* in *acknowledge*.

6. **shipment**   The ship*'* ment of self-help books was delayed a week.
Center on the *ment* in *shipment*. Compare *treatment*.

■ He didn't ac __ no __ l __ dg __ rec __ __ p __ of the shipm __ __ t of self-help books.

7. **completely**   After the experience, she was com plete*'* ly different.
Center on the *ete* in *completely*. Compare *complete*.

8. **forgotten**   He had for got*'* ten what a relief it was to have a close friend in whom to confide.

9. **happened**   The incident had hap*'* pened early in their childhood.
Center on the *ened* in *happened*. MEMO: Happy it happened

■ He had compl __ __ __ ly forg __ t __ __ n the accident that hap __ __ __ ed early in his life.

10. **between**   It's often difficult to choose be tween*'* two options.

11. **connection**   There's a con nec*'* tio*n* between the accident and his nightmares.
Note the three *n*'s in *connection*. Compare *connect*.

12. **source**   Her parents' divorce was a so*urce* of conflict for Marta.
MEMO: We sought the source of the sour soup.

■ What was the so __ r __ e of the con __ e __ __ ion betw __ __ n the two friends?

☐ EXERCISE I

Write each italicized word correctly in the first blank. In the second blank, write the word in dark print that most nearly means the same as that word.

1. *source:*   origin, sorrow, ending   _____   _____

2. *happened:*   thought, occurred, delivered   _____   _____

3. *belief:*   lie, confusion, trust   _____   _____

4. *completely:*   totally, uselessly, hopelessly   _____   _____

5. *soul:*   appearance, spirit, reputation   _____   _____

6. *acknowledge:*   deny, reject, admit   _____   _____

7. *connection:*   link, break, interruption   _____   _____

☐ EXERCISE II

In each sentence, cross out the incorrect word in parentheses. Then write the correct word in the blank.

1. Sandra is (religous—religious).

_____

2. Be (completly—completely) honest.

_____

3. It's my (belief—beleif) that the company will grow.

_____

4. The accident (happened—hapened) today.

_____

5. The secret must remain (between—betwen) us.

_____

6. What's the best (sourse—source) for fresh vegetables?

_____

7. Get a (receipt—reciept).

_____

8. Send the (shippment—shipment).

_____

9. The squabble will soon be (forgoten—forgotten).

_____

10. The sermon was about the (sole—soul).

_____

11. (Acknowledge—Acknowlege) his greeting.

_____

12. There's no (connection—conection) between those two cities.

_____

LESSON 18

The Public Library

You can strengthen and add to your spelling ability by studying the related words presented as memory aids. Study each word carefully. In sentences with missing letters, visualize the whole word, and write in the missing letters.

1. article Tim looked for the title of the ar' ti cle in the card catalog.
      Note the *cle* in *article*. MEMO: An article about the art circle

2. science In which section of the library will I find books on sci' ence?
      Focus on the *sci* in *science*. MEMO: Scott finds science scintillating.

3. referred The numbers on the book's spine re ferred' to its location.
      Note the *rr* in *referred*. Compare *preferred, conferred*.

■ **The librarian ref __ r __ __ __ d the student to an art __ __ l __ on sc __ __ n __ e.**

4. library There are fifty new books in the li' brar' y.
      Pronounce all of the syllables in *library* distinctly.

5. interesting This is a very in' ter est ing article.
      Note the *ere* in *interesting*. Compare *interest, interested*.

6. literature There's a section of the library devoted to English lit' er a ture'.
      Center on the *era* in *literature*. Compare *literary, illiterate*.

■ **Int __ __ __ sting lit __ __ __ t __ r __ can always be found in the lib __ __ __ y.**

7. librarian Ask the li brar' i an about the new book.
      Pronounce *librarian* carefully. Compare *barbarian, vegetarian*.

8. psychology The library contains many good books on psy chol' o gy.
      Focus on the *psych* in *psychology*. Note the silent letters.

9. volume The second vol' ume is not in the library.
      Note that *volume* ends in *me*. Contrast the *mn in column*.

■ **The lib __ __ r __ an showed us the newest vol __ __ __ on __ sy __ __ ol __ gy.**

10. various The library contains thousands of books on var' i ous subjects.
      MEMO: Curious and furious about the various and spurious

11. pamphlet That pam' phlet may be in the library.
      Center on the *ph* in *pamphlet*. MEMO: The emphatic pamphlet about camphor

12. magazine That mag' a zine' can be found in the periodical section.
      Note the *gaz* in *magazine*. Pronounce both *a*'s.

■ **Besides books, there were var __ __ __ s pam __ __ l __ ts and m __ g __ z __ nes.**

☐ EXERCISE I

The following business letter contains many spelling errors. Cross out each misspelled word. Then write the word correctly above the misspelled word.

Dear Mrs. Morrison:

    I read your interisting articel in this month's *Libery Magezine.* I find librery sceince

very interisting, and wondered if you could give me some information on how I could

become a part-time librerian. I am a sophomore in college, taking courses in litterature

and in psichology. Our libraran reffered me to several pamplets from the Liberry Service

and to one or two volums concerning careers in our liberry. I would like to know even

more about varous opportunities open to me in this field and to know if you offer part-

time jobs at your libery.

    Thank you in advance for any assistance.

Sincerely yours,

☐ EXERCISE II

Match each word in Column A with its meaning in Column B. Place the letter of the meaning in the blank in front of the word it defines.

COLUMN A

1. _____ pamphlet

2. _____ librarian

3. _____ magazine

4. _____ volume

5. _____ library

6. _____ literature

COLUMN B

a. novels, poems, essays, etc.

b. a short piece of writing on a subject usually of current interest

c. one of a number of books forming a set

d. a place for reading, study, or reference

e. one who works in a library

f. periodical

A. The following business letter contains many spelling errors. Cross out each misspelled word. Write the word correctly above the misspelled word.

Dear Mayor Hiller:

I am writing to you in your capasity as head of our city government to ask you not to cut back on a valuable city servise. I am referring to your recent anouncement of changes in the ours of operation of our city libary system. I hope that this new policy of closing the library two hours earlie on Tuesdey and Wensday will be temporarry.

I estamate that I use the librery once a week for bussines reasons. I find the chanjable hours confusing and not at all satisfactry.

No other organisation in the city is such a complete sorce of litterature, articels, pamphlits, and magazenes. Research has shown that there is a conection between the standard of living in a city and the library services it offers. I would appreceate you checking into what I feel is a policie erore. I feel that you and the city council have completly foregotten the average citizen by taking the possition that you have. If there is any possibillity of changing this policy, I would apreciate your doing so.

Yours truly,

Each correct answer is worth 2 points.	Total score: 58 points.

B. Write the correct form in each blank. When you have completed the exercise, check your answers in the dictionary.

1. Write the *ing* form of the word *shine*. _____

2. Write the past tense of *refer*. _____

3. Add the suffix *al* to *office* to form an adjective. _____

4. Add the suffix *tion* to *describe* to form a noun. _____

5. Add the prefix *dis* to *appear* to form a verb. _____

6. Write the past tense of *equip*. _____

Each correct answer is worth 1 point.	Total score: 6 points.

C. In each group of words, cross out any misspelled words. Then write each word correctly in the blank. If there are no misspelled words, write a *C* in the blank.

1. rhyme   minite   naturally   _____

2. liberian   journey   tired   _____

3. circumstances   science   lenth   _____

4. scene   shipment   icicle   _____

5. procede   advise   happened   _____

6. religious   sychology   especially   _____

Each correct answer is worth 2 points.   Total score: 12 points.

D. In each sentence, find any misspelled words. Write each word correctly in the blank. If there are no misspelled words, write a *C* in the blank.

_____ 1. Do you know who was the third presidant of the United States?

_____ 2. That child is growing up to be highly independant.

_____ 3. I wonder if the whether will be good for the picnic Saturday.

_____ 4. The cab driver was very curteous.

_____ 5. Why not post that article on the bullatin board?

_____ 6. Call the weather burough for the exact temperature.

_____ 7. The president heads the executive branch of government.

_____ 8. That is a very intresting book.

_____ 9. Please turn down the volume on the radio.

_____ 10. That was really a clever television commerciel.

_____ 11. I acknowledge that I'd forgotten to have my automobeal inspected.

_____ 12. Did you expect the movie to end like that?

Each correct answer is worth 2 points.   Total score: 24 points.

Trains

Note that some words have two accented syllables; one receives a primary accent (′), and another a secondary accent (′). Study each word carefully. In sentences with missing letters, visualize the whole word, and write in the missing letters.

1. **freight**   The workers loaded the fr*eight* into the boxcars.
Note the *eight* in *freight*. MEMO: The weight of eight freight trains

2. **passenger**   Every pas′ *senger* on the train had some luggage.
Note the *ss* in *passenger*. Compare *passed, messenger*.

3. **precede**   Doesn't the engine of a train pre *cede*′ the caboose?
Center on the *cede in precede*. Compare *recede, accede, concede*.

■ The pa __ s __ nger train was to pre __ __ d __ the fr __ __ __ __ t train.

4. **plain**   It was pla*in* to see that the train was coming down the tracks.
Distinguish *plain* from *plane*.

5. **engineer**   The train's en′ *gi* neer′ has a highly responsible job.
MEMO: Imagine an engine without an engineer.

6. **view**   The *view* from the train window was beautiful.
Focus on the *iew* in *view*. MEMO: Preview the view of the review.

■ The eng __ n __ __ r had a pl __ __ n v __ __ w of the tracks ahead.

7. **moving**   You can barely feel the train mov′ *ing*.
Compare *move, moving; shove, shoving; prove, proving*.

8. **territory**   The train crossed through a large portion of very dry ter′ ri to′ ry.
Note the *rr* in *territory*. Compare *terrible, terror*.

9. **toward**   The train eased gradually to′ *ward* the station.
STUDY: He ran *toward* her to *ward* off the mad dog.

■ They were mov __ __ g slowly to __ __ rd the stretch of very hilly ter __ __ t __ ry.

10. **occurred**   It had not oc curred′ to her that she could sleep on the train.
Compare *occur, occurrence*.

11. **tragedy**   The train trag′ *e* dy could have been prevented.
Pronounce *tragedy* (trăj′ ĭ dē) carefully. MEMO: They staged a page from an aged tragedy.

12. **imagine**   I i mag′ *ine* traveling by train would be a fantastic experience.
MEMO: Imagine an engine with nine engineers.

■ I cannot i __ ag __ n __ why such a terrible tr __ __ e __ y oc __ __ r __ ed on the railroad tracks.

☐ EXERCISE I

In each sentence, cross out the incorrect word in parentheses. Then write the correct word in the blank.

1. Did Elizabeth send the package to Detroit by air (freight—frieght)?

_____

2. He plans to study to become an electrical (enginere—engineer).

_____

3. Don't you see that large truck coming (toward—towarrd) us?

_____

4. They were paging a (pasenger—passenger) on the airline's incoming flight.

_____

5. The booklet told of the splendor of the (view—vue) from the Eiffel Tower.

_____

6. Were the employees at the factory when the fire (ocurred—occurred)?

_____

☐ EXERCISE II

In each sentence, find any misspelled words. Write each word correctly in the blank.
If there are no misspelled words, write a *C* in the blank.

_____ 1. Should this part of the report preceed the material devoted to the company's growth?

_____ 2. The dress was plane in design, but it suited the occasion.

_____ 3. The real tradgedy occurred later in the day.

_____ 4. You can't imagin how frightened we were when the car started moving toward the edge of the cliff.

_____ 5. This nation grew when it acquired the Louisiana Territory.

_____ 6. The train was moving quickly tward the stalled car.

_____ 7. Her brother is studying to become an enginier.

_____ 8. Is that a frieght train or a passenger train?

Writing Letters

There is no rule which covers double letters. You must learn each word separately. Study each word carefully. In sentences with missing letters, visualize the whole word, and write in the missing letters.

1. **recall**　　Do you re call′ their zip code?
　　　　　　　Note the *all* in *recall*. MEMO: I will recall all in the hall.

2. **envelope**　The en′ ve lop*e* was not addressed properly.
　　　　　　　Distinguish *en′ ve lope* from the verb *en vel′ op* (to surround).

3. **address**　A complete a*d* dress′ always includes a zip code.
　　　　　　　Note the *add* in *address*.

■ **Do you reca ＿＿ what the ad ＿ re ＿＿ was on the old ＿ nvel ＿ p ＿ ?**

4. **writing**　　He types all his letters because his *writ′* ing is barely legible.
　　　　　　　Omit the *e* in *writing*. Compare *bite, biting; kite, kiting.*

5. **invitation**　They received the wedding in′ vi ta′ *tion.*
　　　　　　　Pronounce the middle *i* in *invitation*. Compare *cite, citation.*

6. **enclose**　　I will en clos*e′* pictures from my vacation with the letter.
　　　　　　　Enclose may also be spelled *inclose.*

■ **We should ＿ nclo ＿＿ an ＿ nv ＿ ta ＿＿＿＿ n in ＿ rit ＿ ng to the group.**

7. **earnest**　　Tasuko was *ear′* nest in her wish to write an interesting letter.
　　　　　　　Note the *ear* in *earnest*. MEMO: Learn to be early in earnest.

8. **discussion**　The class held a dis cu*s′ si*on on how to address an envelope.
　　　　　　　Note the *ss* in *discussion*. Compare *discussed, discussing.*

9. **speech**　　The postmaster delivered a spe*ech* on why letters wind up in the
　　　　　　　dead letter office.
　　　　　　　MEMO: A speedy speech without a screech

■ **The envelope contained a copy of the sp ＿＿ ch that was immediately followed by an ＿＿ rn ＿ st d ＿ scus ＿＿＿ n.**

10. **mentioned**　He never men′ *tion*ed that he hadn't left a forwarding address.
　　　　　　　Center on the *tion* in *mentioned*. Compare *invention.*

11. **additional**　Will this envelope require a*d* di′ *tion* al postage?
　　　　　　　Note the *add* in *additional*. Distinguish from *traditional.*

12. **information**　Is there sufficient in′ for ma′ *tion* on this envelope?
　　　　　　　Note the *formation* in *information*. Stress the *tion.*

■ **The letter men ＿＿＿ n ＿ d the need for ad ＿ i ＿＿＿ n ＿ l i ＿ form ＿＿＿＿ n.**

☐ EXERCISE I

Supply the missing letters in each word.

1. a __ __ itional

2. e __ __ nest

3. informa __ __ on

4. env __ __ ope

5. wri __ __ ng

6. men __ __ oned

7. discu __ __ ion

8. en __ __ ose

9. sp __ __ ch

10. in __ __ tation

11. re __ __ __ l

12. a __ __ re __ __

☐ EXERCISE II

In each sentence, find any misspelled words. Write each word correctly in the blank. If there are no misspelled words, write a *C* in the blank.

_____ 1. Was Mrs. Graham able to recall the day on which the wedding invitations were mailed?

_____ 2. Marion's sister is writing a style manual for the course entitled "Effective Letters."

_____ 3. There will be a discusion period following the legislator's speech.

_____ 4. Address the envalope in a block style as designated on the diagram.

_____ 5. Enclosse the invitation in the envelope before you seal it.

_____ 6. If you are ernest about completing the course, study every night.

_____ 7. Tom needed aditional information on the topic in order to finish his project.

_____ 8. Did the marketing expert mention a sales analysis, or was it menttioned only in the discussion period that followed?

_____ 9. Writeing letters is a good way to keep in touch with people.

_____ 10. They had an earnest discusion about her plans.

_____ 11. The invitacion didn't contain information on how to dress for the party.

_____ 12. I recall that she mencioned buying a car in her last letter.

Air Travel

Always read the sentence which follows each word carefully. Be certain that you have the right meaning in mind. Study each word. In sentences with missing letters, visualize the whole word, and write in the missing letters.

1. **loose**
The flight attendants made sure there was no *loose* luggage.
Distinguish *loose* from *lose*. You may *lose* a *loose* nickel.

2. **aerial**
When you fly, you get a lovely *ae' ri al* view of the countryside.
Pronounce *aerial* carefully. Compare *serial, material.*

3. **receiving**
The pilot was re *ceiv' ing* instructions from the control tower.
Center on the *ei* in *receiving.* Compare *deceiving, receive.*

■ **The passenger was enjoying the a __ ri __ l view instead of rec __ __ v __ ng instructions, so he didn't notice that his seat belt was l __ __ s __ .**

4. **response**
The pilot's re *sponse'* to the engine's failure was immediate.
Note that *response* ends in *se*. Compare *sense, expense.*

5. **could**
Although she was tired, she *could* not sleep on the airplane.
Focus on the *oul* in *could.* Compare *would, should.*

6. **inquiry**
Mike made an *in' quir y* about the flights available.
Look at *inquiry* carefully. Compare *inquire, require.*

■ **I'm sure the flight attendant would have given you a r __ spon __ __ to the inq __ __ r __ if he c __ __ __ d have done so.**

7. **generally**
The airlines claim flying is *gen' er al ly* safer than driving a car.
Note the *rally* in *generally.* MEMO: Generals will generally rally.

8. **noticeable**
The passengers' anxiety was not *no' tice a ble.*
Keep the middle *e* in *noticeable.* Compare *serviceable.*

9. **trouble**
The flight crew knew what to do in case of *trou' ble.*

■ **Any tr __ __ b __.__ that occurs on a flight is gen __ r __ l __ y not noti __ __ __ ble to the passengers.**

10. **hear**
Did you he*ar* about the plane crash in Washington?
Note the *ear* in *hear.* Distinguish *hear* from *here.*

11. **satisfactorily**
The pilot managed to land the plane *sat' is fac' to ri ly.*
Focus on the *ily* in *satisfactorily.* Pronounce each syllable.

12. **impossible**
It is *im pos' si ble* for the plane to take off in this storm.
Note the *ossi* in *impossible.* Pronounce the *i* in *ible.*

■ **It's imp __ __ s __ ble not to h __ __ r that most flights land sat __ sfactor __ __ __ .**

☐ EXERCISE I

In each sentence, cross out the incorrect word in parentheses. Then write the correct word in the blank.

1. Was the cable (lose—loose) before the boat slipped its docking?

_____

2. Mary's behavior is (impossible—imposible) to understand.

_____

3. Carlos is (generaly—generally) known to have a pleasant personality.

_____

4. (Coud—Could) Shakespeare's plays have been written by Bacon or by Marlowe?

_____

5. If you are quiet, you can (here—hear) the roar of the ocean's waves.

_____

6. Mr. Moody's (respons—response) to the address was a moving one.

_____

7. Did you make an (inquiry—enquiry) about the position?

_____

☐ EXERCISE II

Write the correct word in each blank. Choose from the words below.

satisfactorily	receiving	aerial
noticeable	inquiry	trouble

1. My letter of _____ was answered promptly and courteously.

2. Mohammed _____ completed the application and turned it in.

3. Please try not to cause any more _____.

4. She took an _____ photograph from the small plane.

5. The spot on your shirt is not very _____.

6. Are you still _____ so much junk mail?

Protecting Our Resources

The words in this lesson cause many spelling errors. Study each word carefully. In sentences with missing letters, visualize the whole word, and write in the missing letters.

1. fertile   Farmers often use crop rotation to keep their soil fer′tile.
Pronounce *fertile* (fur′til) carefully. MEMO: A hostile reptile in a fertile field

2. field   That f*i*eld of cotton was his sole source of income.
MEMO: The field will yield.

3. yield   Using proper irrigation will produce a better crop y*i*eld.
Note the *i* before *e* in *yield, shield, wield,* and *field.*

■ A fert _ _ _ f _ _ ld of corn will y _ _ ld a large crop.

4. forest   Smoky the Bear reminds us to help prevent for′est fires.
Note the *fore* in *forest.*

5. realize   Do you re′al *ize* how important it is not to pollute the planet?
Note the *a* in *realize.* Pronounce each of the three syllables.

6. necessity   Finding ways to keep our water clean is a ne *ces*′*si* ty.
Center on the *cess* in *necessity.*

■ We r _ _ li _ _ the ne _ e _ _ ity of protecting the fo _ _ st.

7. often   Forest fires are of′*t*en caused by the carelessness of smokers.
Focus on the *oft* in *often.*

8. built   The Native Americans b*u*ilt their traditions on respect for nature.
MEMO: He built a quilt.

9. waste   The old saying "Wast*e* not, want not" is as true today as ever.
Distinguish *waste* from *waist.* MEMO: Don't waste your taste on paste.

■ Fires carelessly b _ _ lt of _ _ n cause great w _ st _ .

10. column   A huge col′um*n* of smoke rose from the forest fire.
Center on the *umn* in *column.* Think of a newspaper columnist.

11. fiery   The forest animals scurried away from their fi′*e* ry home.
Note the three syllables in *fiery.* Contrast *fire, fiery; wire, wiry.*

12. ascend   Pollution from our cars will as *cend*′ into the atmosphere.
Focus on the *sce* in *ascend.* Compare *descend, scene.*

■ The f _ _ ry col _ _ _ _ of smoke and flames began to a _ _ end still higher.

☐ EXERCISE I

Write the correct word in each blank. Choose from the words below.

fertile	field	waste	realize	necessity
often	built	column	fiery	ascend

1. The _____ blaze consumed three buildings before it could finally
   be stopped.

2. That _____ is being prepared for spring planting.

3. The old house was _____ in 1790.

4. A college degree is a _____ if you want to work in that field.

5. To come down was easy, but to _____ was very difficult.

6. We try never to _____ food.

7. That _____ field will be great for a huge garden.

8. We _____ speak of the good time we had in Chicago.

9. Is the _____ supporting the roof beginning to rot?

10. I didn't _____ it was so late!

☐ EXERCISE II

Each sentence contains one or more spelling errors. Cross out each misspelled word.
Then write the word correctly above it.

1. This area is very furtile, but crops will not be planted since a shopping mall will be

   bilt in this feild.

2. We have been told that the feild will yeild a huge crop of onions this spring.

3. I have offen said that it is a waist of time to complain about the neccessity of having

   to work.

4. What a waist to cut down such a beautiful forrest!

5. Did you realise how important that colum was to the building?

6. The natives bilt a shrine deep within the forrest.

Higher Education

Study longer words by syllables. Note the double accents in four words. In sentences with missing letters, visualize the whole word, and write in the missing letters.

1. **professor**   Dr. Spikes is a pro fes′ sor of adult education.
Note the *esso* in *professor*. Compare: *confess, confessor.*

2. **knowledge**   The idea behind a liberal arts education is to gain *knowl′ edge* in a wide variety of areas.
Note the *know* and the *ledge* in *knowledge.*

3. **thorough**   His college physics course was both thor′ ough and difficult.
Focus on the *ough* in *thorough.*

■ The pro __ es __ __ r had a tho __ __ ugh knowle __ __ e of chemistry.

4. **university**   She has been accepted by a u′ ni ver′ si ty of the first class.
Always spell *university* with two *i*'s. Compare *adversity.*

5. **months**   Each of the two college semesters lasted four months.
Center on the *ths* in *months.*

6. **calendar**   The university's academic year was not the same as a cal′ en dar year.
Center on the *dar* in *calendar.*

■ These mon __ h __ are the most important on the un __ ver __ __ ty cal __ nd __ r.

7. **college**   He enrolled in the Col′ *lege* of Engineering.
MEMO: A collection collected in college

8. **dormitory**   The girls liked living in a dor′ mi to′ ry.
Note the *it* in *dormitory*. Contrast the *at* in *reformatory.*

9. **sophomore**   Nancy's daughter is a soph′ o more in college.
Write three *o*'s in *sophomore.*
MEMO: The sophomore commodore

■ The so __ __ __ more stayed in the col __ __ g __ dorm __ t __ ry.

10. **laboratory**   Her college biology course included a lab′ o ra to′ ry section.
Note the *labor* in *laboratory.*

11. **examination**   The professor prepared a final ex am′ i na′ tion.
Notice the *i* in the middle of *examination.*

12. **studying**   The athletes were told to concentrate more on stud′ y ing.
Center on the *y* in *studying*. Compare *burying, copying, carrying.*

■ He was stud __ __ ng for an exam __ nat __ __ n on lab __ r __ t __ ry work.

60

☐ EXERCISE I

Write the correct word in each blank. Choose from the words below.

studying	laboratory	months	university	knowledge
examination	sophomore	college	thorough	professor

1. Margaret found that she had to do more _____ for the course.

2. Didn't that English _____ spend several months in England?

3. Isolda's _____ year was spent at the University of Michigan.

4. In order to learn the truth, one must pursue _____.

5. How many _____ are left in this semester?

6. Sam is making plans to attend a junior _____ for two years.

7. She hopes to enroll in a _____ in England.

8. She took an _____ to enter law school.

9. Steve and Bill gave the old house a _____ cleaning.

10. Each of the science experiments will be available in the _____.

☐ EXERCISE II

The following letter contains many spelling errors. Cross out each misspelled word. Then write the word correctly above the misspelled word.

Dear Marcia,

It seems that I have been in colege for years, but actually it has been only a few monthes. I looked at the calender today and realized that it is almost time to begin studiing for final examanations.

I have really enjoyed living in the dormetory this year, and I am looking forward to my sophomor year. I have really gotten a thorogh grounding in English fundamentals, and my French profesor says I might be able to take an advanced reading knowlege examenation next year. I will also be taking my first biology labratory course next year.

Sincerely,

Consumer Issues

Consult the dictionary whenever you are uncertain about the meaning or pronunciation of a word. Study each word carefully. In sentences with missing letters, visualize the whole word, and write in the missing letters.

1. accept   He could not ac *cept'* the salesperson's excuse.
Distinguish between *accept* and *except*. *Accept* gifts *except* from strangers.

2. explanation   He wrote an ex pla na' *tio*n to the Better Business Bureau.
Note the *plan* in *explanation*. Contrast *explain, explanation*.

3. weird   The new battery made a very w*ei*rd sound.
Focus on the *ei* in *weird*. MEMO: Their weird weight

■ **I didn't __ __ c __ pt the expl __ nat __ on that my car is supposed to make w __ __ rd sounds.**

4. does   Does this coffee maker come with a warranty?
Focus on the *oe* in *does*. Contrast *does, dose, dozen*.

5. since   It hadn't been a month sin*ce* she purchased the faulty product.
Distinguish *since* from *sense*. Compare *convince, prince*.

6. very   The customer was ver'y upset when his watch stopped.
Distinguish *very* from *vary*. Compare *ever, every*.

■ **It do __ __ not seem v __ r __ long sin __ __ we wrote our letter of complaint.**

7. popular   The saleswoman said that this model is more pop'u l*a*r.
Note the *lar* in *popular*. MEMO: The popular poplar

8. commission   The Federal Trade Com mis' *sio*n will discuss that issue.
Note the *mm* in *commission*. Compare *committee, community*.

9. receive   Make sure you re ceive' a receipt for your merchandise.
Focus on the *cei* in *receive*. Compare *deceive, conceive*.

■ **Did the pop __ l __ r salesperson rec __ __ v __ a co __ mis __ __ on?**

10. conceive   It's hard to con *ceive'* that a company could be so dishonest.
MEMO: Can you conceive of the conceit of the receiver's deceit?

11. situation   The Consumer Protection Division knew about the sit'u a' *tio*n.
Pronounce *situation* distinctly. Compare *valuation, continuation*.

12. deceive   Their policy is never to de *ceive'* a customer.
Contrast *deceive, deceit* with *receive, receipt*.

■ **We can conc __ __ v __ of a sit __ __ t __ on in which he can dec __ __ v __ us.**

☐ EXERCISE I

In each sentence, cross out the incorrect word in parentheses. Then write the correct word in the blank.

1. The Congressional budget has been in dispute (sense—since) last week.

_____

2. Many people feel it is important to be (popular—poplar).

_____

3. Would you (except—accept) a settlement in the case?

_____

4. Leticia gave an (explaination—explanation) for her behavior.

_____

5. (Does—Dose) the tribal council meet today?

_____

6. Whether to go to college is a (very—verry) important decision.

_____

7. Did Mr. Wong receive a (comission—commission) on the sale of the painting?

_____

8. That (sitation—situation) called for diplomatic conduct.

_____

9. Because the candidate didn't want to (deceive—decieve) the public, he made his voting record available to the media.

_____

☐ EXERCISE II

Supply *ei* or *ie* in each word. You may check the spelling of each word in the dictionary.

1. conc __ __ ve

2. recip __ __ nt

3. dec __ __ ve

4. rec __ __ ve

5. __ __ ther

6. w __ __ rd

REVIEW 4
Lessons 19–24

A. Supply *ei* or *ie* in each word.

1. v __ __ w

2. f __ __ ld

3. rec __ __ ving

4. dec __ __ ve

5. fr __ __ ght

6. rec __ __ ve

7. y __ __ ld

8. f __ __ ry

9. conc __ __ ve

10. w __ __ rd

Each correct answer is worth 3 points.	Total score: 30 points.

B. The following business letter contains many spelling errors. Cross out each misspelled word. Then write the word correctly above the misspelled word.

Dear Sir:

I am righting to you since I recaul a speach you made on TV that seemed vary ernest to me. You said if any of your customers ever had troble with one of your store's populer brands of dishwashers to let you here about the situaton that has ocurred.

I often have troubel with the new dishwasher I recently purchased at your store. I realise that it is almost impossibel to imagene that an enginear bilt a faulty dishwasher in the labratory of your factory. However, I would appreciate your making an inquirey into the matter so that you can send me through infermation on my lose wires.

I'm sure that the majority of your products are satisfactery, and that you will be anxious to remedy my situation. I realize that no company can achieve perfection all the time. I look forward to your responce.

Sincerely,

Each correct answer is worth 1 point.	Total score: 23 points.

C. In each sentence, find any misspelled words. Write each word correctly in the blank. If there are no misspelled words, write a _C_ in the blank.

_____ **1.** What is the name of your Spanish perfesser?

_____ **2.** She hung the humorous calender on the wall of her office.

_____ **3.** The janitorial service did a through job of cleaning.

_____ **4.** Do you plan to live in the dormetory next year?

_____ **5.** The invitacion was gladly accepted.

_____ **6.** The mayor says that raising revenues is a necesity.

_____ **7.** He has worked for the univercity for over twenty years.

_____ **8.** The earthquake was a trajedy.

_____ **9.** Will you recieve a comision on the sale?

_____ **10.** He mentioned that he might call us later today.

Each correct answer is worth 2 points.	Total score: 20 points.

D. In each group of words, cross out any misspelled words. Then write each word correctly in the blank. If there are no misspelled words, write a _C_ in the blank.

1. sophamore	plain	does	_____
2. enclose	mencioned	often	_____
3. column	waste	asend	_____
4. forest	realise.	studying	_____
5. explaination	moving	toward	_____
6. college	accept	commission	_____
7. examanation	months	discussion	_____
8. territory	preseed	passenger	_____
9. additional	envelope	adress	_____

Each correct answer is worth 3 points.	Total score: 27 points.

Law Enforcement

You will not master these words merely by reading the exercises. Study each word carefully. In sentences with missing letters, visualize the whole word, and write in the missing letters.

1. sheriff The sher′iff was sworn to uphold the law in the town.
Focus on the *iff* in *sheriff*. MEMO: After the tiff, the sheriff was miffed.

2. road The highway patrol barricaded the ro*a*d.
Distinguish *road* from *rode*. The rider *rode* down the *road*.

3. ninety The highway patrol clocked him going nine′ty miles an hour.
Note the *nine* in *ninety*. MEMO: Mine in nineteen-ninety-nine

■ The sh __ r __ __ f pursued him down the ro __ d for n __ n __ ty miles.

4. pursuit The police officer set off in p*ur* su*it*′ of the thief.
Note the *pur* in *pursuit*. MEMO: To suit the purpose of the pursuit

5. brief The victim was able to give only a br*ief* description of the robber.
Note the *ief* in *brief*. MEMO: His belief in the thief was brief.

6. stopped The police officer stop*ped* the speeding car.
Note the double *p* in *stopped*. Compare *hop, hopped*.

■ After a br __ __ f p __ rs __ __ t, the police officer st __ p __ __ __ the car.

7. meant The shot was me*a*nt to wound the robber.
Notice the *ea* in *meant*. MEMO: The flea meant to be mean.

8. cancel Since the suspect confessed, they′ll can′cel the investigation.
Focus on the *cel* in *cancel*. Contrast *canceling* with *cancellation*.

9. certificate The police lieutenant earned a cer tif′i *cate* of merit.
Note the *cert* in *certificate*. Compare *certain, certify*.

■ He m __ __ nt to can __ __ l the offender′s c __ rt __ fic __ t __ .

10. warrant The officer had a war′*r*ant to search the house.
Note the *arra* in *warrant*. Compare *narrate*; contrast *parent*.

11. thought The police tho*ught* Todd was the culprit all along.
Compare *thought, although, brought, thorough, fought*.

12. safety Police protect the citizens′ saf*e*′ty.
Keep the *safe* in *safety*. Contrast *safety* with *crafty*.

■ The sheriff th __ __ __ __ t that public saf __ t __ would war __ __ nt this action.

☐ EXERCISE I

Each sentence contains one or more spelling errors. Cross out each misspelled word. Then write the word correctly above it.

1. The shereff saw the car go off the rode.

2. Could your car have stoped in time to ensure maximum saffety?

3. If a warrent has been issued, only the state can cancal it.

4. The patrol car sped down the highway at ninty miles an hour in persuit of the

   bank robbers.

5. I only ment for you to write a breif report about your business trip.

6. The trust officer thout the certificete was in the defendant's name.

7. He called the sherif because he thouht he saw an intruder.

8. The Halloween prank was only maent to frighten her.

☐ EXERCISE II

Write the correct word in each blank. Choose from the words below.

brief	thought	sheriff	cancel	road
warrant	certificate	pursuit	safety	ninety

1. I want to _____ my subscription to that magazine.

2. For one _____ moment, he thought she recognized him.

3. The _____ never entered his mind.

4. The police chief, constable, and _____ all went to the conference.

5. She was given a _____ of appreciation for her heroism.

6. Shall we issue a _____ for his arrest?

7. Keep your eyes on the _____ when you drive.

8. When Harry turned _____, his family threw him a big party.

9. The child ran across the street in _____ of the ball.

10. The swimming coach emphasized water _____.

Smart Shopping

It will help you if you memorize the short sayings introduced by the word MEMO. Study each word carefully. In sentences with missing letters, visualize the whole word, and write in the missing letters.

1. **cashier** The cash *ier'* checked the expiration dates on the coupons.
Focus on the *ier* in *cashier*. Compare *frontier, pier, financier*.

2. **journal** The jour'nal carries many restaurant coupons every day.
Note the *our* in *journal*.

3. **available** How long will that special price be a v*ail'* a bl*e*?
Note the *ail* in *available*. MEMO: Ailing Able was not available.

■ **The c __ sh __ __ r kept a j __ __ rn __ l of which merchandise was av __ __ l __ bl __ .**

4. **taught** Their parents t*augh*t them to comparison shop.
Focus on the *augh* in *taught*. Compare *caught*; contrast *ought*.

5. **course** The consumer c*ourse* helped Luz become a smarter shopper.
Distinguish *course* from *coarse*.

6. **tuition** You must pay your tu i' *tio*n for the consumer course.
Focus on the *ui* in *tuition*. Pronounce each syllable distinctly.

■ **If you aren't satisfied with the consumer c __ __ rs __ she ta __ __ __ t, she will refund your tu __ t __ on.**

7. **past** In the past, he had not been careful to comparison shop.
Distinguish *past* from *passed*. Refer to the dictionary.

8. **future** In the fu'tur*e*, I will be a more informed shopper.
Stress the *u*'s in pronouncing *future*. Compare *nature*.

9. **latter** I prefer the former brand to the lat' *ter*.
MEMO: The latter letter was fatter and better.

■ **Because I paid too much at the lat __ __ r store in the p __ st, I will not shop there in the f __ t __ r __ .**

10. **medium** The me'di um eggs are a better buy than the small.
Focus on the *iu* in *medium*. Stress the *u* sound.

11. **chose** He carefully cho*se* between the two sale items.
Stress the *ose* in *chose*. Compare *nose, rose, suppose*.

12. **advertising** Ad' ver tis' ing often influences our decisions.
Focus on the *isi* in *advertising*. Compare *advising, rising*.

■ **They ch __ se to direct their adv __ rt __ s __ ng to m __ d __ __ m-sized cities.**

☐ EXERCISE I

The following business letter contains many spelling errors. Cross out each misspelled word. Then write the word correctly above the misspelled word.

Dear Mr. Russo:

We were delighted to receive your recent letter requesting our brochure listing

the coarses we teach relating to the field of advertisinng. We are pleased that

you choze our school, and our brochure is enclosed.

The later part of the brochure lists the advertesing courrses currently being

taght. The tuetion for each coarse is also listed. In the passed we have also offered

coarses in the various graphic medeums, and we hope to be able to make them

avalable again in the near futere.

We would be delighted to accept your application for registration for the fall

semester. Your summer work as a cashiar and as a writer on the *Evening Jornal*

should prove to be valuable experience for you.

                                        Sincerely yours,

☐ EXERCISE II

In each sentence, cross out each incorrect word in parentheses. Then write the correct word in the blank.

1. The (casheir—cashier) counted the money carefully. _____

2. I am almost sure his shirt size is (medium—median). _____

3. She kept a detailed (jernal—journal) of her trip. _____

4. He (chose—choose) not to go to the party. _____

5. The college professor (taut—taught) for thirty-three years. _____

6. Do you think the (latter—ladder) answer is the correct one? _____

7. How much is the (tuition—tuitian) at the state university? _____

8. That was a very interesting psychology (coarse—course). _____

Voting

Take time to review previous lessons. Frequent review is the key to recalling spellings correctly. Study each word carefully. In sentences with missing letters, visualize the whole word, and write in the missing letters.

1. **analyze**   I will an′a lyze both candidates' positions on that issue.
Focus on the *lyze* in *analyze*. Compare *paralyze*.

2. **essential**   Honesty is an es sen′ tial attribute in a candidate for office.
Note the *ess* in *essential*. Compare *essay, necessary*.

3. **scheme**   He came up with a *sche*me to raise money for the campaign.
MEMO: The schedule is not a scheme for a fool.

■ It is e __ sen __ __ al to an __ l __ ze the s __ __ em __ for getting more votes.

4. **assume**   I a*s* sume′ that she has facts to back up her statements.
Note the *ss* in *assume*. Compare *assure, assert, assist*.

5. **much**   There was too much mudslinging during the campaign.
Center on the *uch* in *much*. Contrast *clutch, crutch*.

6. **doubtful**   It looked dou*bt*′ful that her candidate would win.
Observe the *ful* in *doubtful*. Compare *thoughtful, resourceful*.

■ She was do __ __ tful about how m __ c __ she could safely a __ sum __ concerning the candidate.

7. **certainly**   The candidate cer′ta*in* ly had excellent debating skills.
Focus on the *ai* in *certainly*. Compare *certificate, captain*.

8. **proposition**   Will you vote for the prop′o si′ tion to build a new school?
Note the *sit* in *proposition*. Compare *composition, supposition*.

9. **whole**   The *w*hole debate was on that one campaign issue.
Note the *w* in *whole*. MEMO: The whole apple is full of holes.

■ C __ rt __ __ nl __, we must look at the __ hol __ pro __ __ si __ __ on before we vote.

10. **know**   Do you personally *k*now either candidate?
Note the *k* in *know*. Distinguish between know and no.
MEMO: Did he know that the knife would cut his knee?

11. **portion**   One por′ tion of the proposed amendment concerns me.
Note the *port* in *portion*. Compare *apportion, distortion*.

12. **evident**   The fact that he would lose the election was ev′ i dent.
Focus on the *ide* in *evident*. Compare *confident, accident*.

■ We __ no __ it's __ v __ d __ nt that a p __ rti __ __ of the people didn't vote.

EXERCISE I

Write the correct word in each blank. Choose from the words below.

know   assume   essential
much   scheme   analyze

1. I doubt that it would require _____ studying to complete the course.

2. You will be able to reach a solution if you _____ the problem carefully.

3. An ad valorem tax was _____ to the state's economy.

4. When will you _____ whether you can go with us to the boxing match?

5. The gambler's clever _____ to win at cards was finally discovered by the other players.

6. Eva will _____ the responsibilities of a complicated job.

EXERCISE II

In each sentence, find any misspelled words. Write each word correctly in the blank.
If there are no misspelled words, write a *C* in the blank.

_____ **1.** It is essential that we analize our budget carefully before we purchase an automobile.

_____ **2.** It is extremely doutful that such a huge amount of money can be raised so quickly.

_____ **3.** Scott certinly made a good impression when he went in for a job interview.

_____ **4.** The third propersition on the ballot carried by only a small majority.

_____ **5.** We watched the whole thing from our window, and called the police.

_____ **6.** Please give each person an equal porsion of the cherry pie.

_____ **7.** The officer said it was certinly evident that the burglar broke in through the sliding glass door.

_____ **8.** It is evedent that we will be unable to reach the mountains until tomorrow.

_____ **9.** This equipment will be essenchul to you in your new job.

The U.S. Government

Study each word carefully. In sentences with missing letters, visualize the whole word, and write in the missing letters.

1. accurate A census is an ac' cu rate count of the people in the U.S.
Note the *rate* in *accurate*.

2. secretary He works as a sec' re tar' y in the Department of Labor.
Note the *secret* in *secretary*. Contrast *military, dignitary*.

3. society Government brings order to so ci' e ty.
Focus on the *iet* in *society*. Contrast *social, sociable*.

■ The secr __ t __ r __ of the so __ __ __ ty of government workers to which I belong kept an ac __ __ r __ t __ account.

4. statement The mayor made a state' ment to the public.
MEMO: The late statement rates early payment.

5. parliament Members of a par' li*a* ment are similar to our Senators and Representatives.
See the dictionary for the pronunciation of *parliament*.

6. tomorrow The general election is to mor' row.
Stress the two *r*'s in *tomorrow*.

■ The British Prime Minister will make a st __ t __ m __ nt before the Parl __ __ m __ nt tom __ r __ __ w.

7. economy The e con' o my will be an issue in the upcoming election.
Stress the two *o*'s in *economy*. Contrast *enemy*.

8. administration President Reagan's ad min' is tra' *tio*n lasted eight years.
MEMO: I admit I admire the current administration.

9. refer They will probably re fer' the case to the Supreme Court.
Note that *refer* is spelled the same forward and backward.

■ He will r __ f __ r to the need for ec __ n __ __ y in the ad __ in __ s __ __ at __ on.

10. solemn The judge always looked sol' em*n* in court.
Focus on the *mn* in *solemn*. MEMO: The solemn hymn

11. occasion The inauguration was a happy oc ca' sio*n* for the president.
Emphasize the two *c*'s and one *s* in *occasion*.

12. probably He will prob' a bly be elected to another term in the Senate.
Stress the *ab* in *probably*. Compare *notable, notably*.

■ This meeting of the Cabinet will prob __ __ __ y be a s __ l __ __ n oc __ a __ __ on.

☐ EXERCISE I

In each sentence, cross out the incorrect word in parentheses. Then write the correct word in the blank.

1. The wedding was a joyful (occassion—occasion).

_____

2. A healthy (econamy—economy) is necessary to any system of government.

_____

3. (Referr—Refer) to the dictionary if you are not sure of a word's spelling.

_____

4. We will (probablly—probably) leave before the refreshments are served.

_____

5. The newspaper account wasn't (accurate—accurrate).

_____

6. Ms. Perkins has one of the best executive (secretary—secrretary) positions.

_____

7. It was one of the most (solem—solemn) moments in our country's history.

_____

8. Prepare a (statement—statment) for the press, and check all the facts.

_____

☐ EXERCISE II

In each sentence, find any misspelled words. Write each word correctly in the blank. If there are no misspelled words, write a *C* in the blank.

_____ 1. My friend wants to become a secertary and will start school tomorrow.

_____ 2. You may read it if you wish, but I seldom read the sociaty section of the newspaper.

_____ 3. That statement was made in haste.

_____ 4. Parliament will be in session tomorrow, and the prime minister will probably speak.

_____ 5. Do you think that the economy will improve while this adminestration is in office?

_____ 6. It was a solemn occassion when the president announced that troops had been sent to that country.

_____ 7. Do you think his statement that the environment will probably not be endangered by the pipeline is accarate?

The Legal System

Observe the hard spots printed in italics. Study each word carefully. In sentences with missing letters, visualize the whole word, and write in the missing letters.

1. **accommodate**   The jail can *ac* com' *mo* dat*e* two hundred prisoners.
                        Focus on the *cc* in *accommodate*. Compare *account*.

2. **quite**   The jury was q*uite* confused by the conflicting testimony.
                        Distinguish *quite* from *quiet*. He was *quiet* for *quite* a while.

3. **possible**   Is it pos' *si* bl*e* that he could be acquitted?
                        Stress the *sib* in *possible*. Compare *possibly*, *possibility*.

■ It is q __ __ t __ p __ s __ __ bl __ that the prison will ac __ __ m __ __ dat __ a few more inmates.

4. **attorney**   The *at* tor' ney presented the case clearly.
                        Note the *torn* in *attorney*. Focus on the *ey* ending.

5. **persuade**   The attorney hopes to per s*uade'* the jury.
                        Emphasize the *sua* in *persuade*. Compare *person*.

6. **seems**   It really se*ems* like an open-and-shut case.
                        Distinguish *seems* from *seams*. This dress *seems* to have no *seams*.

■ It s __ __ ms the at __ __ rn __ __ could not p __ rs __ __ d __ us.

7. **appeal**   The prisoner made an a*p* pe*al'* to the warden.
                        MEMO: Its appearance appeals.

8. **modifies**   If he mod' i f*ies* his behavior, he could be released early.
                        Observe the *ifi* in *modifies*. Compare *notifies*, *dignifies*.

9. **governor**   Do you think the gov' er nor will grant them amnesty?
                        Stress the *ver* and *nor* in *governor*. Compare *govern*.

■ She m __ d __ f __ __ s her ap __ __ __ l to the g __ v __ __ n __ r.

10. **congratulate**   I want to con grat' u late the winning attorney.
                        Note the *tu* in *congratulate*. Compare *natural*, *saturate*.

11. **innocent**   The jury found the accused woman in' *no c*ent.
                        Note the *cent* in *innocent*.

12. **hoping**   The prisoner was hop' ing for a different verdict.
                        Compare *hope*, *hoping; rope*, *roping; type*, *typing*.

■ His friends believed he was in __ o __ __ nt and were h __ p __ __ g to c __ ngra __ __ l __ t __ him on his acquittal.

☐ EXERCISE I

Write each italicized word correctly in the first blank. In the second blank, write the word or phrase in dark print that most nearly means the same as the word.

1. *appeal:*   **appear, request, applause**   _____   _____

2. *congratulate:*   **wish well, compensate, omit**   _____   _____

3. *modifies:*   **transfers, retires, changes**   _____   _____

4. *persuade:*   **punish, convince, comfort**   _____   _____

5. *possible:*   **strange, feasible, exceptional**   _____   _____

6. *innocent:*   **guilty, faulty, guiltless**   _____   _____

7. *governor:*   **speaker, guest, leader**   _____   _____

8. *attorney:*   **plaintiff, lawyer, defendant**   _____   _____

9. *quite:*   **very, quiet, quit**   _____   _____

10. *seems:*   **appears, lines, seams**   _____   _____

11. *accommodate:*   **remove, avoid, hold**   _____   _____

12. *hoping:*   **wishing, waiting, hopping**   _____   _____

☐ EXERCISE II

Each sentence contains one or more spelling errors. Cross out each misspelled word. Then write the word correctly above it.

1. It will be quiet posible for us to acommodate your party on that night.

2. We were hopeing that it would be posibble to congratalate the new champion.

3. We were hoping that the atorney would prove the defendant innosent.

4. They were hoping to accomodate their guests.

5. The govenor looked quiet handsome in his tuxedo.

6. Do you think she'll be able to pursuade the jury that he is innacent?

7. It seams possible that she'll be promoted to vice president.

8. He will try to pursuade the candidate to change his position.

Buying a House

Refer to the dictionary for the correct pronunciations of *partner* and *mortgage*. Study each word carefully. In sentences with missing letters, visualize the whole word, and write in the missing letters.

1. **partner**   He asked his business par*t'* ner to co-sign his home loan.
Note the *part* in *partner*. Say *partner*, not *pardner*.

2. **extension**   They are giving the seller an ex ten*'* *sio*n of the deadline.
Focus on the *sio* in *extension*.

3. **mortgage**   What will my monthly mor*t'* ga*ge* payments be?
Note the silent *t* in *mortgage*. MEMO: Mort mortgaged it.

■ **Her p __ r __ n __ r asked for an ext __ n __ __ on on the m __ r __ g __ g __ .**

4. **security**   The bank demanded se cu*'* ri ty for the loan.
Stress the *it* in *security*.

5. **customer**   She was the fifth cus*'* tom er to apply for a home loan that day.
Focus on the *usto* in *customer*. Compare *custom, accustomed.*

6. **remit**   Kindly re mit*'* your mortgage payment as soon as possible.
Note the *it* ending in *remit*. Compare *permit, profit.*

■ **If the bank c __ st __ m __ r does not r __ m __ t his loan payment, he will lose the house he used as s __ c __ r __ t __ for the loan.**

7. **application**   I will make an ap*'* *p*li ca*'* *tio*n for our home loan tomorrow.
Focus on the *ppl* in *application*. Compare *apply, applied.*

8. **terms**   They agreed on the terms of the contract.
Stress the *erms* ending in *terms*. Compare *germs.*

9. **quote**   What interest rate did she *qu*ote you for the home loan?
Remember that *q* is always followed by *u*.

■ **Please remember that the t __ rm __ I am about to q __ __ t __ may change by the time you make your ap __ __ __ ca __ __ on.**

10. **approval**   They were anxiously awaiting a*p* prov*'* al of their home loan.
MEMO: We appreciate the appropriate approval.

11. **concession**   The seller of the house made a con ces*'* *sio*n to the buyer.
Focus on the *cess* in *concession*. Contrast *session, possession.*

12. **amount**   What will the total a mount*'* of my house payment be?
Stress the *ount* in *amount*. Compare *mount, mountain.*

■ **The seller gave his ap __ r __ v __ l to a c __ n __ __ s __ __ on in the am __ __ nt of $500.**

☐ EXERCISE I

Write the correct word in each blank. Choose from the words below.

extension	remit	approval	mortgage	amount	security
concession	terms	application	customer	quote	partner

1. Will she and her _____ agree to the _____ of the contract?

2. With the _____ of the credit manager, we will obtain an

   _____ on the loan.

3. Ms. Sato called to verify the _____ owed on your _____ .

4. Each _____ is required to fill out an _____ for credit.

5. No _____ will be made on the amount each buyer is required

   to _____ .

6. He'll _____ her the amount of _____ required for the
   home loan.

☐ EXERCISE II

The following business letter contains many spelling errors. Cross out each misspelled word. Write the word correctly above the misspelled word.

Dear Mr. Haynes:

We have received your letter requesting an extention on the tirms of your

morgage loan. Our senior pardner, Roberta Johnson, submitted your aplication

to our board of directors for their approval.

We are happy to inform you that, since you are a reliable customar of our bank,

the board has approved the extinsion of your morgage loan. This concesion is

made in view of your excellent credit rating. Additional securaty will not be

required, and you may remitt your payment each month as quotted in your

payment book. The total ammount of your loan will not change; however, interest

charges will be added.

We are happy to have served you and look forward to serving you in the future.

Sincerely,

A. In each sentence, find any misspelled words. Write each word correctly in the blank. If there are no misspelled words, write a *C* in the blank.

_____ 1. The safty of that toy is doubtful.

_____ 2. The administration issued a statment denying the allegation.

_____ 3. Gabriela works as a cashier because she needs a regular paycheck.

_____ 4. The govenor is starting a campaign against false advertising.

_____ 5. James thinks the propesition will probably pass.

_____ 6. An extension on our loan will certinly help our financial situation.

_____ 7. He has never stopped trying to earn his father's approval.

_____ 8. The judge's statment was certainly brief.

Each correct answer is worth 2 points.	Total score: 16 points.

B. In each sentence, cross out the incorrect word in parentheses. Then write the correct word in the blank.

1. Has your dog had a rabies shot in the (past—passed) year?

_____

2. The doctor told us she was on the (rode—road) to recovery.

_____

3. Have you (taught—taut) your new puppy any tricks yet?

_____

4. The golf (course—coarse) was designed by a real pro.

_____

5. I don't believe that (warrent— warrant) is valid.

_____

6. The (whole—hole) story appeared to be made up.

_____

7. His entire story (seams—seems) strange to me.

_____

8. I think we should order the (medium—median) pizza.

_____

Each correct answer is worth 3 points.	Total score: 24 points.

C. The following business letter contains many spelling errors. Cross out each misspelled word. Write the word correctly above the misspelled word.

Dear Sirs:

I am writing to apeal the traffic ticket I received on June 21. When the person from the sherrif's office stoped me on the rode after a very breif persuit, he said I was doing ninty miles an hour in a sixty-five mile-an-hour zone. I asume that it is quiet possibel, but I think it was certanly doubtfull that ninty was my acurrate speed. I no I was going munch slower—probibly more like seventy.

In the passed, I have taken a defensive driving coarse and no the ammount of trouble a person who does not obey the traffic laws can get into. I also kno that traffic laws are an important part of our sesiety.

I am hopping that this statement of my solem promise to drive more slowly in the futuer will persuade you to analize the situation and make a concesion this time. While I am not entirely inocent of the speeding charge, I do not believe I was driving as fast as the officer said I was.

Thank you for considering my apeal.

Sincerely,

Each correct answer is worth 1½ points.	Total score: 45 points.

D. In each group of words, find any misspelled words. Then write each word correctly in the blank. If there are no misspelled words, write a _C_ in the blank.

1. morgage   journal   portion   _____

2. congratulate   ment   secretary   _____

3. application   terms   quote   _____

4. analyze   remit   evadent   _____

5. tommorow   refer   modifies   _____

Each correct answer is worth 3 points.	Total score: 15 points.

Physical Fitness

Focus your attention on the double letters in the words below. In sentences with missing letters, visualize the whole word, and write in the missing letters.

1. **instructor**   Tammy is my favorite aerobics in struc′ tor.
MEMO: The professor as instructor was both actor and conductor.

2. **genius**   Even a gen′ ius should develop himself or herself physically.
Focus on the ius in genius. Contrast religious, generous.

3. **brilliant**   Installing fitness equipment at the office was a bril′ liant idea.
MEMO: A brilliant illiterate in Illinois

■ The physical fitness inst __ __ c __ __ r was br __ l __ __ __ nt, but not a g __ n __ __ s.

4. **committee**   The com mit′ tee voted to provide physical fitness equipment.
Note the double letters in committee.

5. **recommend**   Please rec′ om mend′ a good brand of treadmill.
Focus on the mm in recommend. Compare recollect.

6. **equipment**   That athletic club keeps its e quip′ ment in good working order.
Note the equip in equipment. Compare shipment.

■ The com __ __ __ te __ decided to rec __ m __ __ nd buying new physical fitness eq __ __ pm __ nt.

7. **gymnasium**   He usually works out at the gym na′ si um during lunch.
Focus on the gym in gymnasium. Compare gymnast, gypsy.

8. **faculty**   The college began a fitness program for its fac′ ul ty and staff.
Stress the ul in faculty. Compare culture, difficulty.

9. **preferred**   She much pre ferr ed′ walking to jogging.
Focus on the rr in preferred. Compare referred, conferred.

■ Most of the f __ c __ lt __ pre __ __ r __ __ d the new g __ mn __ s __ __ m.

10. **wholly**   He was whol′ ly responsible for his lack of physical fitness.
Note the unusual ll in wholly. Contrast solely, wholesome.

11. **procedure**   What is the pro ce′ dure for enrolling in aerobics classes?
Focus on the ced in procedure. Contrast proceed, proceeding.

12. **concerning**   He is interested in everything con cern′ ing physical fitness.
Note the cer in concerning. MEMO: Concerning the concert

■ They were __ hol __ __ agreed c __ n __ __ rn __ ng the best pr __ __ ed __ r __ for getting in shape.

☐ EXERCISE I

Each sentence contains one or more spelling errors. Cross out each misspelled word. Then write the word correctly above it.

1. We had a conversation conserning his behavior.

2. What is the correct prosedure for obtaining a driver's license?

3. I am wholy convinced that she is telling the truth.

4. He prefered to stay home tonight.

5. What kind of equipement will I need to climb the mountain?

6. She is an excellent instructer.

☐ EXERCISE II

In each sentence, find any misspelled words. Write each word correctly in the blank. If there are no misspelled words, write a *C* in the blank.

_____ 1. Never before had all of the school's facilty attended a meeting of the school board.

_____ 2. Will the appropriations committee recomend passage of the bill?

_____ 3. Our instructor's lecture was brief, but brilliant.

_____ 4. Ms. Mendoza told us that genuss was mostly attention to detail.

_____ 5. The employees were pleased that the new equippment had arrived for the cafeteria.

_____ 6. Martha prefered to read the sports page before the front page.

_____ 7. What did the instructor say concerning our assignment for the remainder of the week?

_____ 8. Albert Einstein was a geneus.

_____ 9. The gymnaseum was filled to capacity.

_____ 10. The program comittee meets today.

_____ 11. It was the most brillient rainbow I had ever seen.

_____ 12. I think Henry will make a good English instructer.

Buying a Car

Study each word carefully. Note the separate syllables. In sentences with missing letters, visualize the whole word, and write in the missing letters.

1. assure   Can you *as* sure' me that this car had only one owner?
Note the *ss* in *assure*. MEMO: I assure you, I will assist you.

2. descend   To see our latest model, descend' the stairs to the showroom.
Focus on the *sce* in *descend*. Compare *ascend*; contrast *decent*.

3. practical   She was looking for a prac' ti cal car rather than a luxury model.
Stress the *cal* in *practical*. Compare *medical, vertical*.

   ■ We as __ __ r __ you that, if you de __ __ __ nd the stairs, we will show you a pr __ ct __ c __ l car.

4. suggest   Can you sug gest' a reputable car dealership in town?
MEMO: I suggest that you suffer from sudden success.

5. syllable   To pronounce the name of the car, stress the first syl' la ble.
Focus on the *syll* in *syllable*. Stress the *able* ending.

6. pronounce   I can't pro nounce' the name of that new foreign car.
MEMO: Pronounce the *ounce* in *announce* and *denounce*.

   ■ I sug __ __ st that you pr __ n __ __ n __ __ each s __ l __ __ bl __ in the new car's name distinctly.

7. desert   He took the car on a test drive in the des' ert.
Note that *des' ert* means a sandy waste; *de sert'*, to abandon.

8. attacked   Roberto *at* tacked' the task of buying a new car with gusto.
Distinguish *attacked* from *attached*.

9. prior   She read a consumer magazine pri' or to buying a car.
Focus on the *or* in *prior*. MEMO: Junior is prior to senior.

   ■ Pr __ __ r to being at __ __ c __ __ d as an unsafe car, it had undergone extensive field tests in the d __ s __ rt.

10. purpose   The pur' pose of a test drive is to see how well a car handles.
MEMO: The purple purse's purpose

11. courtesy   The salesperson extended every cour' te sy to the buyer.
Note the *court* in *courtesy*. Compare *courteous, courage*.

12. oblige   Going for a test drive will not o blige' you to buy a car.
Focus on the *lige* in *oblige*. Contrast *obligation, privilege*.

   ■ The p __ rp __ s __ of her c __ __ rt __ s __ is to obl __ g __ the customer.

☐ EXERCISE I

In each sentence, cross out the incorrect word in parentheses. Then write the correct word in the blank.

1. Jack could (suggest—sugest) only one solution to the problem.

_____

2. The (purpus—purpose) of the move is to acquire more office space.

_____

3. (Pronounce—Pronounse) each word distinctly so that everyone in the audience can hear you.

_____

4. Can you (dessend—descend) the staircase without tripping on the hem of your evening dress?

_____

5. The army (attackted—attacked) the fortress.

_____

6. The nomads stopped at an oasis in the (dessert—desert).

_____

7. If Lindsay's suggestion seems (pracktical—practical), use it in completing the experiment.

_____

8. It is only common (cortesy—courtesy) to ask permission to leave the table.

_____

☐ EXERCISE II

In each sentence, find any misspelled words. Write each word correctly in the blank. If there are no misspelled words, write a *C* in the blank.

_____ 1. I assure you that we will be there prier to the start of the program.

_____ 2. The purpose of that lesson was to make you aware of each sylable in each word.

_____ 3. Great sand dunes in the dessert were being shifted by the strong winds.

_____ 4. It is not practicle to suggest that we can handle all of these projects.

_____ 5. The village was attacked yesterday, but we never understood why.

_____ 6. I suggest that you oblige the mountain-climbing team by providing hot food when they dessend from the mountain.

Marriage

Consult the dictionary for the correct pronunciation of *g* in *privilege, ought, marriage, league,* and *vinegar.* Study each word carefully. In the sentences with missing letters, visualize the whole word, and write in the missing letters.

1. **Christian** Their wedding was conducted in the Chris'tian tradition.
   Note that *Christian* begins with a capital letter.

2. **privilege** I wonder who will have the priv'i le*ge* of being his best man.
   Note the *ivil* in *privilege.* Compare *civil*; contrast *knowledge.*

3. **civilization** Marriage has long been a part of civ'i li za'tion.
   Focus on the *liz* in *civilization.* Note the four *i*'s in *civilization.*

   ■ The C __ r __ st __ __ n minister said the newlyweds should recognize that it is a pr __ v __ le __ __ to live in this civ __ l __ z __ t __ __ n.

4. **ought** They *ought* to have tied the wedding ring to the pillow.
   MEMO: He ought to have thought about what he bought.

5. **marriage** Their mar'*r*iage vows meant a great deal to them.
   Note the *age* in *marriage.* Compare *carry, carriage.*

6. **jealous** If a husband and wife have trust, they won't be j*eal*'ous.
   Note the *a* in *jealous.* MEMO: Better zealous than jealous

   ■ A new couple o __ __ __ t not to be j __ __ l __ __ s after mar __ __ a __ __.

7. **association** The wedding band has an a*s* so'*ci* a'*tio*n with eternity.

8. **league** All the groomsmen were the groom's softball le*ague* friends.
   Note the peculiar *ague* ending in *league.* Contrast *fatigue.*

9. **forty** The Meyers just celebrated for'ty years of marriage.
   Observe that *forty* omits the *u* correctly found in *four.*

   ■ F __ rt __ married couples with young children formed an as __ __ c __ __ t __ __ n called the New Parents L __ __ g __ __.

10. **alcohol** At the wedding reception, there was a punch with al'co hol.
    Note the *oho* in *alcohol.* Stress the *alco* beginning.

11. **vinegar** The bride's mother reminded her, "You can catch more flies with honey than with vin'e *gar.*"
    Note the *vine* in *vinegar.* Compare *cigar.* Contrast *beggar.*

12. **quantity** The bride and groom had a large *quan*'ti ty of gifts to open.

   ■ He said the wedding reception lasted so long that a q __ __ nt __ t __ of wine containing alc __ h __ l changed to v __ n __ g __ r before it was over.

☐ EXERCISE I

In each sentence, find any misspelled words. Write each word correctly in the blank. If there are no misspelled words, write a *C* in the blank.

_____ 1. Who was it that said, "Life begins at fourty"?

_____ 2. An associasion of business executives can do much for the development of new industry in the city.

_____ 3. The history of Roman civilisation reflects the strength of the founders of that nation.

_____ 4. How many teams were needed to complete the leage?

_____ 5. Sara Gomez has been granted the privalege of addressing the state legislature.

_____ 6. Marriage counseling is one of the many services offered.

☐ EXERCISE II

In each sentence, cross out the incorrect word in parentheses. Then write the correct word in the blank.

1. Was there once an advanced (civilization—civilisation) here?

_____

2. It is a (privilige—privilege) to be invited to speak to this group.

_____

3. There is a great (quanity—quantity) of grain stored in that silo.

_____

4. You can certainly taste the (vinegar—vinager) in this salad.

_____

5. The speaker was discussing the (Christian—Christiain) religion.

_____

6. Are you (jealous—jelous) of the attention that your friend is getting?

_____

7. Who won the football (league—leage) championship?

_____

8. That is the largest (association—asociation) in the state.

_____

9. You (ought—auht) to rest for an hour before you go back to work.

_____

10. It isn't wise to drive while drinking (alkohol—alcohol).

_____

Sports

Study each word carefully. In sentences with missing letters, visualize the whole word, and write in the missing letters.

1. **athletics** Skill in ath let'ics requires much practice.
Limit *athletics* to three syllables. Compare *athlete*.

2. **pleasure** You should participate in sports for the ple*as'*ur*e* of it.
Focus on the *lea* in *pleasure*. MEMO: Treasure a measure of pleasure.

3. **exercise** Playing basketball is good ex'er cise.
Focus on the *cise* in *exercise*. Contrast *leisure*. MEMO: It's wise to rise and exercise.

■ Participating in ath __ __ t __ cs gives both pl __ __ s __ re and ex __ r __ i __ e.

4. **athlete** The ath'let*e* increased his endurance greatly.
Limit *athlete* to two syllables. Compare *complete*.

5. **perspiration** The per'spi ra'tio*n* dripped from the runners' faces.
Focus on the *per* and the *spi* in *perspiration*.

6. **tournament** The winner of the tennis tour'na ment was sixteen years old.
Note the *tour* in *tournament*. Compare *tourist, touring*.

■ Every ath __ __ t __ in the t __ __ rn __ m __ nt was covered with
p __ __ __ p __ ration.

7. **amateur** The am'a *teur* golfer played like a professional.
Note the unusual *teur* in *amateur*. MEMO: I am an amateur.

8. **strength** The wrestler's muscular streng*th* is enormous.
Focus on the *gth* in *strength*. Compare *length, width*.

9. **physical** Football is a highly phy'*s*i cal sport.
Note the *physic* in *physical*. Compare *physician, physics*.

■ As an am __ t __ __ r, I work hard to increase my __ h __ sic __ l stren __ __ __ .

10. **practically** The game was prac'ti cal *ly* over before the coach put him in.
Note the *ally* in *practically*. Compare *medically, vertically*.

11. **exhausted** The players seemed ex haust'ed as they left the field.
Focus on the *haus* in *exhausted*. Remember the silent *h*.
MEMO: The exhausted runner exhaled loudly.

12. **bicycle** Always use bi'*cy* cle lanes when they are provided.
Remember that the *bi* in *bicycle* means *two*. Compare *biplane*.

■ The b __ c __ cle rider who just passed was pra __ t __ c __ l __ y
ex __ __ __ sted.

EXERCISE I

Write the correct form in each blank. When you have completed the exercise, check your answers in the dictionary.

1. Don't you think a contractor should have (practically) as well as theoretical knowledge?

2. There were two (amateur) and two professionals on each team.

3. Eric lifts weights in order to shape his body and (strength) his muscles.

4. Are Linda and Carlos (bicycle) today?

5. Winning the title would (pleasure) her greatly.

6. If you are (perspiration) heavily, take a cool shower and change into fresh clothes.

7. The trainer was (exercise) the horses.

8. Although the car wreck frightened her and damaged her car, she was not hurt (physical).

9. Does physical exercise (exhausted) you?

10. She is an extremely (athletics) young woman.

EXERCISE II

In each sentence, cross out the incorrect word in parentheses. Then write the correct word in the blank.

1. The university spends a great deal of money on (atheletics—athletics).

2. Swimming is excellent (excercise—exercise).

3. Tom is going to make a superb (athlete—athelete).

4. The sweatband helped keep the (prespiration—perspiration) from running into his eyes.

5. The (tournament—tournement) will be played this month.

6. She gained a lot of (strenth—strength) over the summer.

Banking

There is no rule to govern the spelling of words ending in *ance*. Learn to associate them with each other. Study each word carefully. In sentences with missing letters, visualize the whole word, and write in the missing letters.

1. **resistance**   The elderly man's family overcame his re sist' ance to keeping his money in a bank.

2. **remittance**   The bank provided a self-addressed, stamped envelope for his re mit' tance.

3. **insurance**   FDIC stands for the Federal Deposit In sur' ance Corporation.

■ He made no re __ ist __ n __ e to paying the re __ it __ __ nce for his __ nsu __ __ n __ e and immediately wrote a check on his bank account.

4. **acceptance**   The bank's ac cept' ance of their home loan application pleased them.

5. **nuisance**   It is a nui' sance when the automatic teller machine is out of order.

6. **accordance**   She filled out the loan application in ac cord' ance with the bank's requirements.

■ Her __ c __ ept __ n __ e of the nu __ s __ __ c __ was in ac __ ord __ n __ e with her good feelings about the bank.

7. **remembrance**   His re mem' brance of the loan officer's helpfulness is the reason he banks there today.

8. **acquaintance**   He ran into an old ac quaint' ance while he was standing in line at the bank.

9. **appearance**   The new bank building gave the ap pear' ance of stability.

■ The ap __ e __ r __ n __ e of his old banking a __ q __ __ __ __ nt __ nc __ brought back many a rem __ __ br __ n __ e.

10. **assurance**   The bank official gave me every as sur' ance about the safety of my deposit.

11. **maintenance**   In return for the main' te nance of a minimum balance in my checking account, I will not pay a service charge.

12. **assistance**   For as sist' ance with your account, call your banker.

■ He received as __ ur __ nc __ of continued as __ ist __ nc __ in the m __ __ nt __ n __ n __ e of his bank records.

☐ EXERCISE I

Write each italicized word correctly in the first blank. In the second blank, write the word or phrase in dark print that most nearly means the same as the word.

1. *assurance:*   **promotion, promise, neglect**   _____ _____

2. *acquaintance:*   **friend, enemy, relative**   _____ _____

3. *acceptance:*   **deliberation, denial, approval**   _____ _____

4. *accordance:*   **agreement, motionless, recount**   _____ _____

5. *appearance:*   **looks, dissipation, language**   _____ _____

6. *assistance:*   **hindrance, help, assignment**   _____ _____

7. *remembrance:*   **renewal, renown, recollection**   _____ _____

8. *resistance:*   **ferocity, opposition, efficient**   _____ _____

9. *remittance:*   **payment, information, method**   _____ _____

10. *maintenance:*   **violence, upkeep, patience**   _____ _____

11. *insurance:*   **guarantee, measurement, payment**   _____ _____

12. *nuisance:*   **aid, promise, pest**   _____ _____

☐ EXERCISE II

The words in this lesson are formed by adding the suffix *ance* to a root word. In the blanks that follow each word, write the root word from which each word is formed. Only one word is not formed from a root word. Write an *X* in the blank that follows that word.

1. resistance _____

2. remittance _____

3. insurance _____

4. acceptance _____

5. nuisance _____

6. accordance _____

7. remembrance _____

8. acquaintance _____

9. appearance _____

10. assurance _____

11. maintenance _____

12. assistance _____

Holidays

The following list contains six pairs of similar words which are frequently confused. Consult the dictionary for the exact meaning of each word. In the sentences with missing letters, visualize the whole word, and write in the missing letters.

1. **forth**   Columbus Day honors the man who set forth on a dangerous voyage to the Indies.
Distinguish *forth* from *fourth*. MEMO: Go forth for a fortune.

2. **fourth**   The Fourth of July is a national holiday.
Note the *four* in *fourth*. Compare *fourteen*; contrast *forty-one*.

3. **piece**   I always eat a p*iece* of pie on Thanksgiving.
Distinguish *piece* from *peace*. MEMO: A piece of pie.

■ They brought f __ __ th the f __ __ rth p __ __ ce of cake for the holiday picnic.

4. **peace**   Veterans' Day honors those who kept p*eace* in our country.
Focus on the *eace* in *peace*. Compare *peaceful*.

5. **principal**   Christmas is the prin' ci p*al* Christian holiday.
MEMO: That school principal is my principle pal.

6. **principle**   We celebrate Lincoln's birthday to honor a man of prin' ci p*le*.
MEMO: A sensible principle

■ The princ __ p __ __ princ __ p __ __ of observing V-J Day is to commemorate the end of World War II and the return of pe __ c __ .

7. **prophesy**   Can you prop*h*' e *s*y the weather for Memorial Day?
Distinguish *prophesy* (to foretell) from *prophecy* (a prediction).

8. **prophecy**   Christmas is celebrated as the fulfillment of a prop*h*' e *c*y.
Stress the *cy* (si) ending of *prophecy*. Focus on the *phe*.

9. **counsel**   She went to a party planner for coun' *sel* on her Easter party.
Distinguish *counsel* from *council*. Focus on the *sel*.

■ Knowing John's ability to pro __ he __ y, we took coun __ __ __ over his pro __ he __ y of rain for the Fourth of July.

10. **council**   The City Coun' *cil* voted to hold a Thanksgiving Day parade.
Focus on the *cil* in *council*. Think of a *city* counc*il*.

11. **compliment**   Marsha received a com' pl*i* ment on her holiday decorations.

12. **complement**   The flags were a perfect com' pl*e* ment to the holiday decor.

■ I would like to compl __ m __ nt the coun __ __ __ on finding the perfect Christmas decorations to compl __ m __ nt our downtown district.

□ EXERCISE I

Write the correct word in each blank. Choose from the words below.

complement   principle   council   peace
compliment   principal   counsel   piece

1. Sam felt the _____ should gather to discuss the question of tribal unity.

2. Ms. Andrews is the school _____.

3. Two colors which _____ each other are blue and yellow.

4. The _____ treaty set down the conditions to be observed by the two countries.

5. Domita found that she could eat only one _____ of the cherry pie.

6. The _____ at stake in that court case is freedom of speech.

7. A simple "Thank you" is the best response to any _____.

8. If you are looking for good advice, it would be wise to seek the _____ of some expert in the field.

□ EXERCISE II

In each sentence, cross out the incorrect word in parentheses. Then write the correct word in the blank.

1. She didn't know how to respond to the generous (complement—compliment).

_____

2. Could you (prophesy—prophecy) the ending of the movie? _____

3. She went to a lawyer for (council—counsel). _____

4. This is the (forth—fourth) time I've asked you to stop. _____

5. The bright tie was a perfect (compliment—complement) to the suit. _____

6. Her (prophecy—prophesy) proved correct. _____

7. The speaker held (fourth—forth) on the subject of poverty. _____

8. The city (council—counsel) meeting will begin at 8:00, and will continue until all items

on the agenda have been discussed. _____

A. The following friendly letter contains many spelling errors. Cross out each misspelled word. Write the word correctly above the misspelled word.

Dear Gary,

I am practically aghausted! I have just returned from a fourty-mile bycicle ride that took all the phisical strenth I had. I realize that getting into shape requires hard work and prespiration. Still I had hoped that the excercise I would get from atheletics would be a pleazure. Instead I am finding it to be a nuisence. I guess I am not a very good amatour athelete.

My brillant fitness instructer is a genieus at motivating people, but even he can't keep me from wanting to give up sometimes. I'm afraid I much prefered using the eqippment in the jimnassium at school even though the facultie there was holy inferior to my current instructer. That I continue in this physical maintainance program is a complement to him, I asure you. I only hope my instructer is not going to sugest that I enter a tennis turnement!

I will close for now with a warm rememberance to you and your family.

Sincerely,

Each correct answer is worth 1½ points.	Total score: 42 points.

B. In each group of words, cross out any misspelled words. Then write each word correctly in the blank. If there are no misspelled words, write a C in the blank.

1. civilization   proceedure   oblige   _____

2. assurance   bicycle   resistence   _____

3. practical   assistance   attacked   _____

4. remmitance   accordance   appearance   _____

Each correct answer is worth 6 points.	Total score: 24 points.

C. Each sentence contains one or more spelling errors. Cross out each misspelled word. Then write the word correctly above it.

1. He said that it was important for the counsel to uphold the principal of fairness to all citizens.

2. Her aunt's acceptence of her wild appearence was appreciated.

3. The insurence salesman gave them his asurance that the policy was a good one.

4. In acordance with the bylaws, the comittee reccomends that the measure be tabled until the next meeting.

5. His best friend made a prophicy concirning his marige.

6. It is wise to consume only a small quantitie of alcahol.

7. It was a privalige to make her aquaintance.

8. The Christan minister asked the congregation to pray for pece.

9. The hermit lived in a cabin in the dessert, far from civilazation.

10. Sarah won her forth bycycle race on Saturday.

11. The princapal will require the asistence of all the teachers to implement the new policy.

12. A sylable is a peice of a word.

13. The asocciation will work in leage with other community organizations to remedy the problem.

14. You shouldn't allow your dog to run back and fourth across the street.

15. Can you profesy the outcome of the ternament?

16. He sought his attorney's consel conserning his financial problems.

17. Desend the icy steps slowly.

Each correct answer is worth 2 points.	Total score: 34 points.

Restaurants

Concentrate on the words that are the most difficult to recall. In the sentences with missing letters, visualize the whole word, and write in the missing letters.

1. **restaurant**   We ate at the new Chinese res' *tau* rant last night.
Focus on the *tau* in *restaurant*.

2. **altogether**   The prices at that restaurant are al' to geth' er too high.
Distinguish *altogether* from *all together*.

3. **fulfill**   The waitress tried her best to ful fill' their every desire.
Fulfill is also spelled *fulfil*, but never *fullfill*.

■ The r __ st __ __ r __ nt didn't a __ t __ g __ th __ r f __ lf __ ll its promise to serve a hot lunch in fifteen minutes.

4. **passed**   Our waiter has pass*ed* us three times without stopping.
Distinguish *passed* from *past*. Compare *passing, passenger*.

5. **tariff**   The restaurant must pay the tar' if*f* on imported foods.
Note the *riff* in *tariff*. MEMO: Even if it is stiff, pay the tariff.

6. **unanimous**   The family's vote on their favorite restaurant was *u* nan' i m*ous*.
Stress each syllable in *unanimous*. Compare *famous*.

■ The restaurant owners' association was not happy that the t __ r __ __ f was pas __ __ __ by a un __ n __ m __ __ s vote.

7. **sugar**   That restaurant offers both sug' ar and a sugar substitute.
Focus on the *ar* in *sugar*. MEMO: No sugar in vinegar

8. **enough**   The steak was large e n*ough*' to feed two people.
Focus on the *ough* in *enough*. MEMO: Rough and tough enough

9. **opportunity**   The couple ate out at every op' por tu' ni ty.
Note the *port* in *opportunity*. Compare oppose, opposite.

■ He took the op __ __ rt __ n __ ty to tell the manager that there wasn't en __ u __ __ s __ g __ r in his lemonade.

10. **invoice**   The restaurant manager signed the in' voi*ce* for the produce.
Note the *oice* in *invoice*. Compare *choice, voice*.

11. **potatoes**   The menu offers either baked or fried po ta' toes.
Note the *toes* in *potatoes*. Compare *tomato, tomatoes*.

12. **supplies**   The shipment of restaurant sup p*l*ies' was delayed.
Focus on the *lies* in *supplies*. Compare *apply, applies*.

■ The inv __ __ c __ listed p __ t __ t __ __ s and kitchen s __ __ pl __ __ s.

☐ EXERCISE I

In each sentence, cross out the incorrect word in parentheses. Then write the correct word in the blank.

1. He will give you an (invoise—invoice) for the office supplies.

_____

2. The recipe calls for two cups of (sugar—sugur).

_____

3. The country will levy a (tarif—tariff) on goods.

_____

4. Have we (past—passed) the park?

_____

5. Bring all the new (supplies—supplys) to the storeroom.

_____

6. Never pass up an (opportunity—oppertunity) to learn.

_____

7. We need (potatos—potatoes) to make salad for the picnic.

_____

8. Can you (fullfil—fulfill) your obligations?

_____

9. We voted to have our luncheon at the Polynesian (Resteurant—Restaurant).

_____

10. There are (enogh—enough) hot dogs for each of us to have two.

_____

☐ EXERCISE II

The following memo contains many spelling errors. Cross out each misspelled word. Then write the word correctly above the misspelled word.

Carlos:

The ABC Company's deliveries to our resturant have become all together

unsatisfactory. The situation has past the point where we can ignore it. Last week

the invoise on the potatos and suger they delivered included a tarriff that I

don't understand.

Please take this oportunity to call them and tell them anough is anough. If they

don't start to fullfill their promises to deliver our suplies, tell them it will be our

unamimus decision to cancel service with their company.

Sincerely,

Funerals

Study each word carefully. In the sentences with missing letters, visualize the whole word, and write in the missing letters.

1. terrible
His sudden death came as a ter' *ri* ble shock to his family and friends.
Note the *rri* in *terrible*. Compare *horrible, irritation*. Contrast *portable, capable*.

2. forehead
The grieving widow rested her fore' head on her hands.
Think of *forehead* as *before-head*. Compare *foretell*.

3. awkward
Talking with a grieving person can be very awk' ward.
Focus on the *awk* in *awkward*. MEMO: An awkward hawk

■ We could tell from her a __ kw __ __ __ manner and the wrinkles on her f __ r __ h __ __ d that she still felt t __ __ r __ bl __ grief.

4. folks
The fo*l*ks at the funeral home were very understanding.
Focus on the *ol* in *folks*.

5. cemetery
In the cem' *e* ter' y there were many new graves.
Focus on the unusual *tery* ending in *cemetery*. Stress the three *e*'s.

6. grieve
The unhappy widower continued to g*rieve*.
Note the *rie* in *grieve*. Compare *retrieve, brief, friend*.

■ His f __ __ ks continued to gr __ __ v __ at the c __ m __ t __ r __ .

7. grateful
They were gr*ate*' ful to the friends who attended the funeral.
Note the *ate* in *grateful*. Compare *hateful, wakeful*.

8. extremely
The widow was ex tr*eme*' ly upset during the funeral.
Focus on the *eme* in *extremely*. Contrast *seem, stream*.

9. sympathy
Many friends expressed sym' pa thy by sending flowers.
Stress the *path* in *sympathy*. Compare *pathetic*.

■ They're extr __ m __ l __ gr __ t __ f __ l for the expressions of s __ mp __ th __ .

10. further
There was nothing f*ur*' ther the priest could do to comfort the bereaved parents.
Note the *fur* in *further*. Distinguish *fur* from *far*.

11. acknowledgment
She sent a prompt ac *knowl*' *edg* ment of their flowers.
The preferred spelling is *acknowledgment*.

12. later
I hope the grieving man will feel better at a lat' er date.
John and Tom are here, but the *latter* (Tom) came *later*.

■ They will make f __ rth __ r ackn __ __ le __ gm __ nt of the wreaths l __ t __ r.

☐ EXERCISE I

Write the correct word in each blank. Choose from the words below.

folks	sympathy	terrible	grateful	extremely
grieve	later	cemetery	awkward	acknowledgment

1. The Simpsons seem like nice _____.

2. Megan sent Brian an _____ of his gift.

3. There was a _____ accident at the racetrack last week.

4. The governor was _____ concerned about unemployment.

5. The gravestones in the old _____ recalled days of heroes long dead.

6. The situation would be very _____ if you invited both Calvin and Carl.

7. We were _____ to the committee for working on our bylaws.

8. Akio tried not to _____ over the death of his pet canary.

9. She knew she could count on her friend's understanding and _____.

10. They are planning to see a movie _____ today.

☐ EXERCISE II

In each sentence, cross out the incorrect word in parentheses. Then write the correct word in the blank.

1. We're (grateful—greatful) for your help.

   _____

2. I sent the widower a (simpathy—sympathy) card.

   _____

3. There will be another bus (later—latter).

   _____

4. The little girl had a (terrable—terrible) dream.

   _____

5. The colt was very (aukward—awkward).

   _____

6. The weather has been (extremely—extremly) warm.

   _____

7. There was no need to question the suspect (further—farther).

   _____

8. She felt his (forhead—forehead) to see if he had a fever.

   _____

The Elderly

This lesson will help you associate these words ending in *ant, ense,* and *ience* with other words having the same endings. Contrast these endings with those in Lesson 35. In the sentences with missing letters, visualize the whole word, and write in the missing letters.

1. ignorant Many people are ig′ no r*a*nt of the special needs of elderly persons.

2. pleasant The atmosphere of the Shady Oaks Retirement Home was extremely ple*a*s′ant.

3. attendant Rosa works as an *at* ten′ d*a*nt at the nursing home.
MEMO: The ant was not a pleasant picnic attendant.

■ **Because he was not ign __ r __ nt of the special needs of older persons, Kyle was a pl __ __ s __ nt a __ tend __ nt.**

4. assistant The nurse served as an as sist′ ant to the doctor of geriatrics.

5. expense Is that an ex pen*se*′ that will be covered by Medicare?

6. defense Elderly people are now working in de fen*se*′ of their rights.
MEMO: There is no defense against expense.

■ **The as __ ist __ nt suggests insurance as a def __ n __ __ against the rising exp __ n __ __ of medical care.**

7. sense Putting his mother in a retirement home seemed to be the option that made the most sen*se*.

8. nonsense It's non′ sen*se* to think that most older people cannot care for themselves.

9. conscience The decision to place her father in a nursing home weighed heavily on her con′ *scie*nce.
Note the *science* in *conscience.*

■ **Your cons __ __ __ n __ __ will tell you more s __ n __ __ than nons __ n __ __ about how to treat the elderly.**

10. experience He hasn't had much ex pe′ ri en*ce* with older people.

11. patience It often takes great pa′ *tience* to deal with the special needs of the elderly.

12. inconvenience The elderly couple found it to be a great in′ con ven′ *ience* not to be able to drive any longer.
MEMO: Science is the result of long experience and great patience.

■ **The geriatric physician learned from exp __ r __ __ n __ __ to meet each inconv __ n __ __ n __ __ with pat __ __ n __ __ .**

☐ EXERCISE I

Arrange the following words in correct alphabetical order. Check the spelling of each word as you write it.

inconvenience	nonsense	assistant	inconvenient	attendance
patience	sense	attendant	patient	ignorance
experience	defense	pleasant	conscious	assistance
conscience	expense	ignorant	defensive	senseless

1. _____

2. _____

3. _____

4. _____

5. _____

6. _____

7. _____

8. _____

9. _____

10. _____

11. _____

12. _____

13. _____

14. _____

15. _____

16. _____

17. _____

18. _____

19. _____

20. _____

☐ EXERCISE II

In each group of words, cross out any misspelled words. Write each misspelled word correctly in the blank. If there are no misspelled words, write a *C* in the blank.

1. assistant   experiance   sense   _____

2. acknowledgment   nonsense   patiance   _____

3. maintenance   consciance   expense   _____

4. plaesant   awkward   defense   _____

5. unanimous   attendant   asistant   _____

6. opportunity   restaurant   enconveneince   _____

7. remittance   ignerant   grieve   _____

8. terrible   forehead   inconvenience   _____

9. further   sence   grateful   _____

10. ignorant   attendent   nonsense   _____

Effective Communication

The following words are often misspelled. Study them carefully. In the sentences with missing letters, visualize the whole word, and write in the missing letters.

1. language We use lan′ *guage* to communicate with others.
Focus on the *uage* in *language*. Note the *age* in *language*.

2. communication Co*m* mu′ ni ca′ *tio*n often takes place via computer networks.
Focus on the *mm* in *communication*. Compare *community*.

3. chief Letters were the ch*ie*f form of communication on the island.
Note the *ie* in *chief*. MEMO: The chief thief came to grief.

■ Lang _ _ _ _ is the ch _ _ f means of co _ m _ n _ cat _ _ n.

4. misspell Written communication is difficult when you mis spell′ words.
Focus on the *ss* in *misspell*. Contrast *mistake* and *mischief*.

5. endeavor Most people en d*eav′* or to communicate clearly.
Note the *eav* in *endeavor*. Stress the *end* and the *or*.

6. grammar Using good gram′ *mar* eases oral communication.
Center on the final *ar* in *grammar*. Contrast *stammer*.

■ End _ _ v _ r not to mis _ p _ _ l words or make errors in gr _ m _ _ r.

7. describe It is often hard for people to de scribe′ their feelings.
Focus on the *des* in *describe*. Stress the pronunciation.

8. discuss The ability to dis cuss′ things leads to better communication.
Note the *cuss* in *discuss*. Compare *discussed, discussion*.

9. would People wo*u*ld communicate more effectively if they listened carefully.
Focus on the *oul* in *would*. MEMO: He would if he could.

■ She w _ _ _ _ d neither d _ scr _ b _ nor d _ sc _ _ s her feelings.

10. evidence The baby's cooing was ev′ i den*ce* that she was trying to communicate.
Focus on the *vid* in *evidence*.

11. opinion He was trying to clearly communicate his o pin′ *io*n.
Focus on the *nion* in *opinion*. Compare *onion, union*.

12. judgment It is my ju*dg′* ment that she is not trying to communicate.
Cut the *judge* to *judg* in *judgment*. Compare *acknowledgment*.

■ She made it clear that her ju _ _ m _ nt was based on ev _ d _ n _ _ and not on op _ n _ _ n.

EXERCISE I

Match each word in Column A with its meaning in Column B. Place the letter of the meaning in the blank in front of the word it defines.

COLUMN A

1. _____ language

2. _____ communication

3. _____ judgment

4. _____ endeavor

5. _____ grammar

6. _____ describe

7. _____ discuss

8. _____ evidence

9. _____ opinion

10. _____ chief

COLUMN B

a. to strive

b. to tell about

c. most important

d. proof

e. the use of the voice and writing to communicate

f. to talk about or debate

g. thought or belief

h. a sentence or decision

i. the rules of language

j. the sharing of ideas or information

EXERCISE II

In each sentence, find any misspelled words. Write each word correctly in the blank. If there are no misspelled words, write a *C* in the blank.

_____ 1. The chief complaint among the members was a lack of comunication with their leaders.

_____ 2. The judge wished to hear all of the evedence before she would give an opinion in the case.

_____ 3. If you really want to master the French language, you must study the grammer and practice speaking it.

_____ 4. You must describe the situation and let us discuss the matter before we can make any jugement.

_____ 5. You should endeavor not to mispell words in your letters.

_____ 6. The jurors wuld not discuss the case with the reporters until all the evidence had been presented.

Public Transportation

There is no rule which covers the use of double letters in spelling. You must learn each word separately. In the sentences with missing letters, visualize the whole word, and write in the missing letters.

1. **route**
This bus *route* will take you downtown.
Distinguish *route* (way or road) from *rout* (defeat and flight).

2. **original**
You can see the o *rig′ i* nal trolley tracks downtown.
Focus on the *igi* in *original*. Stress the vowel sounds.

3. **advice**
Her ad vi*ce′* on which bus to take was helpful.
Distinguish the noun *advice* from the verb *advise*.

■ The dispatcher's advi __ __ was to follow the or __ g __ n __ l r __ __ t __ .

4. **already**
The bus was al r*ead′* y an hour late.
Distinguish *already* (by this time) from *all ready*.

5. **regretting**
I am already re gret′ *t*ing my decision not to take the earlier train.
Focus on the *tt* in *regretting*. Compare *letting, betting*.

6. **numerous**
The company received nu′.mer *ous* calls praising that cab driver.
Stress the *mer* in *numerous*. Compare *number*.

■ Num __ r __ __ s passengers were alr __ __ d __ regr __ __ t __ ng their choice of transportation.

7. **similar**
Bad weather caused sim′ *i* lar delays at airports across the country.
Stress the vowel sounds in *similar*. Compare *regular, popular*.

8. **mutual**
The women on the plane discovered many mu′tu al interests.
Focus on the *ual* in *mutual*. Compare *actual, visual, manual*.

9. **surprise**
To Hector's *sur* prise′, he found the subway in that city to be safe.
Focus on the *sur* in *surprise*. Compare *surface, survey*.

■ It was no s __ rpr __ s __ that the citizens had s __ m __ l __ r complaints and m __ t __ __ l concerns about the Department of Public Transportation.

10. **village**
The train was the only link the vil′ *lage* had to the rest of the world.
Note the *age* in *village*. MEMO: The village will age.

11. **together**
We must work to geth′ er to make the new bus system a success.
Note the *get* in *together*. Compare *whether;* contrast *weather*.

12. **community**
The co*m* mu′ni ty joined together to petition for a bus route.

■ The vil __ __ __ __ and a larger c __ __ m __ n __ t __ will work t __ g __ th __ r to build an airport.

☐ EXERCISE I

In each sentence, cross out the incorrect word in parentheses. Then write the correct word in the blank.

1. You'll have to go out of your way if you want to take the scenic (rout—route).

_____

2. (Numurous—Numerous) experiments will be performed on the new drug.

_____

3. Ms. Rios settled the matter to the (mutall—mutual) satisfaction of the parties.

_____

4. Residents disagreed over activities held in the (comunity—community) center.

_____

5. There are many cities and one (village—villege) tucked among those mountains.

_____

6. It came as no (surprise—serprise) to us that Emily was going to run for office.

_____

☐ EXERCISE II

The following business letter contains many spelling errors. Cross out each misspelled word. Then write the word correctly above the misspelled word.

Dear Ms. Hernandez:

I'm writing to you in your capacity as transportation director for this communitie.

For munberous years, we've needed a bus root in my area. My neighbors and

I are regreting moving to this part of the city.

The originel advise not to extend the bus root to our neighborhood was based

on an all ready outdated idea that we could count on the mutuel support of our

neighbors who all had similiar working hours. This is not true. I hope you will

expand bus service into our neighborhood before the end of the summer.

Sincerely,

The Circus

Always read the sentence which follows each word carefully. In the sentences with missing letters, visualize the whole word, and write in the missing letters.

1. barrel Three circus clowns climbed out of the bar' rel.
Focus on the *rel* in *barrel*. Compare *quarrel, tunnel*.

2. shoes The circus clown's sh*oes* were huge.
Focus on the *oes* in *shoes*.

3. shipped The circus ship*ped* two large wooden crates to Springfield, the site of its next show.
Note the two *p*'s in *shipped*. Compare *shipping, slipped*.

■ **The clowns ship __ __ __ a b __ r __ __ l of sh __ __ s to the needy.**

4. holiday Let's go to the circus on our hol' *i* day.
Stress the *i* in *holiday*.

5. eighth Sam was the *eigh*th person in his family to join the circus and become an acrobat.
Focus on the *eigh* in *eighth*. MEMO: The eighth freight train

6. twelfth We went to the circus on May twe*lf*th.
Note the *elf* in *twelfth*.

■ **The circus performers' h __ l __ da __ is from May ei __ __ th to June tw __ l __ th.**

7. forward The ringmaster moved f*or*'ward to begin the performance.
Note the *for* in *forward*. MEMO: Go forward for forty steps.

8. banquet The ban' *que*t was in honor of the visiting circus performers.
Pronounce the two syllables in *banquet* distinctly.

9. annual The big circus is an an' *nu* al event.
MEMO: Anne announced our annual anniversary.

■ **We looked f __ rw __ rd to the an __ __ __ l circus b __ n __ __ et.**

10. preliminary The clowns were the pre lim' *i* nar' y act in the circus.
Focus on the *imi* in *preliminary*.

11. comparatively The highwire act seemed com par' a tive ly tame after seeing the wild animal act.
Focus on the *ara* in *comparatively*. Contrast *comparison*.

12. preparation Their acrobatic act took many years of prep' a ra' *tio*n to perfect.
Stress the *par* in *preparation*. Compare *prepare, separation*.

■ **The circus needs c __ mp __ r __ t __ vely little pr __ l __ m __ n __ ry pr __ p __ r __ t __ on before performing.**

☐ EXERCISE I

Write the correct word in each blank. Choose from the words below.

| preparation | annual | twelfth | shipped | comparatively | banquet |
| eighth | shoes | preliminary | forward | holiday | barrel |

1. Will all the banks in the city observe the _____ tomorrow?

2. We changed the date of the _____.

3. The Greek olives are stored in a _____ at the back of the store.

4. It will be _____ easy for you to pass the driving test.

5. Jennifer needs at least two pairs of _____ to take on the trip.

6. Ms. Vega will attend the _____ stockholders' meeting this year.

7. Find out if Mr. Olson's order was _____ to Detroit yesterday.

8. Megan was looking _____ to entering the Special Olympics.

9. Joshua took a _____ test before taking the Civil Service test.

10. Luis missed the target on the seventh try, but he hit it on

    the _____.

11. Carolyn finished _____ in the race.

12. I studied hard in _____ for the test.

☐ EXERCISE II

In each sentence, find any misspelled words. Write each word correctly in the blank. If there are no misspelled words, write a *C* in the blank.

_____ 1. He prepared his annuel income tax form on March twelfth.

_____ 2. There was a lot to do in preperation for the banquet.

_____ 3. The preliminary report was comparitively optimistic.

_____ 4. This barrel of grapefruit was shipped from the valley.

_____ 5. This is the eigth pair of shoes the child has ruined.

_____ 6. Are you looking forward to the Thanksgiving holliday?

A. Supply *ei* or *ie* in each word. You may check the spelling of each word in the dictionary.

1. suppl __ __ s

2. ch __ __ f

3. consc __ __ nce

4. inconven __ __ nce

5. __ __ ghth

6. exper __ __ nce

7. gr __ __ ve

8. pat __ __ nce

Each correct answer is worth 4 points.	Total score: 32 points.

B. In each group of words, cross out any misspelled words. Then write each word correctly in the blank. If there are no misspelled words, write a *C* in the blank.

1. opportunity	resterant	tariff	_____
2. invoice	village	cemetary	_____
3. forhead	assistant	nonsense	_____
4. sugar	terrible	suplies	_____
5. awkward	unamimus	further	_____
6. endevor	banquet	route	_____
7. passed	extremely	anuel	_____
8. later	acknowledgment	ignorant	_____
9. comunication	judgment	attendant	_____
10. pleasant	regretting	comperativly	_____
11. preparation	twelvth	community	_____
12. langage	barrel	altogether	_____
13. original	shoes	fullfil	_____
14. advice	cheif	shipped	_____

Each correct answer is worth 2 points.	Total score: 28 points.

C. In each sentence, cross out the incorrect word in parentheses. Then write the correct word in the blank.

1. The errors on his tax form were (numerous—numerus).

_____

2. She wanted to (fullfill—fulfill) her dreams.

_____

3. He played (forword—forward) on the basketball team.

_____

4. The (preliminary—preliminery) evidence against him was strong.

_____

5. There was an old cracker (barrel—barrell) in the store.

_____

6. The dog seemed to have a sixth (sence—sense) about danger.

_____

7. She was a witness for the (defense—defence).

_____

8. His spelling and (grammer—grammar) were not very good.

_____

9. Are there (enough—enugh) chairs for everyone to sit down?

_____

10. I have no (simpathy—sympathy) for those who break the law.

_____

11. Could you (discribe—describe) her to me?

_____

12. Try not to (mispell—misspell) so many words.

_____

13. He arranged the (surprise—suprise) party.

_____

14. They had (similiar—similar) tastes in music.

_____

15. It was to their (mutual—mutuel) benefit to come to an agreement.

_____

16. He was on a tight (expense—expence) account.

_____

17. He was very (gratefull—grateful) for the help.

_____

18. I will (endeavor—endever) to keep my promise.

_____

19. What is your (opinion—opinyon)?

_____

20. Is it (allready—already) time for lunch?

_____

Each correct answer is worth 2 points.   Total score: 40 points.

On the Job

Note that some words have two accented syllables, one receiving a primary accent (´) and another a secondary accent (ˋ). Study each word carefully. In the sentences with missing letters, visualize the whole word, and write in the missing letters.

1. **cooperation** Co op´er a´tion with others is essential in the business world. Pronounce the first two o's in *cooperation* distinctly.

2. **attitude** The new employee certainly has a positive at´ ti tude. Focus on the *atti* in *attitude*. Contrast *gratitude, latitude.*

3. **all right** The employee's work was al*l* right, but his attitude was poor. Note the two *l*'s in *all right*. Compare *all wrong.*

■ **Tatsuo's at __ __ t __ d __ is al __ r __ __ __ t, but he needs to improve his c __ __ per __ t __ on with others.**

4. **suppose** I su*p* po*se*´ my boss will tell me if my work is unsatisfactory. Focus on the double *p* in *suppose*. Compare *supper, supply.*

5. **conscientious** The con´*sci* en´*ti*ous worker did her best. Focus on the *tious* in *conscientious*. Compare *conscious.*

6. **succeed** With his positive attitude, the new employee is bound to suc *ceed*´. *Succeed* is one of the only three words ending in *ceed.*

■ **Do you s __ __ pos __ that the new employee will be c __ ns __ __ __ nt __ __ us enough to suc __ __ ed?**

7. **earliest** Elizabeth usually arrives at work *ear*´li est. Note the *lie* in *earliest*. Compare *early, earlier, earliest.*

8. **humorous** The hu´*mor ou*s seminar about working with others contained valuable information. Focus on the *mor* in *humorous*. Compare *odorous.*

9. **exception** Her boss would not tolerate any ex cep´*tio*n to the rule. Distinguish *exception* (omission) from *acceptance* (approval).

■ **His boss's h __ m __ r __ __ s remarks about who always left the office e __ rl __ __ st showed that he took e __ __ ept __ on to John's leaving early.**

10. **prompt** Her supervisor rated her as prompt, accurate, and dependable. Note the two *p*'s in *prompt*. Pronounce all of the letters.

11. **practice** He would need to prac´*tice* his typing skills to get the job. The spelling *practice* is preferred to *practise*. Compare *practical.*

12. **cordial** The new employee was given a cor´*dia*l welcome. Note the *dial* in *cordial.*

■ **Employees should pr __ ct __ c __ always being pr __ __ __ t and c __ r __ __ al.**

□ EXERCISE I

Each sentence contains one or more spelling errors. Cross out each misspelled word. Then write the word correctly above it.

1. She lives by the saying, "If at first you don't suceed, try, try again."

2. Ms. Newton asked that you answer the invitation at your earlyest convenience.

3. After you file your preliminary report in the suit, you will get promt action.

4. The council needs the cooperasion of each of the members without excepsion.

5. Juan and Huyen accepted Amanda's cordiall invitation to the holliday party.

6. I think that it would be a good practise to be a consciensious student.

7. Do you supose that the barrels of wine could be shipped directly to the owners?

8. Your preparation and your atitude are important in finding a job.

9. The first part of the speech was all rite, but his attempt to be humerous fell flat.

10. Mr. Lopez made a practice of being promt.

11. Would it be alright if I came over?

12. The hostess was cordiel to all of her guests.

13. Your consientious attitude is appreciated.

14. Even if he is prompt, the erliest he should arrive is 5 P.M.

15. Do you suppoze that she meant the remark to be humoris?

□ EXERCISE II

In the first blank that follows each word, write the root word from which each word is formed. In the second blank, write the suffix.

1. earliest _____ _____

2. cooperation _____ _____

3. humorous _____ _____

4. exception _____ _____

5. conscientious _____ _____

The Armed Services

This lesson contains some particularly deceptive words. Consult the dictionary for the correct pronunciations. In the sentences with missing letters, visualize the whole word, and write in the missing letters.

1. necessary
A well-trained military is nec′es sar′y for our country to remain safe and strong.
Focus on the *nec* in *necessary*. Compare *necessity, necessarily*.

2. maintain
It is important to ma*in* ta*in*′ strict discipline in the armed services at all times.
MEMO: Strain to maintain the main mountain train.

3. discipline
The sergeant maintained strict dis′*ci* pli*ne*.
Note the *scip* in *discipline*. Contrast *disappear, disappoint*.

■ It is ne __ es __ __ ry to m __ __ nt __ __ n di __ __ ipl __ n __ in the military.

4. soldier
The sol′*die*r won a medal for bravery.
Note the *die* in soldier. Pronounce it *sol′jer*.

5. arctic
The Navy went on maneuvers in the ar*c*′tic wilderness.
Arctic is capitalized in proper names, such as *Arctic Circle*.

6. transferred
The Army trans ferred′ her to Fort Sill.
Note the *err* in *transferred*. Compare *conferred, deferred*.

■ The sol __ __ __ r tran __ f __ r __ __ __ to a regiment in the Ar __ t __ c Circle.

7. campaign
He served in the first cam p*aign*′ of World War II.
Focus on the *aign* in *campaign*. Note carefully the silent *ig*.

8. lieutenant
The l*i*eu ten′ ant gave the command to fire.
Note that *lieutenant* ends in *ant*. Center on the *lieu*.

9. colonel
Her father is a *colo*′nel in the army.
The *colo* in *colonel* is pronounced *kur*.

■ She began the camp __ __ __ n as a l __ __ __ ten __ nt and ended as a c __ __ __ n __ l.

10. conquer
Do you think our armed forces could con′ qu*er* our enemies?
Focus on the *que* in *conquer*. Compare *conquest, conqueror*.

11. country
The goal of our armed services is to protect this coun′try.
Note the *ou* in *country*. MEMO: You can count on our country.

12. enemies
Our armed services protect us from our en′ e m*ies*.
Note the three *e*'s in *enemies*. Center on the *emie*.

■ If provoked, our armed services would attempt to con __ __ __ r the en __ m __ __ s of our c __ __ ntr __ .

110

☐ EXERCISE I

Write the correct form in each blank without referring to the word list. When you have completed the exercise, check your answers in the dictionary.

1. Write the noun form that uses the same root word as *necessary*.

_____

2. Write the past tense of the verb *discipline*.

_____

3. Write the present tense of the verb *transferred*.

_____

4. Write the singular form of *enemies*.

_____

5. Add the suffix *ing* to *conquer* to form a new word.

_____

6. Write the past tense of the verb *campaign*.

_____

7. Write the adverbial form that uses the same root word as *necessary*.

_____

8. Write the plural form of *country*.

_____

☐ EXERCISE II

In each sentence, find any misspelled words. Write each word correctly in the blank. If all words in the sentence are spelled correctly, write a *C* in the blank.

_____ 1. Colonel Norris will review the troops before the campain.

_____ 2. Did Alexander really cry because there were no more worlds to conquar?

_____ 3. It is often neccesary to maintain rigid discipline among the troops while they are on maneuvers.

_____ 4. The job at hand is to defend our country against all enemys.

_____ 5. The soldier asked to be transfered to a regiment in the Arctic Circle.

_____ 6. Lieutenant Phillips ordered all soldiers to report to the mess hall.

_____ 7. The airplane was lost over a remote part of the Artic Ocean.

_____ 8. The souldier was wounded in the battle.

_____ 9. The luetenant said that the colonel would arrive in an hour.

Newspapers

Study and review these words ending in *ence*. In the sentences with missing letters, visualize the whole word, and write in the missing letters.

1. **existence**   The ex ist' en*ce* of a second newspaper in the town created healthy competition.

2. **reference**   The newspaper article made ref' er en*ce* to the suspect's arrest record.

3. **preference**   Jorge has a pref' er en*ce* for the morning newspaper, but his wife likes the evening edition better.

■ **The newspaper made ref __ r __ n __ e to the e __ ist __ n __ __ of new evidence, and to the prosecutor's pref __ r __ n __ __ that it not be made public.**

4. **conference**   The newspaper carried a brief report on the annual con' fer en*ce* of English teachers.

5. **correspondence**   She made frequent references to current newspaper articles in her cor' *re* spond' en*ce*.

6. **influence**   Newspapers exert a great in' flu en*ce* over what we believe about the issues that affect our lives.

■ **The newspaper received a great deal of co __ r __ spond __ n __ __ about the infl __ __ n __ __ the confer __ n __ __ had on the local economy.**

7. **confidence**   The newspaper's editor had great con' fi den*ce* in the accuracy of the veteran reporter's facts.

8. **presence**   The pres' en*ce* of the newspaper reporters led to a more lively debate between the candidates.

9. **consequence**   One con' se *quence* of careless journalism can be libel.

■ **We were filled with conf __ d __ n __ __ about the report's accuracy as a cons __ qu __ n __ __ of the reporter's pres __ n __ __.**

10. **occurrence**   The oc cur' *rence* of the robbery at the museum was reported in the newspaper.
    Give special study to the word *occurrence*. It is one of the most difficult of all commonly used words. Compare *occur, occurring; recur, recurring.*

11. **sentence**   Read the first sen' ten*ce* of this newspaper article about the nationwide recycling effort.

12. **residence**   The newspaper reported that the res' i den*ce* was totally destroyed by the fire.

■ **A single sent __ n __ __ in the paper mentioned the strange o __ __ ur __ __ n __ __ at the Governor's res __ d __ n __ __.**

☐ EXERCISE I

In each group of words, cross out any misspelled words. Then write each word correctly in the blank. If there are no misspelled words, write a *C* in the blank.

1. resistance influance presence _____
2. ocurrence nonsense sentence _____
3. accordance assurance correspondance _____
4. acceptance preferance insurance _____
5. expense assistance existance _____
6. pleasant reference remittance _____
7. appearance experience conferance _____
8. consiquence conscience acquaintance _____
9. confidance ignorant patience _____
10. attendant nuisance referance _____
11. influence existence resadence _____

☐ EXERCISE II

Supply *ance* or *ence* in each word. In the blank following each word, rewrite the complete word.

1. prefer_____ _____
2. assur_____ _____
3. sent_____ _____
4. remembr_____ _____
5. confid_____ _____
6. refer_____ _____
7. pres_____ _____
8. resist_____ _____
9. exist_____ _____

10. consci_____ _____
11. insur_____ _____
12. experi_____ _____
13. nuis_____ _____
14. occurr_____ _____
15. acquaint_____ _____
16. remitt_____ _____
17. resid_____ _____
18. influ_____ _____

First Aid

You can learn to spell many of these words by giving special attention to the separate syllables. Study each word carefully. In the sentences with missing letters, visualize the whole word, and write in the missing letters.

1. **formerly**   She was for′ mer ly a paramedic, but now she teaches first aid.
Note the *former* in *formerly*. Distinguish from *formally*.

2. **doctor**   Fortunately, a doc′tor was at the scene to give first aid.
Note the *tor* in *doctor*. Compare *actor, victor, debtor*.

3. **rheumatism**   What is the best first aid for *rheu*′ ma tism?
Focus on the *rheu* in *rheumatism*.

■ **He told the d __ ct __ r that he f __ rm __ rl __ had r __ __ um __ t __ sm.**

4. **every**   In this course, you'll learn ev′ *er* y first aid technique.
Note the *eve* in *every*.

5. **repetition**   First aid instructions to children require rep′ e ti′ *ti*on.
Note the double *ti* in *repetition*. Compare *competition, petition*.

6. **sacrifice**   Would you sac′ ri fi*ce* your safety to help someone who was hurt?
Note the *ri* in *sacrifice*. MEMO: I sacrifice the price of ice.

■ **The medical technician made __ v __ ry s __ cr __ f __ ce to avoid r __ p __ t __ t __ on of the problem.**

7. **aggravate**   Applying a tourniquet to stop bleeding can sometimes ag′ gra vate′ an injury.
Focus on the *gg* in *aggravate*. Compare *aggregate*.

8. **relieve**   First aid helped re l*ie* ve′ his pain.
Note the *lie* in *relieve*. Compare *believe, relief*.

9. **considerably**   Prompt administration of CPR can help con sid′er a bly.
Note the *consider* and *ably* in *considerably*.

■ **The bystander was hesitant to administer first aid for fear it would aggr __ v __ t __ his condition c __ ns __ d __ r __ bly and r __ l __ __ v __ nothing.**

10. **leisure**   Emergency medical technicians have little l*ei*′ sur*e* time.
Focus on the *lei* in *leisure*. Note the final *sure*.

11. **agreeable**   The family of the injured man was a gree′ a ble to her trying first aid.
Note the *agree* and *able* in *agreeable*. Compare *passable*.

12. **minimum**   Receiving prompt first aid reduced his pain to a min′ *i* mum.
Pronounce each syllable in *minimum* distinctly.

■ **Jesse Jones was agre __ __ bl __ to having a min __ m __ m of l __ __ s __ r __ time.**

☐ EXERCISE I

Write the correct word in each blank. Choose from the words below.

rheumatism
considerably

agreeable
aggravate

leisure
doctor

relieve
every

1. Were the representatives of management and labor both _____ to the contract?

2. Could noise _____ a person's nervous condition?

3. It requires many years of study to become a _____ .

4. The book was priced _____ higher than Warren had expected.

5. Many times light exercise will help a victim of _____ .

6. Not _____ disease has a cure.

7. This aspirin will _____ your headache.

8. What had you planned to do with your _____ time this summer?

☐ EXERCISE II

In each sentence, find any misspelled words. Write each word correctly in the blank. If there are no misspelled words, write a *C* in the blank.

_____ **1.** She made a sacrafice by donating so much money.

_____ **2.** Does your docter charge extra for weekend visits?

_____ **3.** The economy has improved consideribly this year.

_____ **4.** He was certainly in an agreeable mood.

_____ **5.** Her rumatism was really bothering her.

_____ **6.** There is too much repitition in that song for my taste.

_____ **7.** He was formerlly employed with that company.

_____ **8.** Check evry person who enters this gate.

_____ **9.** There should be a minamum of discomfort.

_____ **10.** I don't have as much liesure time as I would like.

Hotels

Study each word carefully. In the sentences with missing letters, visualize the whole word, and write in the missing letters.

1. **ascertain**   She tried to as'cer t*ain*' which of the two new luxury hotels would be best to host the convention.
Focus on the *sce* in *ascertain*.

2. **precious**   She put her pre'*cio*us jewelry in the hotel safe.
Stress the *cio* in *precious*. Compare *delicious, conscious*.

3. **valuable**   The painting in the hotel lobby is val'u *a* ble.
Note the *lua* in *valuable*. Contrast value with *valuable*.

■ **The hotel management asked her to as __ __ rt __ __ n how v __ l __ __ bl __ her pre __ __ __ us jewelry was.**

4. **convenient**   The hotel was con ven'*i*ent to the convention center.
Focus on the *ent* in *convenient*. Compare *patient, ancient*.

5. **dining**   The hotel had two din'ing rooms.
Note the *ini* in *dining*. Compare *dine, dining; line, lining*.

6. **breakfast**   She ordered bre*ak*'fast from room service.
MEMO: Break the fast at breakfast.

■ **It was c __ nv __ n __ __ nt to have br __ __ kf __ st in the hotel's d __ n __ ng room.**

7. **guess**   The hotel chef tried to *gue*ss how many people would order the fresh salmon.
Focus on the *ue* in *guess*. Contrast *guessed* with *guest*.

8. **stationery**   The hotel provided sta'*tio*n er'y in the desk.
Distinguish *stationery* from *stationary* (not moving).

9. **positive**   She was almost pos'i tive she had stayed at that hotel before.
Note the *s* in *positive*. Compare *position*; contrast *possible*.

■ **You can probably g __ __ ss where I'm staying, but a look at the hotel st __ t __ on __ ry will make you p __ s __ t __ v __.**

10. **pierce**   It required a high speed drill to p*ie*rce the hotel's fire door.
Note the *pie* in *pierce*. MEMO: Pierce the shield.

11. **plane**   As soon as her plan*e* landed, she took a cab to the hotel.
Distinguish *plane* from *plain*. Note the *lane* in *plane*.

12. **easily**   His directions to the hotel could be followed *eas*'i ly.
MEMO: The early sun came up easily in the east.

■ **As soon as his pl __ n __ can p __ er __ __ the cloud cover, he will be able to see the tall hotel e __ s __ ly.**

☐ EXERCISE I

In each sentence, cross out each incorrect word in parentheses. Then write the correct word in the blank.

1. It is important to eat a nutritious (breakfest—breakfast).

_____

2. Linda's bracelet is quite (valuable—valueble).

_____

3. The detective will (ascartain—ascertain) the truth.

_____

4. Sean can (easely—easily) make the trip to Newark in the time allowed.

_____

5. Is three o'clock a (conveneint—convenient) time to meet?

_____

6. I can't (guess—gess) how the movie will end.

_____

7. Did Mei want to have her (stationary—stationery) monogrammed?

_____

8. Were the Murrays (dinning—dining) out when the accident occurred?

_____

☐ EXERCISE II

The following postcard contains many spelling errors. Cross out each misspelled word. Then write the word correctly above the misspelled word.

Dear Heather,

You'll never gess where I wound up on vacation! I got on a convinient plain to Hawaii, and here I am. I am posative that I could eazily live here for the rest of my life! Each moment is so precius and valuble! Each morning, I go to the hotel dinning room for a great breakfist of some type of melon that I've never had before. It is easy to peirce with a knife and is very sweet and juicy. Then I go sun myself on the beach, or swim in the ocean.

I have written so many letters that I ran out of stationary, but I thought you'd like the picture on this postcard. I'll see you soon.

Sincerely yours,

Immigration and Naturalization

Study each word carefully. In the sentences with missing letters, visualize the whole word, and write in the missing letters.

1. advisable   It is ad vis′ a ble to learn as much as you can about our country's immigration laws.
Focus on the *able* in *advisable*. Compare *admirable, movable*.

2. immigration   Im′ mi gra′ tion has increased this country's population.
Stress the *immi* in *immigration*. Distinguish from *emigration*.

3. foreign   Each for′ *eig*n country has its own immigration laws.
Focus on the *reign* in *foreign*. MEMO: Reign in foreign Spain.

■ It seemed adv __ __ abl __ to restrict f __ r __ __ __ __ n im __ __ gr __ t __ on.

4. government   In the United States, immigration and naturalization is controlled by the gov′ er*n* ment.
Note the *govern* in *government*. Compare *governor, governing*.

5. control   Our government exercises strict con trol′ over immigration.
MEMO: Sole control of the whole government dole

6. people   Many p*eo*′ ple come to the United States as immigrants.
Focus on the unusual *eo* of *people*.

■ The g __ v __ r __ m __ nt must c __ ntr __ l the immigration of p __ __ pl __.

7. schedule   The Immigration and Naturalization Service will s*ch*ed′ ule a hearing on his case soon.

8. planned   She plan*n*ed to be naturalized this summer.
Focus on the *nn* in *planned*. MEMO: Anne planned to get tanned.

9. carrying   Are you car′ *ry* ing your green card for identification?
Keep the *y* in *carrying*. Compare *marrying, studying*.

■ The government is car __ __ __ ng out a plan __ __ d immigration sc __ __ d __ l __.

10. delivery   She will become a citizen before her child's de liv′ er y.
Note the *live* in *delivery*. Compare *deliver, delivering*.

11. guarantee   A naturalized citizen has the same guar′ an tee′ of freedom as a citizen born in the U.S.
Focus on the *ua* in *guarantee*.

12. machinery   The Immigration and Naturalization Service is part of the ma ch*in*′ er y of our government.
MEMO: The machinery of the refinery was used by the winery.

■ The company would not g __ __ r __ nte __ prompt d __ l __ v __ ry of the m __ ch __ n __ ry to the Immigration and Naturalization Service.

☐ EXERCISE I

Write the correct form in the blank without referring to the word list. When you have completed the exercise, check your answers in the dictionary.

1. Write the root word of the word *machinery.*

_____

2. Write the past tense of the verb *guarantee.*

_____

3. Write the present tense of the verb form of the word *delivery.*

_____

4. Write the present tense of the verb *carrying.*

_____

5. Write the *ing* form of the verb *schedule.*

_____

6. Write the past tense of the verb *control.*

_____

7. Write the word that describes a person *foreign* to another country.

_____

8. Write the present tense of the verb *planned.*

_____

☐ EXERCISE II

Each sentence contains one or more spelling errors. Cross out each misspelled word. Then write the word correctly above it.

1. It was necessary for our goverment to limit the number of peopel arriving here.

2. Did Mr. Lee schedel a delevery of merchandise for Tuesday?

3. It was adviseble for the foreign couple to check with the imigration officials.

4. Our sales manager will garantee immediate delivary of the machinary.

5. The newspaper planed to print the story in order to help controll the rumors

   circulating through the town.

6. Have you ever visited a forin country?

7. How many peple was the airplane carying?

8. It is advisible to pack clothes for both warm and cool weather.

9. Can you guarauntee that Northwestern's flight 101 will arrive in Washington, D.C.

   on skedule?

A. The following business letter contains many spelling errors. Cross out each misspelled word. Then write the word correctly above the misspelled word.

Dear Sirs:

I find it necesary to initiate this correspondance in referance to the atitude of Joe Parker, one of your employees, who was very rude while making his most recent delivry. He was also not on skedule.

Up to now, I have counted on the co-operation of all your peopel. They have been concientious, promptt, cordiel, posative, and agreable. This is considerbly different from Joe's atitude last Monday.

I gues everyone makes mistakes. I also think it is adviseable to call this acception to the usual practise of your employees to your attention. That way you can maintane controll so there won't be a repetition of this problem. I have evry confidance that you will be able to influance Joe's behavior eazily and garantee me the excelent service that I had formerlly come to expect.

Sincerely,

Each correct answer is worth 2 points.	Total score: 58 points.

B. In each sentence, find any misspelled words. Write each word correctly in the blank. If there are no misspelled words, write a *C* in the blank.

_____ 1. It takes more hard work than good luck to succeed in life.

_____ 2. An artic cold front was bearing down upon the soldier.

_____ 3. How many campain promises have been broken?

_____ 4. He was elected lieutenent governor.

_____ 5. Please let me know as soon as possible whether you plan to attend the confrence.

Each correct answer is worth 1 point.	Total score: 5 points.

C. In each sentence, cross out the incorrect word in parentheses. Then write the correct word in the blank.

1. He collects stamps from (foreign—foriegn) countries.

_____

2. What was the (consiquence—consequence) of your being late to school?

_____

3. The movie wasn't meant to be (humorous—humerus).

_____

4. Is this the Alvarez (resadence—residence)?

_____

5. The drill wasn't able to (pierce—peirce) the heavy steel.

_____

6. The scientists needed to (assertain—ascertain) the depth of the lake.

_____

7. Brothers and sisters often (aggravate—agravate) each other.

_____

8. This city offers many enjoyable (liesure—leisure) activities.

_____

9. Is Sarah a (contientious—conscientious) babysitter?

_____

10. The medicine the doctor prescribed didn't (releive—relieve) her pain.

_____

11. Many Americans suffer from (rheumatism—ruematism).

_____

12. The junkyard was filled with broken (machinery—machinary).

_____

13. I (transfered—transferred) the money into my savings account.

_____

14. Uncle Ed is a (colonel—cornel) in the Army.

_____

15. Would this weekend be a (convenent—convenient) time for me to visit?

_____

16. That jeweler sells rings set with a variety of (precious—pretious) stones.

_____

17. Let us know if there is another (occurrence—occurence) of misbehavior.

_____

18. Are you (positive—posative) he said he'll be here?

_____

Each correct answer is worth 2 points.

Total score: 36 points.

Advertising Techniques

Study each word carefully. In the sentences with missing letters, visualize the whole word, and write in the missing letters.

1. **magnificent**   The young woman featured in the shampoo ad had mag nif′ i cent long black hair.

2. **prominent**   Prom′ i nent people are often hired to advertise products on television.

3. **recent**   The company spent most of its advertising budget on its more re′ cent products.

■ **The re __ ent perfume ad designed by a prom __ n __ nt artist from New York is magn __ fi __ __ nt.**

4. **equivalent**   The ad claims that a small box of the concentrated detergent is e quiv′ a lent to a large box of regular detergent.

5. **intelligent**   In tel′ li gent people are often skeptical about the claims made in TV ads.

6. **excellent**   The company's ad claims that their product is ex′ cel lent for people of all ages.

■ **The new diet drink may be ex __ e __ l __ nt, but no inte __ l __ g __ nt person believes the company's claim that it is equ __ v __ l __ nt to a healthful meal.**

7. **accident**   The model suffered a minor ac′ ci dent while filming the commercial.

8. **confident**   The ad implied that you'd always feel con′ fi dent if you used that deodorant.

9. **superintendent**   The su′ per in tend′ ent likes the TV ad advising kids to stay in school.

■ **The sup __ __ intend __ nt was c __ nf __ d __ nt that the safety ads would prevent another ac __ __ d __ nt.**

10. **management**   Man′ agement always has the final say on the company's proposed advertising budget.

11. **permanent**   By widely advertising its new product, the company hoped to secure a per′ ma nent place in the market.

12. **competent**   The new advertising manager hired by the president was highly com′ pe tent at his job.

■ **It is good man __ g __ m __ nt to employ a comp __ t __ nt advertising team on a perm __ n __ nt basis.**

EXERCISE I

In each group of words, cross out any misspelled words. Then write each word correctly in the blank. If there are no misspelled words, write a *C* in the blank.

1. competant   brilliant   shipment   _____

2. assistant   president   confidant   _____

3. judgment   prominant   present   _____

4. ignorant   intelligant   permanent   _____

5. attendant   accident   superintendant   _____

6. government   management   equivalent   _____

7. excellant   announcement   pleasant   _____

8. lieutenant   judgment   rescent   _____

9. evident   magnificant   innocent   _____

EXERCISE II

Supply *ant* or *ent* in the spaces in each word. In the blank following each word, rewrite the complete word.

1. judgm_____   _____

2. accid_____   _____

3. ignor_____   _____

4. excell_____   _____

5. governm_____   _____

6. compet_____   _____

7. assist_____   _____

8. magnific_____   _____

9. presid_____   _____

10. confid_____   _____

123

LESSON 50

Using Credit

Study each word carefully. In the sentences with missing letters, visualize the whole word, and write in the missing letters.

1. beginning   Be gin′ *n*ing next week, I'll be charged interest on my balance.
Focus on the *nn* in *beginning*. Compare *winning, grinning*.

2. paragraph   Carefully read each par′a gra*ph* of this credit agreement.
Note the middle *a* in *paragraph*. Compare *parallel, parachute*.

3. capital   He uses credit because he doesn't have enough cap′ i t*al*.
Distinguish *capital* (money) from *capitol* (building).

■ At the beg __ n __ __ ng of the third par __ gra __ __ of the loan agreement, the amount of c __ p __ t __ l he was investing was stated.

4. difficult   It can be dif′ *fi* c*ult* to use credit cards wisely.
Focus on the *iffi* in *difficult*. Contrast *deficit, different*.

5. continually   He seemed to con tin′u al *ly* use credit cards instead of cash.
Stress the *ua* in *continually*. Compare *annually, visually*.

6. license   For identification, she was asked to show the clerk her driver's li′ *cense* and a credit card.
Focus on the *cens* in *license*. Compare *expense*.

■ Using a check can be dif __ __ c __ lt, since you cont __ n __ __ __ ly have to show your driver's li __ en __ __.

7. exceed   Be careful not to ex ceed′ your credit card limit.
Exceed is one of the only three words ending in *ceed*.

8. tries   She tr*ies* to pay her credit card balance each month.
Note that *tries* ends in *ies*. Compare *pies, supplies, dries*.

9. achievement   Paying off his credit card balance was quite an a ch*ieve′*ment.
Note the *achieve* in *achievement*. Compare *retrieve, believe*.

■ She tr __ __ s not to ex __ __ ed her credit card limit, and she is proud of this ach __ __ v __ m __ nt.

10. success   His plan to pay off all his charge accounts was a suc cess′.
Focus on the *cc* and *ss* in *success*. Compare *access*.

11. sufficient   She didn't have suf fi′ cient cash, so she had to charge her hotel bill.
Focus on the *cie* in *sufficient*. Compare *efficient, deficient*.

12. partial   They made a par′ t*ia*l payment of their credit card bills.
Note the *tia* in *partial*. Compare *initial, confidential*.

■ Par __ __ __ l suc __ es __ in paying off your bills is not su __ fi __ __ __ nt.

124

□ EXERCISE I

In each sentence, cross out each incorrect word in parentheses. Then write the correct word in the blank.

1. He always (tries—trys) to be polite.

_____

2. Maria plans to invest some of her (capital—capitol) in that business.

_____

3. David thought the math test was (dificult—difficult).

_____

4. She is (continally—continually) looking for a bargain.

_____

5. Did you lose your (lisence—license)?

_____

6. I received (partial—parcial) payment.

_____

7. The letter was only one (paregraph—paragraph) long.

_____

8. Don't (exeed—exceed) the speed limit.

_____

9. Do you have (sufficient—suficient) cash for the trip?

_____

10. The party was a (success—sucsess).

_____

□ EXERCISE II

Each sentence contains one or more spelling errors. Cross out each misspelled word. Then write the word correctly above it.

1. If you achieve even parsial sucess in this venture, you will have done well.

2. If he continues to excede the limit, the game warden will take away his licinse.

3. Make sure you are begining every paregraph of your theme with a capitol letter.

4. It is dificult for Mrs. Higgins to walk with a cane, although she trys very hard.

5. He continualy works to improve his competence, but he rarely meets with sucess.

6. Successfully negotiating the terms of the treaty was a great acheivment.

7. The profit he made on the shirts wasn't sufitient to cover the cost of production.

8. Drivers who often ekseed the speed limit can lose their licenses.

9. True succes is found not in great fortune or fame, but in the achievment of the goals

    one sets for oneself.

125

Landscaping

There is no rule which covers the use of double letters in spelling. Memorize each word. In the sentences with missing letters, visualize the whole word, and write in the missing letters.

1. disappoint The landscaper hated to dis′ap point′ her by telling her that the tree would not grow in her part of the country.
Note the one *s* and two *p*'s in *disappoint*. Compare *disappear*.

2. site The homeowner selected a sunny sit*e* for the new flower bed.
Distinguish *site* (position) from *sight* (vision).

3. beautiful The new landscaping was b*eau*′ ti ful.
Focus on the *eau* in *beautiful*. Compare *beauty, bountiful*.

■ The b __ __ ut __ ful landscaping at the s __ t __ did not d __ sa __ p __ __ nt us.

4. across They planted the tulips a *cross*′ from the daffodils.
Note the *cross* in *across*.

5. particular He was very par tic′ u l*ar* about the landscaping of his yard.
Distinguish *particular* from *peculiar*. Note the *part* beginning.

6. accidentally Flora ac′ci den′tal *ly* broke the flower's stem while planting it.
MEMO: An accidentally accurate account

■ We came acr __ __ s this p __ rt __ c __ l __ r plant ac __ __ d __ nt __ __ ly.

7. brought The landscaper *brought* photos of many lawns he had worked on for them to look at.
Compare *think, thought* with *bring, brought*.

8. February Feb′ *ru* ar′y is the best month to prune rose bushes.
Pronounce both *r*'s in *February*. Focus on the *bru*.

9. variety The couple liked to grow a va ri′ *e* ty of flowers in their garden.
Pronounce each syllable in *variety* distinctly.

■ F __ br __ __ ry br __ __ __ __ __ t a v __ r __ __ ty of weather, making landscaping difficult.

10. effect The cold temperatures had no *ef* fect′ on the young tree.
Focus on the *ff* in *effect*. Compare *affect*; contrast *defect*.

11. raise We decided to r*ai*se vegetables in the garden.
Note the *ai* in *raise*. MEMO: Praise the raise.

12. spirits The colorful garden helped raise their spir′ *it*s.
Note the *it* in *spirits*. Pronounce each syllable distinctly.

■ The ef __ __ ct of the beautiful landscaping was to r __ __ s __ our sp __ r __ ts.

EXERCISE I

In each sentence, cross out the incorrect word in parentheses. Then write the correct word in the blank.

1. Throw the blanket (across—acros) your knees if you are too chilly.

_____

2. A well-balanced diet will have both appeal and (varity—variety).

_____

3. (Spirits—Sprites) were high as the time for the football game approached.

_____

4. Mr. Ross began preparing his income tax statement in (Febuary—February).

_____

5. The speech had a profound (affect—effect) on the audience.

_____

6. The architect surveyed the (sight—site) for the new building.

_____

EXERCISE II

Write the correct word in each blank. Choose from the words below.

disappoint   beautiful   brought
particular   raise   accidentally

1. She didn't want to _____ the child on his birthday.

2. She _____ ran over the ball in the street.

3. He _____ the hostess a beautiful bouquet of flowers.

4. It was a _____ sunset.

5. Did you have a _____ restaurant in mind?

6. He was afraid to ask his boss for a _____.

LESSON 52

Archaeology

Study each word carefully. In the sentences with missing letters, visualize the whole word, and write in the missing letters.

1. **ancient** Archaeologists study an′*cie*nt cultures.
   Note the unusual *cie* in *ancient*. Contrast *receive, deceive*.

2. **interest** He expressed in′*ter*est in ancient Egypt.
   Note the *ter* in *interest*. MEMO: Enter winter interest.

3. **great** She felt *great* excitement on her first dig.
   Distinguish *great* (large) from *grate* (iron bars).

■ The archaeologist showed gr __ __ t int __ r __ st in an __ __ __ nt Rome.

4. **whether** He didn't know *wheth*′er the site would yield any artifacts.
   Distinguish *whether* (which of two) from *weather*.

5. **duplicate** She tried to du′*pli*cate the ancient statue exactly.
   Focus on the *pli* in *duplicate*. Compare *triplicate, implicate*.

6. **genuine** Are these ancient Greek coins gen′u in*e*?
   Focus on the *uine* in *genuine*. Place the accent on *gen*.

■ He wondered wh __ th __ r he would be able to d __ pl __ c __ te the g __ n __ __ ne Ming dynasty vase exactly.

7. **ghost** She believed that the *ghost* of Julius Caesar lingered at the ruins.
   Note the *host* in *ghost*. MEMO: The ghost was a hostile host.

8. **familiar** He was fa mil′i*ar* with many different techniques for preserving fragile artifacts.
   Note the *liar* in *familiar*. Compare *peculiar*; contrast *similar*.

9. **picture** They took a pic′tur*e* of the site where the statue was found.
   Distinguish *picture* (photograph) from *pitcher* (a ballplayer).

■ He could p __ ct __ re the g __ __ st of Sophocles among the f __ m __ l __ __ r ruins of the amphitheater.

10. **although** Al tho*ugh*′ the sun was hot, the archaeologists kept digging.
    Note the one *l* in *although*.

11. **seize** That government has the right to s*eize* artifacts that are important to the country's history.
    Focus on the *ei* in *seize*. Distinguish *seize* from *cease*.

12. **determine** He used radiocarbon dating to de ter′min*e* the age of the skull.
    Note the *mine* in *determine*. Compare *genuine, feminine*.

■ Altho __ __ __ they could not d __ t __ rm __ ne the importance of the site, they decided to s __ __ z __ the opportunity to dig at the old pueblo.

☐ EXERCISE I

Write the correct word in each blank. Choose from the words below.

genuine   seize   familiar   interest
picture   great   ghost   ancient

1. The photographer restored the old _____.

2. Are you _____ with the works of many modern American writers?

3. Could we _____ you in joining our study group in Mexico?

4. There is a rumor that a _____ is haunting the castle.

5. Is that a _____ diamond?

6. The archaeologist walked among the _____ ruins.

7. The coast guard moved quickly to _____ the smuggler's cargo.

8. Cicero was a _____ Roman orator.

☐ EXERCISE II

In each sentence, find any misspelled words. Write each word correctly in the blank. If there are no misspelled words, write a *C* in the blank.

_____ **1.** Can you duplacate her handwriting?

_____ **2.** The thief attempted to sieze her purse.

_____ **3.** The shopping mall cost a grate deal of money to build.

_____ **4.** Can you detourmine which way to go from the map?

_____ **5.** I wonder weather or not we'll be invited.

_____ **6.** He would usually take a plane, all though he hated to fly.

_____ **7.** What a good pitcher of Aunt Alicia!

_____ **8.** The couple danced to the famillier song.

_____ **9.** His affection for his brother is genuwine.

_____ **10.** Professor Thompson has spent many years studying the languages of the ancient world.

129

The Theater

Make sure that you know the correct pronunciation and meaning of each word. Refer to the dictionary. In the sentences with missing letters, visualize the whole word, and write in the missing letters.

1. performance   The actress's per form' ance was superb.

2. affect   The final scene of that play will af fect' the whole audience.
Distinguish *affect* from *effect*. Compare *affection*.

3. appreciation   The audience showed its ap pre' ci a' tion of the fine performance by applauding.
Focus on the *cia* in *appreciation*. Compare *appreciate*.

■ An audience's ap __ re __ __ __ ti __ n of a p __ rf __ rm __ n __ __ can af __ __ ct an actor deeply.

4. neighbor   Our n eigh' bor has tickets to a Broadway musical.
Focus on the *eigh* in *neighbor*. MEMO: Weigh eight neighbors.

5. criticism   The reviewer's crit' i cism of the new play was harsh.
Note the *critic* in *criticism*. Compare *critical, criticize*.

6. disposition   The actress struggled to overcome her shy dis' po si' tion.
Note the *position* in *disposition*. Compare *positive, dispose*.

■ My n __ __ __ __ __ bor's cr __ ti __ __ sm of the play was due to his grumpy d __ sp __ s __ ti __ n.

7. grievous   She played a character who had done a griev' ous wrong.
Focus on the *ie* in *grievous*. Compare *retrieve*; contrast *receive*.

8. dying   The character's dy' ing words were a confession.
Distinguish *dying* (expiring) from *dyeing* (coloring).

9. profession   Acting is a unique pro fes' sion.
Note the single *f* in *profession*. Compare *profess, professor*.

■ The hero made a pr __ f __ __ si __ n of love as he lay d __ __ ng from the gr __ __ v __ __ s wound he received in a duel.

10. guardian   In the movie, the famous actress played the unscrupulous guard' i an of an heir.
Note the *ua* in *guardian*. Distinguish *guardian* from *garden*.

11. handling   The comedian is han' dling the dramatic role well.
Focus on the *dli* in *handling*. Compare *trembling, assembling*.

12. responsible   All actors are re spon' si ble for learning their lines.
Focus on the *sible* ending in *responsible*.

■ She will be r __ sp __ ns __ bl __ for h __ ndl __ ng the role of the g __ __ rd __ __ n.

□ EXERCISE I

In the first blank, write each italicized word correctly. In the second blank, write the word or phrase in dark type that most nearly gives its meaning.

1. *handling:*   **observing, quoting, taking care of**   _____   _____

2. *guardian:*   **caretaker, teacher, locksmith**   _____   _____

3. *profession:*   **objection, vocation, location**   _____   _____

4. *neighbor:*   **enemy, visitor, one who lives nearby**   _____   _____

5. *appreciation:*   **determination, recognition, neglect**   _____   _____

6. *affect:*   **to sleep, to influence, to deliberate**   _____   _____

7. *performance:* **presentation, silence, fight**   _____   _____

□ EXERCISE II

Write the correct form of each italicized word in the blank. When you have completed the exercise, check your answers with the dictionary.

1. Write the present tense of the verb that uses the same root as *performance*.

_____

2. Write the present tense of the verb form that uses the same root word as *criticism*.

_____

3. Write the root word of the verb *dying*.

_____

4. Write the root word of the verb that *grievous* is formed from.

_____

5. Write the root word of the verb that *disposition* is formed from.

_____

6. Add a suffix to *responsible* to form a noun.

_____

7. Write a homonym of the verb *affect*.

_____

Car Maintenance

Study each word carefully. In sentences with missing letters, visualize the whole word, and write in the missing letters.

1. **chauffeur**   It was the ch*auf f*eur''s job to make sure the car was always clean, and to maintain it properly.
Consult the dictionary for the pronunciation of *chauffeur*.

2. **mileage**   The odometer showed the mile' *age* for their trip from Jackson, Mississippi to Washington, D.C.
Note the *mile* and the *age* in *mileage*. Contrast *village*.

3. **getting**   She was get' *t*ing good gas mileage from the subcompact Japanese car she bought last summer.
Note the double *t* in *getting*. Compare *get, getting; bet, betting*.

■ **The ch __ __ f __ __ __ r was g __ t __ __ ng low gas m __ l __ __ g __.**

4. **kerosene**   Oil lamps burn *ker' o sene'*; cars burn gasoline.
Focus on the *ene* in *kerosene*. Contrast *gasoline, vaseline*.

5. **gasoline**   He always tried to buy high-grade *gas' o line'*.
Note the *so* in *gasoline*. MEMO: Old line gasoline gas

6. **carburetor**   The mechanic repaired the *car' bu ret' or*.
Note the *bur* in *carburetor*. Pronounce the *or* ending distinctly.

■ **The k __ r __ s __ n __ mixed with g __ s __ l __ n __ choked the c __ rbur __ t __ r.**

7. **scarcely**   They had scar*ce'*ly left town when the car stalled.
Focus on the *rce* in *scarcely*. Compare *fiercely, pierce*.

8. **mountain**   She wasn't at all confident that her old car could climb the steep moun'tain.
Focus on the *ai* in *mountain*. MEMO: Captain of the mountain

9. **climb**   The c*limb* up the mountain was too steep for the car.
Note the *limb* in *climb*. MEMO: Climb the limb.

■ **The old car could sc __ r __ __ ly cl __ m __ the m __ __ nt __ __ n road.**

10. **finally**   She fi' nal *ly* realized how important frequent oil changes are for maintaining a car's engine.
Note the *ally* in *finally*. Compare *usually, naturally*.

11. **compelled**   The low tread com pelled' them to buy new tires.
Note the *ll* in *compelled*. MEMO: He rebelled, but spelled when compelled.

12. **carriage**   My great-grandfather still calls his car a horseless car' r*iage*.
Focus on the *arri* in *carriage*. Compare *marriage*.

■ **They were f __ n __ __ ly c __ mp __ __ led to sell the old c __ __ r __ __ ge.**

□ EXERCISE

In the sentences, cross out each incorrect word in the parentheses. Then write the correct word in the blank.

1. The novice climbers attempted to scale the (mounten—mountain), but they had to turn back before they reached the summit.

   _____

2. Kristen felt (compelled—compeled) to wash the laboratory equipment even though she had not been the last person to use it.

   _____

3. Are you (getting—geting) any closer to finding the answer to the problem?

   _____

4. Fill your camp lanterns with (kerosien—kerosene).

   _____

5. Check the (milleage—mileage) on your odometer before beginning the trip so you can tell how far you have traveled.

   _____

6. To (climbe—climb) to the top of Mount Everest is his ambition.

   _____

7. Did Joe ride around Central Park in the old-fashioned (cariage—carriage)?

   _____

8. There was (scarcily—scarcely) any pizza left after we had eaten.

   _____

9. Be sure to have the mechanic check the spark plugs and the (carburetor—carbaretor) when you have your car serviced.

   _____

10. The (chaufeur—chauffeur) drove safely.

   _____

11. How many gallons of (gasoline—gasolene) does your car's tank hold?

   _____

12. Ryan's package had (finely—finally) arrived.

   _____

A. In each sentence, cross out the incorrect word in parentheses. Then write the correct word in the blank.

1. Sacramento is the (capitol, capital) of California. _____

2. Hard hats were required on the construction (site, sight). _____

3. She (accidently, accidentally) hit the batter with the baseball.

   _____

4. Valentine's Day always falls on (Febuary, February) 14. _____

5. The weather has a profound (effect, affect) on my mood.

   _____

6. They (raze, raise) the flag every morning. _____

7. Do you think Reagan was a (great, grate) president? _____

8. Did you ask the child (whether, weather) he wanted to go?

   _____

9. You should (seize, seas) the opportunity. _____

10. The change in rates did not (affect, effect) us. _____

11. She noticed that the flowers were (dyeing, dying). _____

12. After ten rings, she (finally, finely) answered the phone. _____

Each correct answer is worth 3 points.	Total score: 36 points.

B. Supply *ei* or *ie* in each word.

1. tr __ __ s

2. ach __ __ vement

3. suffic __ __ nt

4. s __ __ ze

5. n __ __ ghbor

6. var __ __ ty

7. anc __ __ nt

8. gr __ __ vous

Each correct answer is worth 3 points.	Total score: 24 points.

C. The following business letter contains many spelling errors. Cross out each misspelled word. Write the word correctly above the misspelled word.

Dear Mr. Lyle:

I feel compeled to write you after my resent experience. I hired one of your limousines to take me to my hotel. I'm confidant that we avoided an accedent because of the exellent driving performince of the chaufer, Mr. Ed Smith.

We were driving accross town when a car tryed to cut our limousine off. It was a dificult acheivement to avoid an accident. Mr. Smith had sucess in doing so because he was compatent and responseable in handleing the problem.

Because the other driver tried to excede the speed limit and, in particuler, because he tried to cut in front of us, he should lose his driver's lisence.

Usually, letters bring critisism and not apreciation. I want to express my genuin appreciation to the managment of your company and to Mr. Smith for being a gardian of my safety. Mr. Smith certainly sets a magnifisent example for his profesion.

Sincerely,

Each correct answer is worth 1 point.	Total score: 25 points.

D. In each sentence, find any misspelled words. Write each word correctly in the blank. If all words in the sentence are spelled correctly, write a *C* in the blank.

_____ 1. The superintendant met with the principals.

_____ 2. Children usually try hard not to disapoint their parents.

_____ 3. That man looks familar to me.

_____ 4. Can you determine which way we should turn?

_____ 5. The baby had a wonderful dispositon.

_____ 6. The mechanic told me my carborator needs adjusting.

_____ 7. My gasolene gauge isn't accurate.

Each correct answer is worth 2 points.	Total score: 14 points.

Melodramas

Concentrate on the hard spots which appear in italics. In the sentences with missing letters, visualize the whole word, and write in the missing letters.

1. **villain**   He grew a moustache to play the vil′l*ai*n in the melodrama.
     MEMO: The villain of the mountain fountain

2. **character**   Which *char*′ac ter will you play in the melodrama?
     Note the *act* in *character*. Contrast *chorus, chemistry*.

3. **establish**   The heroine in the melodrama tried to es tab′lish her credibility.
     Focus on the *est* in *establish*. MEMO: Establish an estimate.

■ The v __ __ l __ __ n had to est __ bl __ sh that he had a bad c __ ar __ ct __ r.

4. **possession**   The villain took pos ses′*sio*n of the heroine's homestead.
     Note the four *s*'s in *possession*.

5. **principally**   The actors in the melodrama were prin′ci pal *ly* amateurs.
     Note the *ally* in *principally*. Compare *practically, accidentally*.

6. **mysterious**   The villain disappeared in a *mys* te′ri ous cloud of smoke.
     Focus on the *mys* in *mysterious*. Note the *ious* ending.

■ The m __ st __ r __ __ __ s villain obtained p __ __ ses __ __ __ n of the homestead pr __ nc __ p __ __ ly by being dishonest.

7. **decide**   The Bakers could not de *c*ide′ when to go to the melodrama.
     Focus on the *c* in *decide*. Compare *decision*; contrast *beside*.

8. **majority**   A ma jor′i ty of the audience hissed at the villain.
     Note the *major* in *majority*.

9. **arrangement**   She made the *ar* range′ment for tickets to the melodrama.
     Focus on the *ge* in *arrangement*. Compare *changeable*.

■ It took a m __ j __ r __ ty of the cast of the melodrama to d __ c __ d __ on the ar __ __ ng __ m __ nt of the scenery.

10. **American**   The melodrama is one form of A mer′i can theater.
     Always begin *American* with a capital *A*. Clearly pronounce the *i*.

11. **niece**   She took her n*ie*ce to the melodrama.
     Focus on the *ie* in *niece*. MEMO: My niece wants a piece of pie.

12. **allowance**   The child spent his entire a*l* low′ *ance* for the month on tickets to the melodrama.
     Stress the *ance* in *allowance*.

■ Her Am __ r __ c __ n n __ __ c __ spent her al __ __ w __ nc __ to take her to the melodrama.

☐ EXERCISE I

In each sentence, find any misspelled words. Write each word correctly in the blank. If there are no misspelled words, write a *C* in the blank.

_____ 1. It will be hard for the jury to deside the fate of the defendant.

_____ 2. Ms. Newsome's most cherished posession is the ring.

_____ 3. Selena asked for an advance on next month's allowence.

_____ 4. The musical arrangment was done by the conductor.

_____ 5. The partners each put up an equal amount of capital to establish the business.

_____ 6. Was the customer principaly interested in antiques?

_____ 7. Mr. Olson's neice is visiting him from Des Moines, Iowa.

_____ 8. Misterious sounds came from the old house.

_____ 9. The judge was a person of fine caracter.

_____ 10. The American flag is a symbol of democracy.

☐ EXERCISE II

The following postcard contains many spelling errors. Cross out each misspelled word. Then write the word correctly above the misspelled word.

Dear Latonia,

I am having a great time here in Buffalo. I am principaly just relaxing. Last night I couldn't dicide what I wanted to do, so my little eight-year-old neice spent her allowence and took me downtown to the Amercan Theater to see a melodrama.

The arrangment of the seats was wonderful, and I could see everything. I especially enjoyed watching the caracter who played the misterious villian. He was able to establesh such dislike among the audience that the majorety of us who were in posession of popcorn used it to toss at him! It was a fun evening.

Sincerely,

137

Public Opinion

The words in this lesson cause many spelling errors. Study them carefully. In the sentences with missing letters, visualize the whole word, and write in the missing letters.

1. volunteer He served as a vol′ un teer′ for the public opinion survey.
Focus on the *un* in *volunteer*. Compare *voluntary, profiteer*.

2. allowed Public opinion favored smoking not being al lowed′ in the building.
Note the *owe* in *allowed*. Distinguish *allowed* from *aloud*.

3. captain She was elected cap′ tain of the public opinion pollsters.
Focus on the *tai* in *captain*. Compare *mountain, fountain*.

■ The pollsters a __ lo __ __ d the v __ l __ nteer to be made c __ pt __ __ n.

4. different Because people have dif′ fer ent opinions, polls are taken.
Note the *ent* in *different*. MEMO: Silent, violent, and different

5. apartment They polled every person living in the a part′ ment complex.
Note the *apart* in *apartment*. MEMO: A part of an apartment

6. convenience Telephones are a con ven′ ience for public opinion pollsters.
Focus on the *ience* in *convenience*. Compare *science, experience*.

■ A d __ f __ __ r __ nt pollster will come to your ap __ rtm __ nt at your
c __ nv __ n __ __ n __ __.

7. basis A public opinion poll showing 40% of the voters undecided was the ba′ sis of the candidate's optimism.
Note the *is* in *basis*. MEMO: His basis is the oasis.

8. definite The pollster soon learned that the man had a def′ i nite opinion on each of the issues.
Focus on the *ite* ending in *definite*. Compare *infinite*.

9. criticize The candidate was quick to crit′ i cize his opponent's opinion poll as irrelevant to the campaign.
Keep the *critic* in *criticize*. Compare *critical, criticism*.

■ She had a d __ f __ n __ t __ b __ s __ s on which to cr __ t __ c __ ze the poll.

10. personal That is my per′ son al opinion, not necessarily public opinion.
Note the *al* in *personal*. MEMO: A personal pal is not critical.

11. argument The latest public opinion poll created a heated ar′ gu ment between the two candidates.
Note the omitted *e* when *argue* changes to *argument*.

12. prejudice A recent survey polled the public's attitude on pr ej′ u dice.
Focus on the *ej* in *prejudice*. Compare *judicial, injustice*.

■ The poll on p __ rs __ n __ l pr __ j __ di __ __ caused a lengthy arg __ m __ nt.

☐ EXERCISE I

In the first blank, write each italicized word correctly. In the second blank, write the word or phrase in dark type that most nearly means the same as the word.

1. *criticize:*   **assist, reproach, confuse**   _____   _____

2. *volunteer:*   **offer, offend, withdraw**   _____   _____

3. *different:*   **same, insane, unusual**   _____   _____

4. *argument:*   **debate, comment, experiment**   _____   _____

5. *allowed:*   **loud, permitted, debated**   _____   _____

6. *basis:*   **airport, diameter, foundation**   _____   _____

7. *prejudice:*   **intolerance, inactivity, pride**   _____   _____

8. *captain:*   **shipmate, employee, leader**   _____   _____

9. *apartment:*   **store, department, place to live**   _____   _____

10. *definite*   **sorrowful, unpopular, distinct**   _____   _____

11. *personal:*   **solemn, private, dignified**   _____   _____

12. *convenience:*   **difficulty, occupation, ease**   _____   _____

☐ EXERCISE II

Each sentence contains one or more spelling errors. Cross out each misspelled word. Then write the word correctly above it.

1. The captin alowed his first mate to go ashore on personel business.

2. She worked for the political campaign on a voluntier basiss.

3. His new apartement is equipped with every conveniance.

4. In the heat of the argeument, she couldn't help but critasize his prejidice.

5. Each had a difrent, defanite opinion.

6. The capitain vollenteered for another tour of duty.

7. For your conveneince, the store will be open until 9:00.

Community Service

In the sentences with missing letters, visualize the whole word, and write in the missing letters.

1. disease She passed out pamphlets about the dis *ease'*.
Stress the *dis* in *disease*.

2. stating He read a brochure stat'*ing* what services were available.
Omit the *e* in *stating*. Compare *state, stating; skate, skating*.

3. extraordinary She was recognized for her ex tr*aor'* di nar'*y* service to the city's homeless population.
Note that *traor* is one syllable in *extraordinary*.

■ The volunteer was quoted as st __ t __ ng that an extr __ __ rd __ n __ ry number of citizens had the d __ s __ __ se.

4. recognize The banquet will rec'*og* ni*ze* eight service organizations.
Pronounce the *g* in the middle syllable of *recognize*.

5. difference Teresa's voluntary service made a dif'*fer* en*ce* in the city.
Note the *ence* in *difference*. MEMO: A difference in evidence

6. sensible Be sen'*si* b*le* about taking on community service obligations.
Focus on the *sib* in *sensible*. Compare *defensible, responsible*.

■ Do you r __ c __ gn __ __ __ e any s __ ns __ bl __ d __ f __ __ r __ nc __ between the two community service organizations?

7. divided John d*i* vid'*ed* his time between work and community service.
Stress the *i*'s in *divide*. Compare *inside, division*.

8. fundamental Lauren has a fun'*da* men'*tal* belief in community service.
Pronounce each syllable in *fundamental* distinctly.

9. opposite They did volunteer work for groups with op'*po* site goals.
Stress the *po* in *opposite*. Compare *opportunity, opposition*.

■ The volunteers were d __ v __ d __ d into groups with op __ __ s __ te opinions about their f __ nd __ m __ nt __ l purpose.

10. merely She did not volunteer at the hospital mere'*ly* to pass time.
Note the *mere* in *merely*. Compare *sincerely*; contrast *nearly*.

11. pressure The group put no pres'*sure* on her to volunteer.
MEMO: Be sure to stress the *press* in *pressure*.

12. vicinity Marta will collect donations from homes in her vi cin'*i* ty.
Focus on the *cin* in *vicinity*. Stress the three *i*'s in *vicinity*.

■ I m __ r __ l __ put pr __ s __ __ re on the city to stop dumping in the vi __ __ n __ ty.

☐ EXERCISE I

Each sentence contains one or more spelling errors. Cross out each misspelled word.
Then write the word correctly above it.

1. The arguement will not end until they agree on the fundemental point.

2. Would you volenteer to help in the disese prevention program?

3. Mr. Perkins was stateing the basus for a two-party system of politics.

4. Although he held the oposite opinion, he did not critisize the legislator.

5. The legislature was dividded on the question of personel income tax.

6. The captein was amazed at the extrordinary conduct of the crew.

7. Could you recognise Ashley's apartement building?

8. The child was not alowed mearly to cross the street.

9. The group made a definate move to exert presure for the passage of the bill.

☐ EXERCISE II

The following letter contains many spelling errors. Cross out each misspelled word.
Then write the word correctly above the misspelled word.

Dear Silvia,

   This letter of commendation is to recognize your extraordenary community service

work over the past five years. When you began, you statted that combatting a dread

decease among neighbors in your immediate vacinity was your fundimental goal, and

you really have made a big diference.

   Before your effort, the community's awareness of the disese was merly superficial.

Now it is just the oppasite. There is preasure to take a more senseable approach and

not be devided on the issue of the disease's cause.

   Congratulations on your caring attitude, hard work, and dedication!

Sincerely,

Photography

Note that some words have two accented syllables, one receiving a primary accent (′) and another a secondary accent (′). Study each word carefully. In the sentences with missing letters, visualize the whole word, and write in the missing letters.

1. **attention** — Photographers must pay close a*t* ten′ *tio*n to detail.
Note the three *t*'s in *attention*. Compare *invention*.

2. **sincerely** — The couple sin *cere*′ ly appreciated the photographer's care in taking their wedding pictures.
Keep the *sincere* in *sincerely*. Compare *merely, entirely*.

3. **respectfully** — The photographer treated his subjects re spect′ful *ly*.
Note the *respect* and the *fully* in *respectfully*.

■ The photographer s __ n __ __ r __ ly, r __ sp __ ctf __ __ ly asked for at __ __nt __ __n.

4. **affectionately** — The photographer spoke a*f* fec′ *tio*n ate ly of his subjects.
Focus on the *ely* in *affectionately*. Compare *approximately*.

5. **really** — The photographer real′ *ly* had a great eye for unique angles.
Focus on the *all* in *really*. Compare *totally, locally, naturally*.

6. **characteristic** — Patience is a necessary char′ ac ter is′tic for a successful photographer.

■ It is r __ __ __ ly c __ __ r __ ct __ rist __ c of her to treat the animals she photographs af __ __ ct __ __ n __ t __ ly.

7. **comparison** — He made a com par′ *i* son of the two photos.
Focus on the *ison* ending of *comparison*.

8. **relative** — She learned the basics of photography with rel′ *a* tive ease.
Focus on the *la* in *relative*. Pronounce the *a* distinctly.

9. **competition** — There will be stiff com′ pe ti′*tio*n in the photo contest.
Note the *petition* in *competition*. Focus on the *eti*.

■ The judge of the c __ mp __ t __ t __ __ n made a c __ mp __ r __ s __ n of the photos and decided on their r __ l __ t __ ve merits.

10. **representative** — The photos were rep′ re sent′ a tive of different interests.
Focus on the *at* in *representative*. Stress the *a* sound.

11. **conscious** — Photographers must be con′ *scio*us of their surroundings.
Focus on the *scio* in *conscious*. Compare *glorious*.

12. **individual** — Our in′ di vid′ u al tastes influence our choice of subjects.

■ To create a portrait that is r __ pr __ s __ nt __ t __ ve of an ind __ v __ d __ __ l, a photographer must be c __ n __ __ __ __ ous of the subject's personality.

EXERCISE I

Write the correct form in each blank. When you have completed the exercise, check your answers in the dictionary.

1. Write the past tense of the verb form that uses the same root word as *attention*.

_____

2. Drop the suffix from *sincerely* to form an adjective.

_____

3. Drop the suffixes from *respectfully* to form a noun.

_____

4. Drop the suffixes from *affectionately* to form a noun.

_____

5. Drop the suffix from *really* to form an adjective.

_____

6. Drop the suffix from *characteristic* to form a noun.

_____

EXERCISE II

In each sentence, find any misspelled words. Write each word correctly in the blank. If there are no misspelled words, write a *C* in the blank.

_____ **1.** A close comperisin of the two brands showed that there was little difference between them.

_____ **2.** Is he a reletive of yours?

_____ **3.** Do you plan to enter the cooking compatition?

_____ **4.** The Olympic athlete was proud to be a repersentative of her country.

_____ **5.** He was not conscious of his inconsiderate behavior.

_____ **6.** That private school stresses the development of individial creativity in young children.

_____ **7.** Close attention to detail is charicteristic of a fine craftsman.

Hobbies

Study each word carefully. Refer to the dictionary for the correct pronunciation of the difficult words in this lesson. In sentences with missing letters, visualize the whole word and write in the missing letters.

1. **vacuum** His hobby included studying how objects behave in a vac′u um.
Focus on the *uu* in *vacuum*. Stress all three syllables.

2. **apparently** She was ap par′ent ly engrossed in her hobby.
Note the *rent* in *apparently*. Compare *transparent, parent*.

3. **propeller** The model airplane was finished except for its pro pel′ler.
Focus on the *elle* in *propeller*. Compare *speller*; contrast *propel*.

■ Ap __ __ r __ ntly the va __ __ __ __ m cleaner sucked up the model's prop __ __ l __ r.

4. **forfeit** She'd have to for′feit time for her hobby to take the three-week trip to Hawaii.
Note the *ei* in *forfeit*. Compare *surfeit, counterfeit*.

5. **guest** He discovered that his gue st also collected stamps.
Focus on *ue* in *guest*. Distinguish *guest* from *guessed*.

6. **embarrass** It will em bar′rass him if he doesn't win first place at the African violet show.
Focus on the *rr* and the *ss* in *embarrass*.

■ The girl would f __ rf __ __ t her hobby for a week if she were to embar __ __ __ __ s the g __ __ st.

7. **purchase** He went to the store to *pur′* chase another model train.
Note the *pur* in *purchase*. MEMO: Purchase the purple purse.

8. **orchestra** Her hobby was playing in the city's symphony or′*ch*es tra.
Focus on the *ch* in *orchestra*. Note the *tra* syllable.

9. **piano** She played the piano as a hobby.
Pronounce the three syllables in *piano* distinctly.

■ Eric will p __ rch __ s __ the old p __ __ n __ from the orc __ __ str __.

10. **treasurer** Guillermo was elected treas′ur er of the men's garden club.
Note the *sure* in *treasurer*. Compare *measure, pleasure*.

11. **superstitious** Breeding black cats is a bad hobby for the su′per sti′tious.
Focus on the *tious* in *superstitious*. Compare *superstition*.

12. **shepherd** His hobby was raising German *Shep′ herd* puppies.
Note the *shep* and the *herd* in *shepherd*. Focus on the silent *h*.

■ The s __ p __ rst __ t __ __ __ s tr __ __ sur __ r is afraid of the German Sh __ p __ __ rd.

□ EXERCISE I

Cross out each incorrect word in the parentheses. Write the correct word in the blank.

1. The (Treasurer—Tresurer) of the United States signs our paper money.

_____

2. Sounds cannot echo in a (vaccum—vacuum).

_____

3. Consuela could not afford to (purchass—purchase) a new wheelchair.

_____

4. The old plane had only one (propellar—propeller).

_____

5. The young (shepherd—shepheard) will watch over the flocks.

_____

6. If you fail to appear at the tournament, you will (forfit—forfeit) the prize.

_____

7. Jiro wanted to play the (pianno—piano) solo at Tuesday's concert.

_____

8. The (guest—guessed) list for the dinner will be published in the paper.

_____

9. It would (embarass—embarrass) him if we sang in the restaurant.

_____

□ EXERCISE II

Cross out any misspelled words in each group of words. Write each misspelled word correctly in the blank. If there are no misspelled words, write a *C* in the blank.

1. aparently	attention	attitude	_____
2. vacuum	really	embarrass	_____
3. shepherd	orcestra	individual	_____
4. supersticious	forfeit	sincerely	_____
5. treasurer	guest	piana	_____

145

Nutrition

Study each word carefully. In sentences with missing letters, visualize the whole word, and write in the missing letters.

1. **irresistible** Even though it wasn't on her diet, Jamie had an *ir′ re sist′ i*ble desire for chocolate.
   Focus on the *rr* in *irresistible*. Note the *ible* ending carefully.

2. **apparatus** The nutritionist had all sorts of chemical ap *pa ra′ tus* in her lab.
   Focus on the double *p* in *apparatus*.

3. **current** The *cur′ r*ent literature is full of information on proper nutrition.
   Note the *rr* in *current*.

■ The ap __ __ r __ t __ s that pops corn without oil, and which runs on an alternating cur __ __ nt, is ir __ __ s __ st __ ble to the health-conscious.

4. **destroy** Eating too many fatty foods can de stroy′ a healthful diet plan.
   Focus on the *des* in *destroy*. Compare *destruction, despise*.

5. **siege** Bernardo decided to lay *siege* to her poor nutritional habits.
   Focus on the *ie* in *siege*. MEMO: Relieve the field by siege.

6. **concrete** Nutritional standards are not set in con′ cr*ete*.
   Note the *ete* ending of *concrete*. Compare *complete, athlete*.

■ The aim of the media s __ __ g __ was to d __ str __ y the dietary hoaxes that seemed to be set in c __ ncr __ t __.

7. **substitute** Many people now sub′ st*i* tut*e* margarine for butter.
   Focus on the *sti* in *substitute*. Compare *constitute, institute*.

8. **auxiliary** The nutritionist worked in the hospital's *aux* il′ *ia* ry kitchen.
   Note the *liar* in *auxiliary*. Focus on the unusual *aux* beginning.

9. **instead** More people are now eating fruit for dessert in st*ead′* of cakes and cookies.
   Focus on the *ea* in *instead*.

■ The dietition was forced to s __ bst __ t __ te an a __ x __ l __ __ ry meal plan in __ t __ __ d of the original.

10. **anything** He ate *an′ y* thing he wanted in moderation.
    Note that *any* and *thing* combine to make *anything*.

11. **stationary** She ate carefully, but her weight remained sta′ *tion* ar′ y.
    Distinguish *stationary* (fixed) and *stationery* (paper, etc.).

12. **desirable** To maintain a de sir′ a bl*e* weight, you must eat healthfully.
    Note the *rable* ending of *desirable*. Compare *admirable*.

■ His weight remaining st __ ti __ n __ ry was an __ th __ ng but d __ s __ r __ ble.

146

☐ EXERCISE

In each sentence, find any misspelled words. Write each word correctly in the blank. If there are no misspelled words, write a *C* in the blank.

_____ **1.** Mrs. Endo decided to substitutte meat for fish at the dinner party.

_____ **2.** I don't think I will need anything from either the drugstore or the market.

_____ **3.** The electric curent surged through the wire.

_____ **4.** The soldiers planned the sieg of the fortress in great detail.

_____ **5.** The car was stationery when it was hit from behind by a red pickup truck.

_____ **6.** The architect will check the foundation before the concreat is poured for the slab.

_____ **7.** Many women think it is desireable to be thin.

_____ **8.** If the water rises, it will distroy their home.

_____ **9.** Let's eat at home insted of going out.

_____ **10.** The gym was full of exercise aparatus.

_____ **11.** The new bulding on 5th Street will serve as an auxiliary to the old town hall.

_____ **12.** The chocolate mousse was iresistible.

_____ **13.** He likes to keep up with curant events.

_____ **14.** Will they distroy the old house?

_____ **15.** The officer candidates studied a famous seige.

_____ **16.** The workmen are pouring concerete for the sidewalk.

_____ **17.** Would you prefer a sugar substatute?

_____ **18.** Is the house in a desireable neighborhood?

_____ **19.** Would you like inything to eat?

_____ **20.** Turn on the auxiliery generator.

147

A. Write the correct form in each blank without referring to the word list. When you have completed the exercise, check your answers in the dictionary.

1. Write the past tense of the verb that uses the same root word as *dividing*.

_____

2. Add a suffix to *apparent* to form an adverb.

_____

3. Change *mere* from an adjective to an adverb.

_____

4. Add a suffix to *possess* to form a noun.

_____

5. Add a suffix to *sense* to form an adjective.

_____

6. Add a prefix to *resistible* to form a word that means unable to be resisted.

_____

7. Add a suffix to the root word of *convenient* to form a noun.

_____

8. Add a suffix to *principal* to form an adverb.

_____

9. Add a suffix to *propel* to form a noun.

_____

10. Add a suffix to *major* to form a noun.

_____

Each correct answer is worth 4 points.	Total score: 40 points.

B. The following note contains many spelling errors. Cross out each misspelled word. Write the word correctly above the misspelled word.

Dear Jeff,

I sinserely appreciate the reely extrordinary tie you sent me for my birthday. I reconize your personel attenshun in selecting it. I have never seen anythin so iresistable. It is perfect for the curent style. The thoughtfulness you showed is so caracteristic of you. The tie is so diferent and individuel that it has already become a favorite possesion of mine. I will wear it for my piana solo in the orcestra next month.

Affectionatly,

Each correct answer is worth 1 point.	Total score: 16 points.

C. Each sentence contains one or more spelling errors. Cross out each misspelled word. Then write the word correctly above it.

1. Which cheracter in the movie is supposed to be the villein?

2. The orcestra desided to perchase a new piana.

3. The Romans laid sieje to Troy.

4. He works for the hospital on a voluntier basiss.

5. The crew could not critasize the captin.

6. Stateing her opinion respectfuly was the best way to deal with her boss.

7. His neice was alowed to spend her alowance in any way she chose.

8. Her apartement is oposite the cleaners, in the vacinity of the shopping mall.

9. We must find a substatute for the currant tresurer.

10. The researchers were under presure to find a cure for the misterious disaese.

11. He has a definit prejidice against Americun cars.

12. After their argumint, he sent her a flower arangment.

13. It was desireable to astablish the witness's good character.

14. What made you deside to enter the compatition?

15. The fundamentel diffrence between the two vacum cleaners was their quality.

16. It was difficult to keep the aparatus stationery.

17. He worked as an auxilary to the Representetive.

18. They tried to distroy the concerete water tank.

19. She felt like a gest insted of a reletive.

20. His comperasin of the two boys wasn't meant to emberass them.

21. She wasn't contious of being supersticious.

22. The sheperd will forfit his right to be believed if he lies about the wolf.

Each correct answer is worth 2 points.	Total score: 44 points.

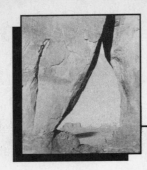

Part Two
The Technical Gateway

Practical Spelling and Dictionary Habits

Complete mastery of the 720 words in Part 1 of *Gateways to Correct Spelling* will eliminate most mistakes in spelling. Part 2 is presented for those who wish to go beyond the basic list of spelling words, and attain mastery of a greater variety of words important both in business and literature. The lessons ahead are designed to meet the practical needs of these students.

Part 2 of *Gateways to Correct Spelling* makes three practical contributions to the language needs of its students:

1. It presents additional words especially useful for general literary and business needs.
2. It shows how to become an expert in the use of the dictionary, giving the student the necessary skills to gain correct understanding and use of all words.
3. It applies the rules and principles of spelling in an objective manner that contributes to better spelling and improved speech.

Students should continue to use the whole-word, hard-spot method of study described in Part 1 of this book. The proper use of a comprehensive dictionary is so important to practical progress in spelling that it becomes a major objective in the lessons to follow.

The Dictionary

A good dictionary is an essential aid to practical spelling and, in addition, opens the way for general language improvement. The business of buying, selling, advertising, writing letters, using the telephone, and preparing reports, is dependent upon the correct choice and spelling of words. The lessons which follow in *Gateways to Correct Spelling* show how to use the dictionary as an aid to correct spelling. Fortunately, the proper use of a dictionary for purposes of correct spelling also contributes to the better use of a dictionary for general language purposes.

The student should carefully study the directions in the front part of the dictionary which tell how to use it. Dictionaries differ considerably in the information they present and in the exact form and place in which they present it.

Study the sample dictionary entries below. Note that there are three entries for the word *spell*. Each entry is marked with a small superscript number. *Spell* has three separate dictionary entries because the word has three different meanings: "to write a word," "a magical formula," and "a period of time."

Following each entry word is the phonetic spelling, shown in parentheses. The phonetic spelling tells you how to pronounce the word. You will learn how to read phonetic spellings in Part 2.

The phonetic spelling is followed by a letter in italics. This letter gives the word's part of speech: *v* for verb, *n* for noun, etc. Note that two of the entries for *spell* are nouns, and one is a verb.

Now look at the etymology for each of the entries. The etymology is shown in brackets. It tells how a word came into our language. The etymology of each of the entries is different. The three meanings of *spell* came into the Modern English language from two different Middle English words. The meanings "to write a word" and "a magical formula" originally came from an Old English word, and the meaning "a period of time" originally came from an Old French word.

Note that each entry has more than one definition. The different definitions of the entry word are indicated by numbers and lower-case letters. Look at the second entry of the word *spell*. This entry has three definitions: "an incantational word or formula," "compelling attraction," and "a bewitched state."

spell¹ (spĕl)—*v.* **spelled** *or* **spelt** (spelt), **spell•ing, spells.** [ME *spellen,* to read letter by letter < OFr. *espelir,* of Germanic orig.]—*vt.* **1.** To name or write in order the letters constituting (a word or part of a word). **2.** To be the letters of (a word). **3.** To mean: signify <a policy that *spells* disaster> —*vi.* To form a word or words correctly by means of letters. **—spell down.** To defeat in a spelldown. **—spell out. 1.** To make perfectly clear. **2.** To comprehend by study.
spell² (spĕl) *n.* [ME, discourse < OE, story.] **1.** An incantational word or formula. **2.** Compelling attraction: FASCINATION. **3.** A bewitched state: TRANCE. —*vt.* **spelled, spell•ing, spells.** To put under a spell.
spell³ (spĕl) *n.* [<ME *spelen,* to spare < OE *spelian,* to represent.] **1.** A short yet indefinite time period. **2.** *Informal.* A period of weather of a given kind <a wet *spell*> **3.** A period of work: SHIFT. **4.** *Informal.* **a.** A period, as of irritability. **b.** A sudden bout of illness. **5.** *Informal.* A short distance. —*v.* **spelled, spell•ing, spells.** —*vt.* **1.** To relieve (another) from work temporarily by taking a turn. **2.** To allow to rest a while. —*vi.* To rest for a time from an activity.
★*syns;* SPELL, ACCESS, ATTACK, FIT, SEIZURE *n. core meaning:* a sudden, often acute manifestation of a disease <experienced frequent *spells* of indigestion>

The final value of any dictionary depends upon your ability to find words quickly and to interpret the accompanying information correctly. The lessons which follow show you how to do this.

Finding Words in the Dictionary

The exercises below are planned to give you practice in finding where different kinds of words are located in your dictionary. If you have trouble finding any of the words, consult the Table of Contents or the Directions for Use in the front of your dictionary.

1. Speed in locating a word may be attained by following the two guide words which appear at the top of each page in the dictionary. The first guide word is the first entry on the page; the second guide word is the last entry on the page. See how quickly you can find the following words in your dictionary.

   disagree
   accordingly
   leaves

   whistle
   luncheon
   mechanical

2. Abbreviations, foreign words, and names of places and persons are often listed separately at the end of a dictionary. Some words, for example, *adiós*, may be listed both in the main body and at the end of a dictionary. Look for the following words in your dictionary. It is possible that some may not be listed.

   f.o.b.
   IRS
   petite
   Charles
   YMCA

   Moses
   Washington
   e pluribus unum
   Chinese

☐ VISUAL DRILL

As you look at each word, try to visualize the whole word with the missing letters in place. Then check yourself by looking at the word as it appears above. Finally, fill in the blanks. Check the spelling again, and make any necessary corrections.

dis __ gr __ __

ac __ ordin __ l __

le __ v __ s

Mo __ __ s

__ ashin __ t __ n

__ harl __ __

w __ is __ le

lun __ __ e __ n

me __ __ anic __ __

Ch __ n __ s __

pet __ t __

☐ EXERCISE

Find each word in your dictionary. In the first blank, indicate the word's part of speech. In the second blank, give the word's meaning. If more than one meaning is indicated in your dictionary, give the first meaning.

1. installment _____ _____

2. maladjustment _____ _____

3. Fahrenheit _____ _____

4. personnel _____ _____

5. *laissez-faire* _____ _____

6. copier _____ _____

7. stereophonic _____ _____

8. centrifugal _____ _____

9. cogitate _____ _____

10. perpendicular _____ _____

11. undulate _____ _____

12. mercurial _____ _____

13. *fait accompli* _____ _____

14. atheistic _____ _____

15. fallaciously _____ _____

16. indictment _____ _____

17. perpetuity _____ _____

18. homogeneous _____ _____

19. commitment _____ _____

20. legerdemain _____ _____

21. chemotherapy _____ _____

22. swatch _____ _____

Understanding Phonetic Spelling

Each of the words listed in alphabetical order in a dictionary is called an entry. Most dictionaries print the entry words with the syllables separated by hyphens, spaces, or dots. Note how your own dictionary prints its entries. Make sure you understand your dictionary. Consult the Directions for Use.

Each entry in the dictionary is followed by a phonetic spelling. For example, the word *va cant* is followed by the phonetic spelling (vā′ kənt). Phonetic spellings show how words should be pronounced. Be careful not to confuse phonetic spellings with correct spellings.

Listed below are six words with illustrative sentences to show their meanings. Find each word in your dictionary. Notice the correct spelling, the dictionary entry spelling, and the phonetic spelling of each word.

despair	The drowning person gave up in *despair*.
hygiene	The science of *hygiene* deals with health.
luncheon	The *luncheon* was served at noon.
permit	They would not *permit* me to go.
salmon	The *salmon* is an edible fish.
watch	Be sure to *watch* your pronunciation.

☐ VISUAL DRILL

As you look at each word, try to visualize the whole word with the missing letters in place. Then check yourself by looking at the word as it appears above. Finally, fill in the blanks. Check the spelling again, and make any necessary corrections.

d __ sp __ __ r   h __ g __ __ ne   lunc __ __ __ n

p __ rm __ t   s __ __ m __ n   w __ __ ch

☐ EXERCISE I

Find each word in your dictionary. Write the correct spelling, the dictionary entry spelling, and the phonetic spelling of each word.

WORD	CORRECT SPELLING	DICTIONARY ENTRY	PHONETIC SPELLING
Ex: machinery	machinery	ma-chin-er-y	mə shē′ nə rē
1. illustrate	_____	_____	_____
2. horticulture	_____	_____	_____
3. lingerie	_____	_____	_____

WORD	CORRECT SPELLING	DICTIONARY ENTRY	PHONETIC SPELLING
4. metabolism	_____	_____	_____
5. combustion	_____	_____	_____
6. transaction	_____	_____	_____
7. qualification	_____	_____	_____
8. illiteracy	_____	_____	_____
9. exotic	_____	_____	_____
10. upholstery	_____	_____	_____
11. pedagogy	_____	_____	_____
12. retractable	_____	_____	_____
13. calculator	_____	_____	_____
14. fuselage	_____	_____	_____
15. archipelago	_____	_____	_____
16. judicial	_____	_____	_____
17. penicillin	_____	_____	_____

☐ EXERCISE II

Study the phonetic spelling of each of the following words. Try to figure out the correct spelling of each word, and write it in the blank. Check your efforts by looking at the words in Exercise I above. Make any necessary corrections.

PHONETIC SPELLING

CORRECT SPELLING

1. rĕnch _____

2. pĕn′ ĭ sĭl′ ĭn _____

3. ĭ lĭt′ ər ə sē _____

4. kwŏl′ ə fĭ kā′ shən _____

5. ĭg zŏt′ ĭk _____

How To Study Words in the Dictionary

It is very important, for both spelling and speech, that you take the right steps in studying the dictionary. Whenever you look up a word to determine its spelling or how to pronounce it, take the following steps:

1. Make sure that you have the right word.
2. Observe how the word is syllabified.
3. Observe how the word is accented.
4. Observe letters pronounced differently than usual.
5. Observe silent or extra letters.
6. Strengthen your visual image of the word.

The method and importance of these steps will become clearer as you consider them in greater detail in the lessons to follow.

Step 1. Making Sure That You Have the Right Word

Always look at the meanings of a word given in the dictionary to make sure that you are not confusing it with some other word. For example, do not confuse *accept* with *except*, or *essay* with *assay*. Confusion of this sort accounts for a surprisingly large number of spelling errors. (See Lessons 3 and 36.) Look up the following pairs of words in your dictionary, and contrast them as to spelling, pronunciation, and meaning.

biannual	A bi an′ nu al event occurs twice a year.
biennial	A bi en′ ni al event occurs once in two years.
dairy	We get our milk at the dair′ y.
diary	I write something in my di′ a ry every night.
eligible	Morgan was not el′ i gi ble for membership.
illegible	Mary's handwriting was almost il leg′ i ble.
eminent	She is an em′ i nent person.
imminent	Another major strike seemed im′ mi nent.
moral	His mor′ al acts were right and just.
morale	The team's mo rale′ was very low.
receipt	The re ceipt′ showed that he had paid the bill.
recipe	Roger has a good rec′ i pe for making biscuits.

☐ VISUAL DRILL

As you look at each word, try to visualize the whole word with the missing letters in place. Then check yourself by looking at the word as it appears above. Finally, fill in the blanks. Check the spelling again, and make any necessary corrections.

bi __ n __ __ al	di __ __ y	__ min __ nt	mor __ l __
bi __ n __ ial	eli __ __ b __ __	__ mmin __ nt	re __ e __ p __
d __ ir __	ill __ __ ib __ __	mor __ __	re __ ip __

☐ EXERCISE I

Look up the meanings of each pair of words in your dictionary. Write the meaning of each word in the blank.

1. elicit _____

   illicit _____

2. envelop _____

   envelope _____

3. expansive _____

   expensive _____

4. extant _____

   extent _____

5. formally _____

   formerly _____

☐ EXERCISE II

Write one of the following words in each blank. Study each sentence carefully.

moral   imminent   eligible
morale   eminent   illegible

1. Thomas Carlyle, an _____ scholar and historian, spoke at the graduation ceremony.

2. Did the economist predict that a depression was _____?

3. If you are _____ for membership in the club, you will be nominated by the committee.

4. The signature in the old family Bible was _____.

5. Nothing the owner could say would help boost the _____ of the employees.

6. The _____ of Aesop's fable of the fox and the grapes is still applicable today.

157

Making Sure You Have the Right Word

This lesson gives you additional practice in studying the dictionary. Study the different spellings of the following pairs of similar words. Some words are pronounced exactly the same but have different spellings and meanings. These words are called homonyms. Examples of homonyms in this lesson are complement-compliment and council-counsel. When you look at a word, be sure that you have its exact meaning in mind. If you are uncertain about the pronunciation or meaning of any word, consult your dictionary.

adapt	You should a dapt' to new conditions.
adopt	The club refused to a dopt' the motion.
complement	Music is a com' ple ment to a fine meal.
compliment	The com' pli ment was sincere.
continual	The rain kept up a con tin' u al patter.
continuous	There was a con tin' u ous stretch of bad roads.
council	The city coun' cil has five members.
counsel	Wise people give good coun' sel.
healthy	The laborers were not health' y.
healthful	This climate is health' ful.
lightening	There was no way of light' ening the load.
lightning	The light' ning struck the same tree twice.
prescribe	What did the doctor pre scribe'?
proscribe	Some churches pro scribe' card playing.
respectfully	He spoke re spect' ful ly to his father.
respectively	The stamps cost five cents and twenty-five cents, re spec' tive ly.
stature	Six feet is more than average stat' ure.
statute	The legislature passed another stat' ute.

☐ VISUAL DRILL

As you look at each word, try to visualize the whole word with the missing letters in place. Then check yourself by looking at the word as it appears above. Finally, fill in the blanks. Check the spelling again, and make any necessary corrections.

ada __ __   coun __ il

cont __ n __ a __   st __ t __ r __

r __ spe __ __ f __ __ ly   he __ lthf __ __

cont __ nu __ __ s   r __ sp __ __ t __ v __ ly

li __ __ t __ ning

☐ EXERCISE I

Look up the meanings of each pair of words in your dictionary. Write the meaning of each word in the blank.

1. appraise _____

   apprise _____

2. immigrate _____

   emigrate _____

3. liable _____

   libel _____

4. persecute _____

   prosecute _____

5. perspective _____

   prospective _____

☐ EXERCISE II

Use each word in a complete sentence that illustrates the meaning of the word.

1. adopt _____

   _____

2. healthful _____

   _____

3. council _____

   _____

4. proscribe _____

   _____

5. stature _____

   _____

Observing How a Word Is Syllabified

Carefully noting how the dictionary divides a word into syllables is the second step in dictionary study. Careful observation of the different syllables will help you spell and pronounce words correctly.

Some words are syllabified differently in the phonetic spelling. The phonetic syllables shown are solely for purposes of pronunciation. Do not confuse the phonetic syllables with the correct syllables.

The following words are frequently misspelled or mispronounced because a syllable is overlooked or confused. Note the different syllables carefully; then pronounce each word distinctly. If you are not certain how to pronounce a word, look it up in your dictionary.

actually	The dog ac′tu al *ly* walked on two legs.
bachelor	The bach′ *e* lor said that he would never marry.
botany	Bot′ *a* ny is a science.
chocolate	Most people like choc′ o l*ate* candy.
diamond	The di′ *a* mond is a precious stone.
granary	A gr*an*′ a ry is a storehouse for grain.
history	The his′ to ry traced the rise of civilization.
hungry	The children were hu*n*′ gry.
interrupt	The noise did not in′ te*r* rupt′ the speaker.
omelet	The om′ *e* let was made with three eggs.
sentinel	The sen′ ti n*el* kept watch all night.
slippery	The wet pavement was very slip′ *per* y.
temperature	The thermometer showed the exact tem′ per *a* tur*e*.

☐ VISUAL DRILL

As you look at each word, try to visualize the whole word with the missing letters in place. Then check yourself by looking at the word as it appears above. Finally, fill in the blanks. Check the spelling again, and make any necessary corrections.

t __ mp __ r __ t __ r __   d __ __ mon __

cho __ __ lat __   inte __ __ up __

a __ t __ __ l __ y   hun __ __ __

b __ ch __ l __ r   om __ l __ t

gr __ n __ ry   bot __ __ y

slip __ __ __ y   his __ __ __ __

sent __ n __ __

160

☐ EXERCISE

Find each word in your dictionary. Write the correct spelling, the dictionary entry spelling, and the phonetic spelling of each word.

WORD	CORRECT SPELLING	DICTIONARY ENTRY	PHONETIC SPELLING
1. actually			
2. bachelor			
3. chocolate			
4. diamond			
5. history			
6. hungry			
7. interrupt			
8. omelet			
9. slippery			
10. temperature			
11. botany			
12. granary			
13. sentinel			
14. ticklish			
15. medieval			
16. ruffian			
17. preposition			
18. legislature			
19. liable			
20. bibliography			

Observing Accented Words

Observing accents is the third step in dictionary study. When you look at words in the dictionary, look for the accent marks in the phonetic spellings. Some words have two syllables accented. In most dictionaries, the primary (heavy) accent is shown by a heavy mark (´), while the secondary (light) accent is shown by a light mark (´).

The accent in certain words changes the pronunciation and meaning. For example, con duct´ (a verb) means to guide; con´ duct (a noun) means behavior. Note the change of meaning in the following words according to the change in accent.

abstract	Ab´ stract ideas are difficult to understand.
	The doctor failed to ab stract´ the sliver.
convict	The con´ vict was imprisoned.
	The jury voted to con vict´ the man.
desert	The stranger was lost in the des´ ert.
	We must not de sert´ those in need.
entrance	There was but one en´ trance to the room.
	The music seemed to en trance´ them.
essay	Janet wrote a good es´ say.
	The girl prepared to es say´ her strength.
increase	There was an in´ crease in traffic.
	The newspaper tried to in crease´ its circulation.
insult	Her harsh words were an in´ sult.
	The remark seemed to in sult´ the visitor.
present	John was happy with his birthday pres´ ent.
	Juan will pre sent´ his gift later.
progress	They made little prog´ ress.
	The truck began to pro gress´ rapidly.
record	We bought a new rec´ ord for the dance.
	I will re cord´ the conversation.

☐ VISUAL DRILL

As you look at each word, try to visualize the whole word with the missing letters in place. Then check yourself by looking at the word as it appears above. Finally, fill in the blanks. Check the spelling again, and make any necessary corrections.

ab __ tr __ c __   in __ ul __

__ n __ re __ se   de __ __ rt

conv __ __ t   pr __ s __ nt

__ ntr __ n __ __   pr __ gr __ s __

e __ s __ y   re __ __ rd

Write a complete sentence using each word. Observe the accent mark. Be sure your sentence shows the correct meaning of each word.

1. re cord' _____

_____

2. con' duct _____

_____

3. prog' ress _____

_____

4. pre sent' _____

_____

5. in' sult _____

_____

6. in' crease _____

_____

7. es' say _____

_____

8. en trance' _____

_____

9. con' vict _____

_____

10. des' ert _____

_____

11. ab stract' _____

_____

12. con duct' _____

_____

13. rec' ord _____

_____

A. Locate each of the following words in your dictionary. In the blank, write the word's part of speech.

1. hygiene _____
2. botany _____
3. disagree _____
4. actually _____
5. mechanical _____
6. interrupt _____

7. luncheon _____
8. imminent _____
9. granary _____
10. despair _____
11. accordingly _____
12. temperature _____

Each correct answer is worth 2 points.   Total score: 24 points.

B. Carefully observe the accented words in parentheses in the following sentences. Select the correctly accented word, and write it in the blank.

1. He didn't really intend to (in sult'—in' sult) her dress.

   _____

2. Did the construction (prog' ress— pro gress') quickly?

   _____

3. I would like to (pres' ent—pre sent') Ms. Jameson to you.

   _____

4. She set a new (re cord'—rec' ord).

   _____

5. The jury will (con vict'—con' vict) him.

   _____

6. Where is the building's (en trance'—en' trance)?

   _____

7. Should I (in' crease—in crease') your allowance?

   _____

8. What a great birthday (pres' ent— pre sent') that will make!

   _____

9. Don't (des' ert—de sert') him.

   _____

10. I like (ab stract'—ab' stract) art.

   _____

Each correct answer is worth 3½ points.   Total score: 35 points.

164

C. Place one of the following words in the blank in each of the sentences. Determine which word is needed by studying each sentence carefully.

adapt	compliment	biannual	eligible	respectfully
continual	adopt	respectively	biennial	complement
illegible	prescribe	healthy	healthful	continuous
stature	statute	council	counsel	proscribe

1. That person's signature was completely _____.

2. A _____ line of cars stretched down the highway.

3. They will get a chance to vote at the _____ meeting every two years.

4. Are you _____ to vote in the next election?

5. Keith has always been a _____ person.

6. Abraham Lincoln was a man of great _____.

7. The _____ meeting of the association was held every six months.

8. He is in a _____ state of panic.

9. Are you sure you are eating a variety of _____ foods?

10. Was the _____ entered on the books during the last session?

11. Do you think the Alaskan can readily _____ to the hot summer weather?

12. The scarf was a good _____ to her new sweater.

13. The doctor will _____ a special diet.

14. They will have to _____ a more cooperative attitude.

15. He didn't want to accept the doctor's _____.

16. When is the next city _____ meeting?

17. The children were eight and nine years of age, _____.

18. She received a _____ on her new sweater.

19. Does your new diet _____ ice cream?

20. He treats his grandmother _____.

Each correct answer is worth 2 points.	Total score: 40 points.

Letters with Unusual Pronunciations

Learning to pronounce foreign words is the fourth step in dictionary study. Some letters, particularly in words of foreign derivation, are pronounced differently than they are in most English words. The *Gi* in *Gila* monster, for example, is pronounced *he*. When you discover a word of this type, focus your attention on the peculiar letters and pronounce the word distinctly several times.

Practice pronouncing the following words while you look at them carefully. If you are uncertain about the correct pronunciation of any of the words, consult your dictionary. By mastering this lesson, you can make a big advance in both spelling and speech.

antique	The odd-looking chair was an an t*ique'*.
asphalt	The as'*ph*alt will be used to pave this road.
author	Dickens was the au'th*or* of many books.
beggar	The beg'*ga*r asked everyone for money.
buffet	We keep our best china in a bu*ffet'*.
cafe	We went to the ca f*e'* for a cup of coffee.
cello	The c*el' l*o looks like a violin.
collar	Robert's col' *l*ar was too large for his neck.
comptroller	The c*omp* trol' *l*er handled all expenditures.
crepe	The box was covered with a thin cr*epe* cloth.
debris	The storm left piles of de br*is'* everywhere.
editor	Cynthia Rogers was also ed' *it*or of a newspaper.
etiquette	We should observe the rules of et' i *quette.*
mirage	The m*i* rage' of water on the desert seemed real.
reign	Queen Victoria's *reig*n lasted sixty-four years.
rumor	There was no truth to the widespread ru' m*or*.
sphere	A true *sphere* is perfectly round.
suede	The s*uede* cloth looked like leather.

☐ VISUAL DRILL

As you look at each word, try to visualize the whole word with the missing letters in place. Then check yourself by looking at the word as it appears above. Finally, fill in the blanks. Check the spelling again, and make any necessary corrections.

ant __ q __ __	caf __	d __ br __ __	rum __ __
as __ hal __	c __ l __ o	ed __ t __ __	s __ __ er __
a __ th __ r	col __ __ r	et __ q __ __ t __ __	su __ d __
beg __ __ r	com __ __ rol __ __ r	m __ ra __ __	
buf __ e __	cr __ p __	r __ __ gn	

166

☐ EXERCISE I

Find each word in your dictionary. In the first blank, write the phonetic spelling. In the second blank, give the definition of each word.

1. repertoire   _____   _____

2. subpoena   _____   _____

3. quorum   _____   _____

4. dessert   _____   _____

5. strata   _____   _____

6. alumnae   _____   _____

7. chameleon   _____   _____

8. melee   _____   _____

9. rendezvous   _____   _____

☐ EXERCISE II

Use each word in a complete sentence that illustrates the meaning of the word.

1. sphere   _____

2. buffet   _____

3. antique   _____

4. suede   _____

5. asphalt   _____

6. cafe   _____

7. crepe   _____

8. reign   _____

9. mirage   _____

10. etiquette   _____

Observing Silent Letters

Learning to spell words that contain silent letters is the fifth step in dictionary study. It would be much easier to spell words correctly if so many of them did not contain silent letters. The phonetic spellings given in the dictionary leave out all silent letters, so you must be certain to note any that may be in the original entries. Always look at the true spelling when you practice pronouncing a word. In this way you can keep from associating the wrong image with the correct pronunciation.

Note the silent letters in the words listed below.

achieve	The lawyer failed to a chieve′ her purpose.
commence	Fumio should com mence′ his work earlier.
coupon	This cou′ pon entitled us to another ride.
depot	Get your train ticket at the city de′ pot.
entries	The dictionary contained many new en′ tries.
grief	His sudden death caused widespread grief.
indict	No evidence to in dict′ the suspect could be found.
irrigate	The canal brought fresh water to ir′ ri gate the farm.
ledger	The clerk posted the charge in the ledg′ er.
offense	Her act was an of fense′ against the law.
plague	The plague spread rapidly, and many people died.
pneumonia	Both lungs were inflamed with pneu mo′ ni a.
scissors	The new scis′ sors have sharp blades.
thief	A thief stole our garden hose last night.
tongue	The baby stuck out its tongue.
vengeance	We swore ven′ geance against the attackers.
wrench	The sudden wrench broke off the handle.
yacht	They sailed away in the racing yacht.

☐ VISUAL DRILL

As you look at each word, try to visualize the whole word with the missing letters in place. Then check yourself by looking at the word as it appears above. Finally, fill in the blanks. Check the spelling again, and make any necessary corrections.

com __ en __ __   ind __ __ t   c __ __ p __ n   gr __ __ f

__ n __ umon __ a   plag __ __   ir __ ig __ t __   le __ __ er

ven __ e __ n __ e   __ ren __ __   s __ i __ s __ rs   ya __ __ t

entr __ __ s   of __ en __ __   th __ __ f

t __ ng __ __   ach __ __ v __   d __ p __ t

☐ EXERCISE I

Find each word in your dictionary. Write the phonetic spelling in the blank.

1. achieve _____

2. commence _____

3. coupon _____

4. depot _____

5. entries _____

6. grief _____

7. indict _____

8. irrigate _____

9. ledger _____

10. offense _____

11. plague _____

12. pneumonia _____

13. scissors _____

14. thief _____

15. tongue _____

16. vengeance _____

17. wrench _____

18. yacht _____

☐ EXERCISE II

Write the correct form in each blank. When you have completed the exercise, check your answers in the dictionary.

1. Add a suffix to *achieve* to form a noun.

_____

2. Write the *ing* form of *commence*.

_____

3. Write the singular form of *entries*.

_____

4. Add a suffix to *indict* to form a noun.

_____

5. Add a suffix to *irrigate* to form a noun.

_____

6. Add a suffix to *offense* to form an adjective.

_____

7. Write the plural form of *scissors*.

_____

8. Write the plural form of *thief*.

_____

☐ EXERCISE III

Supply *ei* or *ie* in each word. Don't look at the words' spellings in the book until you have finished.

1. th __ __ f

2. ach __ __ ve

3. entr __ __ s

4. gr __ __ f

169

Strengthening the Visual Image

The final step in studying the dictionary is strengthening the visual image of a word. It will be helpful at this point to review all six steps:

1. Make sure you have the right word.
2. Observe how the word is syllabified.
3. Observe how the word is accented.
4. Observe letters with unusual pronunciations.
5. Observe silent letters.
6. Strengthen the visual image of the true spelling.

Throughout this book, emphasis has been placed on the importance of retaining correct visual images of spelling words. There is a real danger that the syllabified and phonetic spellings in the dictionary may blur rather than strengthen the correct visual image of a word. For this reason, the student should keep the correct image clearly in mind at all times during the six steps of dictionary study.

Whenever you study a difficult word, give special emphasis to the correct visual image. First, examine the word carefully as directed in the various steps for dictionary study. Then, as you look away, strengthen the correct visual image by writing, printing, or typing the word several times.

Find the following words in your dictionary. Study each word by the six-step method. Keep this practice up whenever you consult your dictionary. Before long, the steps will become automatic. You will have mastered an exceedingly useful method of word study.

boulder   A heavy bo*ul'* der rolled down the mountain.
honorable   The *hon' or a bl*e thing to do is to apologize.
dangerous   Automobile racing is not the most dan' ger *ou*s occupation.
readily   The singers responded re*ad' i* ly to the request.
drowned   The swimmer dro*w*ned before the rescue unit arrived.
weighed   We w*eig*hed ourselves on the scales.

☐ VISUAL DRILL

As you look at each word, try to visualize the whole word with the missing letters in place. Then check yourself by looking at the word as it appears above. Finally, fill in the blanks. Check the spelling again, and make any necessary corrections.

bo __ ld __ __   r __ __ d __ ly

__ on __ r __ ble   dr __ __ n __ d

dan __ er __ __ s   w __ __ g __ ed

EXERCISE I

Find each word in your dictionary. In the first blank that follows each word, write the phonetic spelling. In the second blank, write the definition of the word.

1. equity _____ _____

2. voucher _____ _____

3. illustrate _____ _____

4. facade _____ _____

5. militia _____ _____

6. furlough _____ _____

7. motif _____ _____

8. synthetic _____ _____

9. reclamation _____ _____

10. suffrage _____ _____

11. isthmus _____ _____

12. matriculate _____ _____

EXERCISE II

Study each word carefully. Then cover the word. Write each word correctly in the blank that follows it. Check your spelling as you complete each word.

1. boulder _____

2. honorable _____

3. dangerous _____

4. readily _____

5. drowned _____

6. weighed _____

7. equity _____

8. voucher _____

9. illustrate _____

10. militia _____

11. furlough _____

12. synthetic _____

13. reclamation _____

14. suffrage _____

15. isthmus _____

16. matriculate _____

Pronouncing Words Correctly

Although the chief emphasis of this book is on correct spelling, students should not overlook the contribution that the study of spelling makes to correct speech. The first step in clear speech is to utter each word distinctly. In the same way, each syllable of a word should be spoken clearly and distinctly.

Your dictionary can help you to improve your speech. Whenever you look up a word, take time to pronounce it slowly, distinctly, and correctly. This should be done syllable by syllable. It is essential that you know the sounds indicated by the diacritical marks used in the phonetic spellings in your dictionary.

The Pronunciation Key given below is similar to, although somewhat simpler than, the key found in most dictionaries. It is presented here so that you can use it for quick reference in the next several lessons.

Pronunciation Key

a as in *ale*	ā	**i** as in *pier*	î	**u** as in *burn*	û		
a as in *at*	ă	**o** as in *go*	ō	**th** as in *thin*	th		
a as in *care*	â	**o** as in *odd*	ŏ	**th** as in *though*	*th*		
a as in *father*	ä	**o** as in *orb*	ô	**a** as in *about*			
e as in *eve*	ē	**oo** as in *foot*	oo	**e** as in *manner*			
e as in *get*	ĕ	**oo** as in *noon*	ōo	**i** as in *edible*		ə (schwa)	
i as in *ice*	ī	**u** as in *union*	ū	**o** as in *history*			
i as in *hit*	ĭ	**u** as in *under*	ŭ	**u** as in *status*			

To get the most out of the exercises which follow, first count the syllables and note which ones are accented. Next, check the diacritical marks, referring to the Pronunciation Key when you are uncertain of the exact sounds. Then read the note which accompanies each drill, and speak the word distinctly several times. Finally, read the sentence indicating the correct use of the word aloud.

experiment (ĭk spĕr′ ə mənt) The professor performed the *experiment*. NOTE: Do not say *ek spear′ mint*. Sound all four syllables.

genuine (jĕn′ yōo ĭn) It was a *genuine* diamond. NOTE: The last syllable is *in*, not *wine*.

heroine (hĕr′ ō ĭn) The *heroine* in the story was pretty. NOTE: Do not say *heer o een′*. Accent the first syllable.

Italian (ĭ tăl′ yən) Caruso was an *Italian* singer. NOTE: Do not say *eye tal′ e an*; say *i tal′ yan*.

rinse (rĭns) Be sure to *rinse* the clothes. NOTE: Do not say *wrench* or *rense*, but *rinse*.

suite (swēt) They rented a *suite* of four rooms. NOTE: Pronounce *suit* like *fruit*, but *suite* like *sweet*.

☐ VISUAL DRILL

As you look at each word, try to visualize the whole word with the missing letters in place. Then check yourself by looking at the word as it appears above. Finally, fill in the blanks. Check the spelling again, and make any necessary corrections.

e __ per __ m __ nt

__ en __ in __

her __ __ n __

__ tal __ __ n

r __ n __ __ __

s __ __ t __

☐ EXERCISE

Check your dictionary to find out how each word is syllabified. Divide each word into syllables with diacritical markings in the first blank. In the second blank, write the word's meaning. Pronounce each word correctly when you have finished.

1. saccharin _____ _____

2. zwieback _____ _____

3. bituminous _____ _____

4. illuminate _____ _____

5. hemorrhage _____ _____

6. calipers _____ _____

7. neuralgia _____ _____

8. perpetuity _____ _____

9. tourmaline _____ _____

10. chronicle _____ _____

11. injunction _____ _____

12. subpoena _____ _____

13. idyll _____ _____

14. soliloquy _____ _____

15. corrosion _____ _____

16. quotient _____ _____

17. portraiture _____ _____

18. cohesion _____ _____

19. static _____ _____

20. inhibition _____ _____

21. psychic _____ _____

Pronouncing the O Sounds

If you wish to speak correctly, you must distinguish between the short *o* (ŏ) and the circumflex *o* (ô). (See the Pronunciation Key in Lesson 70.) The short *o* is like the *a* sound in *swan*, *what*, and *squander*. Most people pronounce the *o* correctly in *top*, *spot*, and *rot*; but for *fog*, *from*, and *of*, many say *fawg*, *frum*, and *uv*.

The circumflex *o* is like the *o* sound in *lord*, *fork*, and *order*. Note the *o* sounds in the following sentence: He was sorry for the poor dog. Some words pronounced correctly with the short *o* change their meaning if given the circumflex *o* sound. For example, *not* becomes *naught* when the ŏ is pronounced with the ô sound. In the same manner, *nod* becames *gnawed*, *stock* becomes *stalk*, *pod* becomes *pawed*, *odd* becomes *awed*, *clod* becomes *clawed*, and *tot* becomes *taught*.

Observe the *o* sounds in the following sentences:

across (ə krôs′) George swam *across* the river.
NOTE: Sound the circumflex *o*. Do not say *a krost′*.

coyote (kī ō′ tē *or* kī′ ōt′) The dogs chased the *coyote*.
NOTE: The first *o* is silent; the second *o* is long.

forehead (fôr′ ĭd) The hair grew down on his *forehead*.
NOTE: Say the *o* as in *hot*, not as in *for* or *fore*. Instead of *head*, say *ed*.

Florida (flôr′ ĭ də) *Florida* is a southern state.
NOTE: Do not say *Flow′ ri da* or *Flaw′ ri da*. Sound the *o* as in *lord*.

foreign (fôr′ ĭn) She came from a *foreign* country.
NOTE: Sound the *o* as in *hot*. Do not say *for′ in*.

horrible (hôr′ ə bəl) The explosion created a *horrible* scene.
NOTE: This is the same short *o* as in *hot, forehead,* and *Florida*.

iron (ī′ ərn) Steel is made from *iron* and carbon.
NOTE: It seems strange, but the *ron* in *iron* is pronounced *ern*.

recognized (rĕk′ əg nīz) Magda *recognized* us immediately.
NOTE: Do not say *rek′ a nize*.

was (wŏz) The hour *was* too late.
NOTE: Do not say *wuz* or *wawz*.

☐ VISUAL DRILLS

As you look at each word, try to visualize the whole word with the missing letters in place. Check your efforts by looking at the word as it appears above. Finally, fill in the blanks. Check the spelling again, and make any necessary corrections.

a __ ros __   for __ __ g __

co __ __ te   h __ r __ __ ble

for __ __ ead   ir __ n

Fl __ r __ da   re __ o __ ni __ ed

☐ EXERCISE I

Each word contains at least one *o* sound. In the blank that follows each word, give the diacritical marking for each *o* sound in each word.

1. opera _____ _____

2. accord _____ _____

3. geopolitics _____ _____

4. focus _____ _____

5. occupation _____ _____

6. nonsense _____ _____

7. overtime _____ _____

8. vote _____ _____

9. depot _____ _____

10. studio _____ _____

11. ego _____ _____

12. October _____ _____

13. morning _____ _____

14. mortar _____ _____

15. chorus _____ _____

16. hydrometer _____ _____

17. ceremony _____ _____

18. tort _____ _____

19. odometer _____ _____

20. overconfident _____ _____

☐ EXERCISE II

Study the diacritical marks over the o's in parentheses. Cross out each incorrectly marked word and write the word and its correct diacritical mark in the blank.

1. Where did you learn to play the (cellŏ, cellō?)

   _____

2. He got a letter today from the (comptrōller, comptrôller).

   _____

3. The salad (fŏrk, fôrk) goes to the outside of the dinner fork.

   _____

4. They should be arriving very (sōon, soon).

   _____

5. What is your (ōccupation, ŏccupation)?

   _____

6. The (swôrd, swörd) was made of fine steel.

   _____

7. He seemed like a very (hônorable, hŏnorable) man.

   _____

8. The inside of their chimney was black with (sōot, soot).

   _____

Pronouncing Letters and Syllables

If you study the dictionary as directed, you will be able to avoid speech errors which are frequently made by careless speakers. Sound all of the letters and syllables indicated in the phonetic spellings. Avoid adding letters or syllables which do not appear in the phonetic spellings. The following words are frequently mispronounced.

arctic (ärk′ tĭk) It is very cold in the *arctic* region.
NOTE: Do not say *artic*. Sound the *c* after the *r*.

attacked (ə tăkt′) In his speech, he *attacked* the new senator.
NOTE: Do not say *at tac′ ted*. There are only two syllables.

deteriorate (dĭ tîr′ ē ə rāt) The perfume seemed to *deteriorate*.
NOTE: Sound all five syllables. Do not say *de ter′ i at*.

diphtheria (dĭf thîr′ ē ə) The patient was ill with *diphtheria*.
NOTE: The first syllable is *dif*, not *dip*. Sound the long *e* in *ther*.

evening (ēv′ nĭng) The church bells rang Tuesday *evening*.
NOTE: Do not say *ev′ en ing*. The syllables are *eve* and *ning*.

library (lī′ brĕr′ ē) The *library* lends many of its books.
NOTE: Do not say *li′ bar ee*. Sound the two *r*'s, the short *e*, and the short *i* in *breri*.

overalls (ō′ vər ôlz′) The workers wore heavy *overalls*.
NOTE: Do not say *holls* for *olz*. There is no *h* in *overalls*.

parliament (pär′ lə mənt) A *parliament* deals with legislation.
NOTE: Sound the short i. Omit the second *a* sound in *parliament*.

rind (rīnd) The flavor came from lemon *rind*.
NOTE: Say *rind*, not *rine*. Sound the long *i* and the *d*.

secretary (sĕk′ rĭ tĕr′ ē) Her *secretary* answered the letters.
NOTE: Do not say *sek′ re tree* or *sek a tar′ ee*. The chief accent is on the first syllable.

strictly (strĭkt′ lē) The information is *strictly* confidential.
NOTE: Sound the *t* in such words as *strictly, compactly, exactly*.

united (yo͞o nīt′ ĕd) *United* we stand; divided we fall.
NOTE: Do not say *yoo ni′ ted*. Pronounce the *u* as in *humane*.

☐ VISUAL DRILL

As you look at each word, try to visualize the whole word with the missing letters in place. Then check yourself by looking at the word as it appears above. Finally, fill in the blanks. Check the spelling again, and make any necessary corrections.

di __ __ th __ r __ __	over __ __ ls	stri __ __ ly	ar __ ti __
par __ __ __ m __ nt	se __ r __ t __ ry	ev __ __ in __	rin __
det __ r __ __ r __ t __	at __ ac __ __ __	lib __ __ r __	__ nit __ d

☐ EXERCISE I

Many of the following words contain spelling errors. Write each misspelled word correctly in the blank. If the word is spelled correctly, write a *C* in the blank. Pronounce each word correctly as you write it.

1. suitte _____
2. horibble _____
3. evenning _____
4. strickly _____
5. conspiracy _____
6. librery _____
7. foriegn _____
8. recognized _____
9. artic _____
10. readily _____
11. honorible _____

12. deficitt _____
13. forhead _____
14. secertary _____
15. united _____
16. attackted _____
17. overhalls _____
18. parliment _____
19. deteriate _____
20. heroinne _____
21. experment _____
22. genuin _____

☐ EXERCISE II

In each sentence, find any misspelled words. Write each word correctly in the blank. If there are no misspelled words, write a *C* in the blank. Pronounce each word correctly as you write it.

_____ 1. The queen will address parlement tomorrow.

_____ 2. I met the author of that book in the libery.

_____ 3. His brother has diftheria.

_____ 4. He didn't want to get his new swayed coat wet.

_____ 5. What would you like for dessert this evening?

_____ 6. The movie star did not want to be reconized in the grocery store.

A. The following postcard contains many spelling errors. Cross out each misspelled word. Then write the word correctly above the misspelled word.

Dear Dora,

Despite any nasty rumer you may hear to the contrary from Ted, he and I are having a wonderful time in Paris. Our hotel suit is beautiful. Just this afternoon, we had a delightful luncheon bouffet in a caffe accross from a museum. I especially enjoyed the seafood crape I had. We were entertained by chello music as we dined.

After lunch, Ted and I explored an old bookstore where we bought an anteak book covered in genuwine swayed.

Sincerely,

Each correct answer is worth 3 points.	Total score: 30 points.

B. In each sentence, find any misspelled words. Write each word correctly in the blank. If there are no misspelled words, write a _C_ in the blank.

_____ 1. Do you think he will ever acheive his dream?

_____ 2. The yaught was anchored at the marina.

_____ 3. She swore vengence on her attacker.

_____ 4. The baby's tongue was swollen where he had bitten it while jumping in his crib.

_____ 5. Do you have an extra pair of sissors that I may borrow?

_____ 6. She was hospitalized with a severe case of neumonia.

_____ 7. The bookkeeper couldn't get the accounts in the leger to balance.

_____ 8. Because of the severe drought, the farmers were forced to irigate their crops.

_____ 9. Do you think the grand jury will indite her?

_____ 10. The train slowly pulled into the depot.

Each correct answer is worth 2 points.	Total score: 20 points.

C. **In each sentence, cross out the incorrect word in parentheses. Then write the correct word in the blank.**

_____ 1. Who was the (auther—author) of that book?

_____ 2. I need to get a new (collar—coller) for my dog.

_____ 3. The (controller—comptroller) is responsible for the state's finances.

_____ 4. The man will be served with a (subpoena—supoena) if he doesn't voluntarily appear in court.

_____ 5. The guest of honor has arrived; let the party (commense—commence)!

_____ 6. The excess (morter—mortar) is oozing from between the bricks.

_____ 7. He has a very inflated (eggo—ego).

_____ 8. Have you come (across—acrost) your missing file yet?

_____ 9. The (motif—motiff) of their home was primarily oriental.

_____ 10. That was my favorite chemistry (experimint—experiment).

_____ 11. Do you (rinse—rince) your hair thoroughly after you shampoo it?

_____ 12. Her diary was a (chronicel—chronicle) of her youth.

Each correct answer is worth 2 points.	Total score: 24 points.

D. **Study the phonetic spelling of each of the following words. Try to figure out the correct spelling of each word and write it in the blank.**

1. də brē′ _____

2. ĕd′ ĭ tər _____

3. sfîr _____

4. fôr′ ĭd _____

5. lī′ brĕr′ ē _____

6. dān′ jər əs _____

7. hôr′ ə bəl _____

8. sĕk′ rĭ tĕr′ ē _____

9. ko͞o′ pŏn′ _____

10. jĕn′ yo͞o ĭn _____

11. ĭ tăl′ yən _____

12. plāg _____

13. ĭl′ ə strāt _____

Each correct answer is worth 2 points.	Total score: 26 points.

Watching the Accent

In Lesson 66, your attention was called to the importance of noticing how words are accented. There are many words in the English language which serve as nouns when accented on the first syllable, and as verbs when accented on the second syllable. Besides those listed in Lesson 66, such words include:

confine	contrast	imprint	project	refuse
conflict	convert	insert	protest	subject
contest	digest	produce	rebound	transport

No rules govern the accents given to most words. Check your dictionary to avoid mistakes.

admirable (ăd′ mər ə bəl) His conduct was not *admirable.*
NOTE: Accent the first syllable. The *i* in *mi* is short.

applicable (ăp′ lĭ kə bəl) The description is not *applicable.*
NOTE: Do not say *a plik′ a bul.* Sound the *ca* syllable.

bronchial (brŏng′ kē əl) The *bronchial* tubes lead to the lungs.
NOTE: Do not say *bron′ i chal.*

contrary (kŏn′ trĕr′ ē) They parked *contrary* to the sign.
NOTE: Do not say *kon trar′ e.* Accent the first syllable.

exquisite (ĕk′ skwĭ zĭt) Your friend has *exquisite* taste.
NOTE: Accent the first syllable. Avoid accenting *skwiz.*

hospitable (hŏs′ pĭ tə bəl) The Smiths are exceptionally *hospitable.*
NOTE: Sound the *o* as in *hot.*

interested (ĭn′ trĭ stĭd) Mrs. Jones is very *interested* in painting.
NOTE: Accent the first syllable only. Do not say *in tres′ ted.*

mischievous (mĭs′ chə vəs) Bobby disliked *mischievous* pranks.
NOTE: There are only three syllables. Do not say *mis che′ vi us.*

museum (myo͞o zē′ əm) The *museum* was full of ancient statues.
NOTE: Do not say *mu′ ze um.* Accent the second syllable.

theater (thē′ ə tər) There is a new movie at the *theater.*
NOTE: Say *the′ a ter*, not *the a′ ter.* Sound the *th* as in *thin.*

☐ VISUAL DRILL

As you look at each word, try to visualize the whole word with the missing letters in place. Then check yourself by looking at the word as it appears above. Finally, fill in the blanks. Check the spelling again, and make any necessary corrections.

adm __ r __ b __ __	__ ont __ __ __ y	mi __ ch __ __ v __ __ s
ap __ li __ ab __ __	e __ __ u __ s __ t __	mu __ e __ m
br __ n __ __ i __ l	h __ spit __ b __ __	th __ __ t __ __
int __ r __ sted		

180

☐ EXERCISE I

Use each word in a complete sentence that illustrates the meaning of the word. Be sure your sentence illustrates the part of speech in parentheses.

1. confine (noun) _____

2. conflict (verb) _____

3. contest (verb) _____

4. contrast (noun) _____

5. convert (verb) _____

6. digest (verb) _____

7. imprint (noun) _____

8. insert (noun) _____

9. produce (verb) _____

10. project (verb) _____

☐ EXERCISE II

Match each word in Column A with its meaning in Column B. Place the letter of the meaning in the blank in front of the word it defines.

COLUMN A

1. _____ admirable

2. _____ applicable

3. _____ contrary

4. _____ exquisite

5. _____ hospitable

6. _____ interested

7. _____ mischievous

8. _____ theater

COLUMN B

a. suitable

b. welcoming to guests

c. opposite, contradictory

d. concerned

e. delicate, beautiful

f. playful, annoying

g. building where plays and musicals are performed

h. praiseworthy

Pronouncing Foreign Words

Many English words come from foreign languages. These words often retain their foreign pronunciation and spelling. The words on this page are among the most commonly misspelled words of foreign derivation.

adobe (ə dō′ bē), sun-dried mud brick
adios (ăd′ ē ōs′), good-bye among Spanish-speaking peoples
ad infinitum (ăd ĭn′ fə nī′ təm), to infinity; endlessly
attaché (ăt′ ə shā′), member of a staff or an embassy
au revoir (ō′ rə vwär′), good-bye till we meet again
bona fide (bō′ nə fīd), in good faith; genuine
chef (shĕf), skilled cook
clique (klēk), a social set
coiffure (kwä fûr′), headdress; the way one's hair is arranged
connoisseur (kŏn′ ə sûr), one who knows a subject thoroughly
debris (də brē′), fragments; rubbish; remains; ruins
éclair (ā klâr′), small, coated pastry with a cream filling
elite (ĭ līt′), the wealthiest or most powerful members of a group
ennui (ŏn wē′), extreme boredom; weariness; dissatisfaction
ensemble (ŏn sŏm′ bəl), all together; a group that makes a whole
entree (ŏn′ trā), entrance to society; the principal dish of a meal
esprit de corps (ĕ sprē′ də kŏr′), group spirit
faux pas (fō pä′), false step; social blunder
hacienda (hä′ sē ĕn′ də), large Spanish-American estate; ranch
liaison (lē′ ā zŏn′), a relationship; communication
lingerie (län′ zhə rā′), linen goods; undergarments
menu (mĕn′ yoo), list of dishes served
penchant (pĕn′ chənt), strong liking
premiere (prĭ mîr′), first or chief; first performance
protege (prō′ tə zhā′), one under the care of another
résumé (rĕz′ oŏ mā′), a summary; condensed outline
sauté (sō tā′), fry in small amount of fat
table d'hote (tä′ bəl dōt′), complete meal served at a fixed price
tamale (tə mä′ lē), Mexican dish of chopped meat and corn meal

☐ EXERCISE

Use each word in a complete sentence that illustrates the meaning of the word.

1. adobe _____

_____

2. attaché _____

_____

3. bona fide

_____

_____

4. chef

_____

_____

5. connoisseur

_____

_____

6. debris

_____

_____

7. elite

_____

_____

8. ensemble

_____

_____

9. entree

_____

_____

10. faux pas

_____

_____

11. liaison

_____

_____

12. penchant

_____

_____

13. premiere

_____

_____

14. protege

_____

_____

15. resume

_____

_____

Use of Hyphens To Separate Syllables

Many spelling mistakes are made in the use of hyphens. The hyphen is used in two ways: (1) to separate syllables and (2) to separate words. This lesson is concerned with the use of the hyphen to separate syllables.

If your dictionary uses hyphens to separate syllables, note what symbol is used to indicate a true hyphen. Dictionaries that use hyphens between syllables usually use a long hyphen (—) or a double hyphen (=). For example, the compound word *go-between* will be probably be entered either as *go—be-tween* or, using the double hyphen, as *go=be-tween*. Look up the following words in your dictionary to see (1) how the syllables are separated and (2) how the hyphen is printed in the compound word.

ammunition	employee	freshwater	quality	wholesale
cafeteria	four-footed	muscle	snowbound	

A hyphen is always used to separate syllables when a word is broken at the end of a line. Whenever possible, a line should be ended with a complete word. When this is not possible, the last word in the line should be broken at the end of a syllable and a hyphen placed after that syllable. When it is necessary to divide a word, observe the following rules:

1. Never divide a word of one syllable; for example, *rhyme*.
2. Never divide a four-letter word of two syllables; for example, *diet*.
3. Never separate a one-letter syllable at the beginning or end of a word; for example, *a-bout, ever-y*.
4. In a word with three or more syllables, any one-letter syllable should be written on the first line; for example *privi-lege*.
5. Divide two vowels which are pronounced separately; for example, *situ-ation*.
6. Separate compound words at the hyphen; for example *blue-eyed*.

☐ VISUAL DRILL

As you look at each word, try to visualize the whole word with the missing letters in place. Then check yourself by looking at the word as it appears above. Finally, fill in the blanks. Check the spelling again, and make any necessary corrections.

a __ m __ n __ t __ __ n

ca __ __ ter __ __

__ mpl __ y __ __

f __ __ r-f __ __ ted

fr __ __ h w __ t __ __

sno __ bo __ nd

__ u __ l __ ty

__ hol __ sal __

mu __ __ le

☐ EXERCISE I

In the blank following each word, show how the word is hyphenated. If the word cannot be hyphenated, write it as one word in the blank. Be sure your hyphens are clearly printed.

1. plan _____

2. community _____

3. among _____

4. within _____

5. happy _____

6. prayed _____

7. eventful _____

8. command _____

9. camera _____

10. demonstrate _____

11. snowbound _____

12. employee _____

13. wholesale _____

14. cafeteria _____

15. four-footed _____

16. muscle _____

17. ammunition _____

18. fresh-water _____

19. quality _____

☐ EXERCISE II

Choose the one correctly hyphenated word in each of the following word pairs. Write the correctly hyphenated word (with its hyphens) in the blank.

1. math-e-mat-ics, math-e-ma-tics

_____

2. kin-der-gar-ten, kin-der-gart-en

_____

3. rhy-me, rhyme _____

4. o-mis-sion, o-mi-ssion _____

5. quart-er, quar-ter _____

6. cal-cu-la-tor, cal-cu-lat-or

_____

7. di-et, diet _____

8. fourt-een, four-teen _____

9. marr-y, mar-ry _____

10. coun-se-lor, coun-sel-or

_____

☐ EXERCISE III

Choose the correct hyphenation of the following words as if they were at the end of a line and needed to be separated. Write the correctly hyphenated word (with hyphen) in the blank. If a word cannot be hyphenated, write it as one word in the blank.

1. among, a-mong _____

2. pray-ed, prayed _____

3. four-footed, four foot-ed

_____

4. sit-uation, situ-ation _____

5. diet, di-et _____

6. mathe-matics, math-ematics

_____

Use of Hyphens in Compound Words

Compound words are words that are used together so much that they eventually become one word. New compounds are usually hyphenated. After a hyphenated compound has been used for a long time, the hyphen is usually dropped. For example, *to day* became *to-day,* and finally *today.*

1. Consult your dictionary to find out how the following words are currently spelled:

inasmuch	in so far	to-day
postmark	post office	good-by
half-dollar	per cent	co-operate
remake	re-mark	eighty-eight

2. Study the spelling of the words listed below. Note how each word is built up from two or more words. Consult your dictionary if you are uncertain about the meaning of any of the words. Some of the words may not be in your dictionary.

afternoon	elsewhere	nevertheless
aircraft	everywhere	ten-year-old boy
bankrupt	first-class	northeast
battlefield	gentlemen	oversight
cheerful	antislavery	self-employed
someone	hardware	vice-president
wireless	hitherto	50 horsepower
doubtless	in spite of	chairperson
dreadful	midnight	pro-British

There are a number of rules which govern the use of hyphens in compound words, but it is better to learn each word by itself. The use of the hyphen, moreover, is to some extent a matter of personal taste. The most helpful rules follow:

1. A hyphen is used in all compound numerals from twenty-one to ninety-nine.
2. When two or more words are used as one adjective before a noun, the words are connected with hyphens. For example, they are public-spirited people.
3. When a verb is made up of two or more words, the words are connected with hyphens. For example, to blue-pencil the mistakes.

☐ EXERCISE I

In the blank that follows each expression, write the expression correctly. Use hyphens where needed.

1. door to door salesperson _____

2. five year old child _____

3. a meeting after school _____

4. a do gooder _____

5. great-great grandmother _____

6. twenty five barrel load _____

7. Governor elect Milburn _____

8. commander in chief _____

9. one half of the students _____

10. up to date model _____

11. one hundred dollars and seventy six cents _____

☐ EXERCISE II

In each sentence find any errors in hyphenation. Write each word or phrase correctly in the blank. If there are no hyphenation errors, write a *C* in the blank.

1. She hated to say good-by to her grandmother. _____

2. The two year old child got lost in the crowd. _____

3. He'll be traveling north-east for his vacation. _____

4. The public service announcement was heard on the radio. _____

5. He wanted to deep-six the memo. _____

6. His boss requested more up to date figures for the report. _____

7. Only one half of the eligible voters made the effort to vote. _____

8. The store is at Forty-third and Maple. _____

9. Stan was an eager beaver student. _____

10. He was told to high tail it to the principal's office. _____

The Apostrophe

Many mistakes in spelling are caused by the incorrect use of the apostrophe ('). The apostrophe has three chief uses:

1. An apostrophe is used in contractions to take the place of one or more omitted letters. For example, John *can't* go; *tomorrow's* too late.
2. An apostrophe is used to indicate the plurals of letters and other symbols. For example, Dot your *i's*. There are six *5's* in that number.
3. An apostrophe is used to indicate possession. (See Lesson 78.)

Do not use an apostrophe with the following pronouns: *its, hers, his, ours, theirs, yours*. Note the difference in the meanings of *their* and *they're*; *it's* and *its*; *you're* and *your*.

It's their business, not ours.
They're all here for a vacation.
I can't go because it's raining.
What's its color when it's wet?
You're wrong about it this time.
'Tis hers, not yours or mine.
There are three 5's in 555.
Type a line of x's for practice.

☐ EXERCISE I

Write the word or words that each contraction stands for.

1. aren't _____
2. 'twere _____
3. can't _____
4. don't _____
5. couldn't _____
6. we're _____
7. isn't _____
8. they're _____
9. o'clock _____
10. I've _____

11. let's _____
12. mustn't _____
13. she'd _____
14. what's _____
15. won't _____
16. 'twould _____
17. who's _____
18. doesn't _____
19. hadn't _____
20. hasn't _____

☐ EXERCISE II

Write the contraction that may be used for each expression.

1. he would _____

2. did not _____

3. she is _____

4. they have _____

5. should not _____

6. should have _____

7. there is _____

8. you have _____

9. you are _____

10. you will _____

11. they would _____

12. we are _____

13. it is _____

14. what is _____

15. it would _____

16. I will _____

17. could have _____

18. would have _____

☐ EXERCISE III

Each sentence contains one or more spelling errors. Cross out each misspelled word. Then write the word correctly above it. Remember: a word is misspelled if an apostrophe is omitted.

1. Can you tell me how many *i*s, how many *s*s, and how many *p*s are in the word Mississippi?

2. Their uncertain as to how they can arrange to obtain interest on they're account.

3. Its too bad that the dog has lost it's collar.

4. Dont become confused when you see the number of *x*s and *y*s left out of the words.

5. You're plan will work if your certain of all you're enemy's negotiations.

6. Ill have to be sure that the wrench is our's and not they'res.

7. Lets put the presents that are her's in one box and your's in another.

8. They're four 8s in 8888.

9. Im not going if she doesnt go too.

10. He needs to be sure that hes minding his own business and not her's.

Words That Show Possession

The apostrophe (') is also used to show possession or ownership. Dictionaries do not usually show the possessive forms of nouns. To spell possessive words correctly, you will have to learn some rules. The following general rules will be of most help.

1. If a noun, singular or plural, does not end in an *s*, add an apostrophe followed by an *s*. For example, the *girl's* coat, the *world's* champion, the *women's* club. If a singular word ends in *s*, add an apostrophe and *s*. For example, *Carlos's* coat. Study the spelling of the following words:

gentlemen's	Law is merely a gentlemen's agreement.
box's	The box's top and bottom were broken in.
advertisement's	The advertisement's format was appealing.
attorney's	We paid the attorney's fees at once.
witness's	The witness's testimony was not trustworthy.
press's	It's the press's obligation to report news fairly.
boss's	It was the boss's duty.
princess's	The princess's car is late.

2. If a plural word ends in a single *s*, add an apostrophe. For example, the *girls'* glee club, the *Germans'* prisoners. Study the spelling of the following words:

days'	The firm owed the laborer three days' wages.
ladies'	The ladies' luncheon will be held at noon.
babies'	Their baby's photo won a prize; several other babies' pictures also won.

3. When a phrase is put into the possessive case, the apostrophe or *'s* is added to the last word. For example, his *son-in-law's* manners. Study the spelling of the following words:

half an hour's	There was half an hour's delay.
Sam and Cooper's	Sam and Cooper's store was open.
somebody else's	This is somebody else's fault.

☐ EXERCISE I

In the blank that follows each word, write the word's possessive form.

1. Brown and Sanders _____

2. woman _____

3. spectacles _____

4. Amalgamated Motors _____

5. everyone _____

6. authors _____

7. firm _____

8. it _____

9. oxen _____

10. brother-in-law _____

11. children _____

12. James _____

13. U.S.A. _____

14. notebooks _____

15. ladies	_____	23. week	_____
16. everyone else	_____	24. days	_____
17. employees	_____	25. attorney general	_____
18. telephones	_____	26. half an hour	_____
19. editor-in-chief	_____	27. process	_____
20. gentlemen	_____	28. travelers	_____
21. month	_____	29. actors	_____
22. committee	_____	30. manager	_____

☐ EXERCISE II

Each sentence contains one or more errors in the use of possessives. Cross out each error. Then write the possessive correctly above it.

1. Will tonights party be held at Amys house?

2. At the wedding, the bride's father shook his new son's-in-law hand.

3. Do you know who knocked down the Smiths's mailbox?

4. He took somebody's else lunch sack by mistake.

5. That universitys' computer science department is excellent.

6. Jim's and Rob's science project won first place at the contest.

7. The view of the city from those apartment building's is beautiful.

8. The new restaurants menu is in the shape of a cow.

9. Whose car is this, Johns' or Heathers'?

10. The defendant disagreed with the jurys' decision.

11. My parent's house is the most beautiful of all the house's on their block.

12. Jennifers new business is selling T-shirt's at the mall.

13. My wifes' brownie's are the best in the world!

14. The athletes victory brought glory to her country.

A. Use each word in a complete sentence. Be sure your sentence illustrates the part of speech in parentheses. In the blank, break the word into syllables. Show which syllable is accented.

1. produce (noun) _____

_____

_____

2. transport (verb) _____

_____

_____

3. refuse (noun) _____

_____

_____

4. project (noun) _____

_____

_____

5. confine (verb) _____

_____

_____

6. subject (noun) _____

_____

_____

7. contrast (verb) _____

_____

_____

| Each correct answer is worth 7 points. | Total score: 49 points. |

B. Use each of the following words in a complete sentence that illustrates the meaning of the word. In the blank, break the word into syllables. Show which syllable is accented.

1. sauté _____

_____

_____

2. menu _____

_____

_____

3. esprit de corps _____

_____

_____

4. eclair _____

_____

_____

5. lingerie _____

_____

_____

6. ad infinitum _____

_____

_____

7. au revoir _____

_____

_____

| Each correct answer is worth 7 points. | Perfect score: 49 points. |

Capital Letters

Many mistakes in spelling are due to the misuse of capital letters. Capital letters should be used to begin every sentence, every line of poetry, every important word in the title of a book, every direct quotation, every proper noun or adjective, and all titles when used with the names of individuals. When in doubt, consult the dictionary.

Many spelling errors result from confusion about when a word should be capitalized. Study the following examples of correct capitalization of some of the more troublesome words. Note the spelling of all the italicized words.

North	The *North* and the *South* are independent. (regions)
north	Turn *north*, not *south*, at the crossroads. (directions)
Mountains	The Rocky *Mountains* are *west* of the Missouri River.
mountains	Many rivers have their source in the *mountains*.
Tuesday	It happened on *Tuesday*, not *Wednesday*.
February	The month of *February* follows *January*.
winter	The *winter* months were very cold.
University	The *University* of Oregon is in Eugene, Oregon.
university	Every *university* lost a number of students.
Avenue	Dr. Chapa lived on *Fourth Avenue*.
avenue	Go to the third *avenue*; then turn *east*.
Capitol	The *Capitol* was the city's highest building.
capital	The *Empire Building* is in the *capital* city.
Venus	The planets include *Venus, Jupiter,* and *Mars*.
earth	We learned about the *earth, moon,* and *stars*.
Superintendent	He had seen *Superintendent* McClure.
superintendent	A *superintendent* of schools has many duties.
professor	Our most-loved *professor* is *Professor* Jones.
Uncle	All of our family love *Uncle* John.
uncle	He is my only *uncle*, but I have two *aunts*.

☐ VISUAL DRILL

In each blank, write a small letter or a capital letter.

1. The __ niversity of Chicago is __ orth of the Tennessee __ ountains.

2. The __ inter term included five __ uesdays in __ ebruary.

3. The __ apitol is the largest __ uilding in the __ apital city.

4. It is on the longest __ venue in the __ apital.

5. The __ arth is larger than __ enus.

194

☐ EXERCISE

Write the correct word in each blank. Choose from the words below.

North	Tuesday	Avenue	Venus
north	February	avenue	earth
Mountains	University	Capitol	Uncle
mountains	university	capital	uncle

1. Can you locate the Ural _____ on the map?

2. The St. Patrick's Day parade traditionally passes down Fifth _____ in New York City.

3. If you head due _____, you will soon come to City Park.

4. Marie was very fond of _____ Martin, and he mentioned her in his will.

5. Do you know the difference between a college and a _____?

6. We had planned the picnic for Monday but had to change the date

   to _____.

7. How many campaigns did the _____ win during the Civil War?

8. Didn't Juanita's _____ die only two weeks after her aunt's death?

9. We will take our vacation near the end of the month of _____.

10. Paula attended the summer session at the _____ of Southern California.

11. The _____ of the state is one of the state's historic monuments.

12. Were you planning to go to the seashore or to the _____ for your vacation?

13. Do you turn right or left at the fourth _____?

14. The legislators arrived in the _____ city two days before the opening of the legislative session.

15. The satellite was heading for the planet _____.

16. Geology is the study of the _____ and all of its products.

Spelling by Rules

Few rules are really helpful in learning to spell. It is well to know that the letter *q* is always followed by *u* in a word and to realize that proper nouns and adjectives should begin with capital letters. In this text, certain rules are listed which govern the use of periods, hyphens, and apostrophes. Despite the value of these and a few other general rules, most students will do better in the long run to learn each word separately. For this reason, the main emphasis of Part 2 will continue to be placed upon words rather than upon rules.

Many spelling rules have to do with the formation of derivatives. A derivative is a word formed from another by adding a prefix or a suffix or by internal change. Thus, from the word *use* are formed such derivatives as *misuse, disuse, uses, used, usage, using, user, usable* and *useless.* The following rules apply to the spelling of certain derivatives:

1. **Words ending in silent *e* drop the final *e* before the addition of suffixes beginning with a vowel.**
   EXAMPLES: come, coming; use, usable; please, pleasure.
2. **Words ending in silent *e* keep the final *e* before the addition of suffixes beginning with a consonant.**
   EXAMPLES: care, careful; tire, tireless; like, likeness.

Some important exceptions to these rules are listed below. Study them carefully. They show how dangerous it is to rely upon spelling rules.

advantage, advantageous	notice, noticeable	judge, judgment
canoe, canoeing	outrage, outrageous	true, truly
dye, dyeing	argue, argument	whole, wholly
mile, mileage	awe, awful	wise, wisdom

Another spelling rule that is frequently quoted is: Put *i* before *e* except after *c*, or where sounded like *a* in *neighbor* and *weigh.*

Be sure to learn the following exceptions to this rule.

ancient	species	seize	counterfeit
forfeit	leisure	weird	science
height	neither	foreign	either

☐ VISUAL DRILL

As you look at each word, try to visualize the whole word with the missing letters in place. Then check yourself by looking at the word as it appears above. Finally, fill in the blanks. Check the spelling again, and make any necessary corrections.

mil __ __ ge	h __ __ g __ t	n __ __ ther	w __ __ rd
anc __ __ nt	l __ __ sur __	jud __ m __ nt	for __ __ __ n
forf __ __ t	sp __ c __ __ s	s __ __ ze	c __ __ nterf __ __ t
tr __ __ y	whol __ __	sc __ __ nce	__ ' __ ther

☐ EXERCISE I

Form derivatives of the words below as directed. Check the spelling of the derivatives in the dictionary.

1. Add a prefix to *advantage* to form a new word. _____

2. Add a suffix to *advantage* to form a new word. _____

3. Add a prefix and a suffix to *notice* to form a new word. _____

4. Add a suffix to *outrage* to form a new word. _____

5. Add two different suffixes to *argue* to form two new words.

_____   _____

6. Add two different suffixes to *judge* to form two new words.

_____   _____

7. Add two different suffixes to *awe* to form two new words.

_____   _____

8. Add four different suffixes to *use* to form four different words.

_____   _____   _____   _____

9. Add two different suffixes to *care* to form two new words.

_____   _____

10. Add two different suffixes to *whole* to form two new words.

_____   _____

☐ EXERCISE II

Supply *ei* or *ie* in each word. Do not refer to the visual drill.

1. w __ __ rd

2. h __ __ ght

3. anc __ __ nt

4. n __ __ ther

5. for __ __ gn

6. spec __ __ s

7. counterf __ __ t

Some Troublesome *ei* and *ie* Words

Although they conform to the spelling rule quoted in Lesson 80, the words listed below cause many spelling errors. Consult your dictionary for the correct pronunciation.

TROUBLESOME *ei* WORDS

ceiling	The ceil'ing of the room was high.
conceit	Mary's con ceit' over her wealth was unfortunate.
conceived	Jane con ceived' many new ideas.
deceit	A liar prefers de ceit' to truth.
heir	There is no heir to the estate.
perceive	I did not per ceive' his change in attitude.
receipts	The cash re ceipts' exceeded our expectations.
received	The crowd re ceived' him well.
rein	Her pull on the rein turned the horse.
veil	The face was covered by a new veil.
vein	A vein carries blood toward the heart.
weighed	The man weighed about three hundred pounds.

TROUBLESOME *ie* WORDS

achieve	Many people do not a chieve' their aims.
apiece	They got three apples a piece'.
diet	The doctor prescribed a limited di'et.
fiend	Only a fiend could commit such a crime.
fierce	The fierce snarls of the wolves scared him.
grievance	His griev'ance was caused by an unjust accusation.
pier	The stone pier jutted into the lake.
priest	The Catholic priest chanted the prayer in Spanish.
shriek	The child uttered a shriek of happy surprise.
twentieth	We live in the twen'ti eth century.
wield	Some kings wield little power.
fortieth	Tuesday was his for'ti eth birthday.

☐ VISUAL DRILL

As you look at each word, try to visualize the whole word with the missing letters in place. Then check yourself by looking at the word as it appears earlier in the lesson. Finally, fill in the blanks. Check the spelling again, and make any necessary corrections.

c __ __ ling	d __ __ t	perc __ __ ve	pr __ __ st	w __ __ ld
ach __ __ ve	dec __ __ t	gr __ __ v __ nce	shr __ __ k	v __ __ n
ap __ __ ce	h __ __ r	p __ __ r	r __ __ n	w __ __ g __ ed
con __ __ __ ved	f __ __ nd	rec __ __ p __ s	v __ __ l	f __ __ t __ __ th
conc __ __ t	f __ __ rce	rec __ __ ved	tw __ nt __ __ th	

☐ EXERCISE I

In each group of words, cross out any misspelled words. Then write each word correctly in the blank. If there are no misspelled words, write a *C* in the blank.

1. ceiling   conciet   conceived   _____

2. pier   priest   percieve   _____

3. acheive   apiece   deceit   _____

4. fortieth   twenteith   weighed   _____

5. receipts   rein   recieved   _____

6. heir   feind   fierce   _____

7. diet   shreik   grievance   _____

8. rein   veil   ceiling   _____

☐ EXERCISE II

Arrange the following group of words in correct alphabetical order. Check the spelling of each word as you write it.

perceive   achieve   wield
ceiling   fortieth   fierce
received   conceived   receipts
conceit   veil   weighed
grievance   fiend   shriek

1. _____   9. _____

2. _____   10. _____

3. _____   11. _____

4. _____   12. _____

5. _____   13. _____

6. _____   14. _____

7. _____   15. _____

8. _____

Forming Plurals

Although most plurals are formed according to established rules, there are enough exceptions to make it unsafe to depend entirely on rules. Each plural is a separate problem. The plurals of most English nouns are formed according to three rules:

A. Add *s* to the singular form. EXAMPLES: 1. birth, births 2. burglar, burglars 3. page, pages

B. Add *es* to the singular when it ends with *s* or a similar sound, such as *ss, ch, x, sh*.
 EXAMPLES: 1. mass, masses 2. box, boxes 3. dispatch, dispatches

C. Change the *y* to *ies* when the singular ends in a consonant and *y*.
 EXAMPLES: 1. ally, allies 2. boundary, boundaries 3. baby, babies

   Study the spelling of the various plurals given below. They are frequently misspelled because they do not follow the rules above. The singular form is listed first and is followed by the plural form in an illustrative sentence.

attorney	There were more *attorneys* than legal business.
bacterium	All soil contains *bacteria.*
basis	Religion is founded on many *bases.*
cargo	The ships carried *cargoes* of wheat and clothes.
corps	Several *corps* of workers sold the new product.
criterion	There were three evaluation *criteria* listed.
datum	The writer gathered *data* for her article.
hero	Three people that I know are *heroes.*
Kelly	There were three *Kellys* in the class.
loaf	Each family was given two *loaves* of bread.
mosquito	Some *mosquitoes* carry disease.
phenomenon	All the *phenomena* of nature were described.
stimulus	Our ears are sensitive to sound *stimuli.*
thief	The bank was robbed by three *thieves.*
turkey	The farmers sold their *turkeys.*
valley	The river *valleys* were covered with water.
veto	The three bills received early *vetoes.*

☐ VISUAL DRILL

As you look at each word, try to visualize the whole word (in plural form) with the missing letters in place. Then check yourself by looking at the word as it appears above. Finally, fill in the blanks. Check the spelling again, and make any necessary corrections.

attorn __ __ __   cor __ __   lo __ __ es   th __ __ __ es

ba __ ter __ __   dat __   mosq __ __ t __ __ __ __   t __ rk __ __ __ __

bas __ __   her __ __ __   __ henome __ __   va __ l __ __ __ __

cargo __ __   Kell __ __   stimu __ __   vet __ __ __ __

cr __ t __ r __ __

☐ EXERCISE

In each blank, write the plural form of the word. You may use a dictionary.

1. tally _____

2. fly _____

3. desire _____

4. loaf _____

5. datum _____

6. cargo _____

7. neighbor _____

8. stimulus _____

9. attorney _____

10. pony _____

11. stitch _____

12. child _____

13. hero _____

14. pass _____

15. solo _____

16. face _____

17. man _____

18. mass _____

19. party _____

20. debt _____

21. receipt _____

22. baby _____

23. business _____

24. valley _____

25. secretary _____

26. duty _____

27. piece _____

28. goose _____

29. ally _____

30. tax _____

31. mouse _____

32. typist _____

33. act _____

34. house _____

35. ax _____

36. lady _____

37. cotton _____

38. economy _____

39. apparatus _____

40. moose _____

41. clothes _____

42. consortium _____

Using Abbreviations

An abbreviation is the shortened form of a word, such as *Dr.* for *Doctor*. An abbreviation should almost always be followed by a period. Many abbreviations are the initial letters of foreign words, such as *e.g.* for the Latin *exempli gratia* (for example). Abbreviations should be written accurately and legibly since they are easily and frequently misinterpreted. The following list includes fifty-four abbreviations that are frequently used, together with their English meanings.

A.D.	in the year of the Lord	lb.	pound or pounds
A.M.	before noon	lieut. or lt.	lieutenant
Apr.	April	M.A.	Master of Arts
asst.	assistant	Mar.	March
atty.	attorney	M.D.	Doctor of Medicine
Aug.	August	memo	memorandum
Ave.	Avenue	mgr.	manager
B.A.	Bachelor of Arts	m.p.h.	miles per hour
B.C.	before Christ	Mr.	Mister
B.S.	Bachelor of Science	Mrs.	Mistress
capt.	captain	No.	number
Co.	Company	Nov.	November
C.O.D.	collect or cash on delivery	Oct.	October
D.D.	Doctor of Divinity	oz.	ounce or ounces
Dec.	December	Ph.D.	Doctor of Philosophy
dept.	department	P.M.	afternoon
doz.	dozen or dozens	P.O.	post office
Dr.	Doctor	pp.	pages
e.g.	for example	P.S.	postscript
etc.	and so forth (et cetera)	Rev.	Reverend
Feb.	February	R.S.V.P.	*Please respond*
f.o.b.	free on board		(Repondez S'il Vous Plait)
ft.	foot or feet	Sept.	September
i.e.	that is (id est)	Sr.	Senior
in.	inch or inches	St.	Street
Jan.	January	supt.	superintendent
Jr.	Junior	vol.	volume
		vs.	against

No periods are used after *1st, 2nd, 3rd,* etc.; after *memo* or *percent*; or after government agencies commonly known by their abbreviations (*IRS, FBI, FDIC,* etc.).

☐ EXERCISE I

In the blank, write the correct abbreviation for each word.

1. Doctor of Philosophy _____   3. for example _____

2. that is _____   4. Bachelor of Arts _____

5. manager _____

6. assistant _____

7. number _____

8. pound or pounds _____

9. before noon _____

10. Bachelor of Science _____

11. ounce or ounces _____

12. September _____

13. postscript _____

14. against _____

15. foot or feet _____

16. captain _____

17. Company _____

18. department _____

19. Doctor of Medicine _____

20. April _____

21. superintendent _____

22. Please respond _____

23. post office _____

24. before Christ _____

☐ EXERCISE II

In the blank, write the word or words for which the abbreviation stands.

1. A.D. _____

2. M.A. _____

3. Rev. _____

4. C.O.D. _____

5. P.M. _____

6. doz. _____

7. atty. _____

8. Jr. _____

9. pp. _____

10. etc. _____

11. Sr. _____

12. vol. _____

13. in. _____

14. Mr. _____

15. Ave. _____

16. memo _____

17. St. _____

18. Dec. _____

19. Nov. _____

20. m.p.h. _____

21. Dr. _____

22. Aug. _____

Abbreviations of States and Territories

Abbreviations of states and territories are frequently misspelled. This often results in improper mail delivery. Study the list of abbreviations given below. They should be used only in conjunction with a city. It is correct to write, "He went to Sioux Falls, SD," but it would be incorrect to write, "He went to SD."

Notice that these two-letter abbreviations recommended by the U.S. Postal Service do not require periods.

ABBREVIATION	STATE OR TERRITORY	ABBREVIATION	STATE OR TERRITORY
AL	Alabama	MT	Montana
AK	Alaska	NE	Nebraska
AZ	Arizona	NV	Nevada
AR	Arkansas	NH	New Hampshire
CA	California	NJ	New Jersey
CO	Colorado	NM	New Mexico
CT	Connecticut	NY	New York
DE	Delaware	NC	North Carolina
DC	District of Columbia	ND	North Dakota
FL	Florida	OH	Ohio
GA	Georgia	OK	Oklahoma
GU	Guam	OR	Oregon
HI	Hawaii	PA	Pennsylvania
ID	Idaho	PR	Puerto Rico
IL	Illinois	RI	Rhode Island
IN	Indiana	SC	South Carolina
IA	Iowa	SD	South Dakota
KS	Kansas	TN	Tennessee
KY	Kentucky	TX	Texas
LA	Louisiana	UT	Utah
ME	Maine	VT	Vermont
MD	Maryland	VA	Virginia
MA	Massachusetts	VI	Virgin Islands
MI	Michigan	WA	Washington
MN	Minnesota	WV	West Virginia
MS	Mississippi	WI	Wisconsin
MO	Missouri	WY	Wyoming

☐ EXERCISE I

Write the correct abbreviations for each of the following states.

1. New Jersey _____

2. Wyoming _____

3. District of Columbia _____

4. Maine _____

5. Massachusetts _____

6. Mississippi _____

7. Oklahoma _____

8. Arizona _____

9. South Dakota _____

10. Pennsylvania _____

11. Georgia _____

12. Alaska _____

13. Puerto Rico _____

14. West Virginia _____

15. Texas _____

16. Illinois _____

17. Kentucky _____

18. Montana _____

19. Louisiana _____

20. Utah _____

21. Iowa _____

22. Nevada _____

23. Virginia _____

24. Ohio _____

☐ EXERCISE II

Write out the state or territory for which each of the following abbreviations stands.

1. KS _____

2. MI _____

3. CA _____

4. MO _____

5. MN _____

6. GU _____

7. CO _____

8. NV _____

9. OR _____

10. RI _____

11. CT _____

12. NY _____

13. IN _____

14. MD _____

15. FL _____

16. NE _____

17. HI _____

18. OH _____

19. WA _____

20. WI _____

21. TX _____

22. AL _____

23. LA _____

24. IA _____

A. In each sentence, cross out the incorrectly capitalized word in parentheses. Then write the correctly capitalized word in the blank.

1. The Rocky (mountains, Mountains) are the highest (mountains, Mountains) I have

   ever seen. _____ _____

2. (January, january) is generally our coldest month and (july, July) our warmest.

   _____ _____

3. The (capitol, capital) building was the tallest building in Austin, the (capitol,

   capital) of Texas. _____ _____

4. Twelfth (Avenue, avenue) will be the fourth (Avenue, avenue) on your left.

   _____ _____

5. Most major (universities, Universities) had decreases in enrollment last spring except
   the (university, University) of Michigan.

   _____ _____

6. We haven't had a good (Superintendent, superintendent) since (Superintendent,

   superintendent) Taylor resigned. _____ _____

7. My favorite (Professor, professor) is (Professor, professor) Young.

   _____ _____

8. (uncle, Uncle) Richard is my favorite (Uncle, uncle).

   _____ _____

9. You need to turn (North, north) at the next intersection.

   _____

10. The (North, north) and the (South, south) fought during the (civil, Civil) War.

    _____ _____ _____

11. Is your (Uncle, uncle) coming to visit you this (February, february)?

    _____ _____

12. In the (Winter, winter) the trees along Marshall (Avenue, avenue) are bare.

    _____ _____

Each correct answer is worth 2 points.	Perfect score: 24 points.

B. Each sentence contains one or more spelling errors. Cross out each misspelled word. Then write the word correctly above it.

1. Trying to pass that counterfiet bill was advantagous to niether person.

2. The sience teacher read about an anceint spechies of fish.

3. The aweful scar across his cheek was very noticable.

4. The gas milage he got with his new car was holy unacceptable.

5. They had an outragous arguement over his poor judgement.

Each correct answer is worth 3 points.   Perfect score: 15 points.

C. Supply *ei* or *ie* in each of the following words. Do not refer to your book.

1. c __ __ ling

2. rec __ __ pts

3. ap __ __ ce

4. conc __ __ ved

5. gr __ __ vance

6. ach __ __ ve

7. w __ __ ld

8. rec __ __ ved

9. pr __ __ st

10. dec __ __ t

11. f __ __ rce

12. perc __ __ ve

13. twent __ __ th

14. f __ __ nd

15. p __ __ r

16. v __ __ n

17. anc __ __ nt

18. h __ __ ght

19. spec __ __ s

20. l __ __ sure

21. conc __ __ t

22. d __ __ t

23. w __ __ rd

24. for __ __ gn

25. counterf __ __ t

26. forf __ __ t

27. sc __ __ nce

28. __ __ ther

29. h __ __ r

30. perc __ __ ve

Each correct answer is worth 2 points.   Perfect score: 60 points.

Prefixes and Suffixes

A prefix is a word element placed before a word stem to change the stem's meaning, such as *un* in *unkind*. A suffix is a word element placed after a word stem to change its meaning, such as *ly* in *kindly*. A knowledge of the more common prefixes and suffixes (see lists below) is very helpful in learning word meanings. Some prefixes and suffixes, such as *auto, anti, trans,* and *ful,* are always spelled the same way. Many others have more than one spelling, such as *ible* and *able; ous, ious,* and *tious;* etc. Words with these prefixes and suffixes present special spelling problems, and should be studied independently (see lessons to follow).

COMMONLY USED PREFIXES

ad, a, ac, af, al, ap, at—to, toward
ante—before
anti—against
con, co, col, com—together, with
de—down, from, away from
dis, di, dif—apart, opposite
ex, e, ec, ef—out of, from, away
in, il, im, ir—in, into, not
inter—between, among

ob, o, oc, of, op—in the way, against
per—through, by means of
post—after, behind
pre—before
pro—before, for, forth, forward
re—back, again
sub, suc, suf, sug, sum, sup—under
trans—across
uni—one

COMMONLY USED SUFFIXES

able, ible, ble—that may or can be
al, ial—relating to, pertaining to
an, ain—pertaining to
ance, ancy, ence, ency—act of, state of being
ant, ent—being
ate, fy, ize, yze—to do or make
d, ed (past tense, past participle)—did
dom—power, office, state
ee—one to whom

er, or, eer, ier—one who, that which
ful—full of
ing (present participle)—continuing to
ion, sion, tion—act of, state of being
ity, ty, ment—condition, state of being
ness—state of being
ory, ery—place where
ous, ious, tious—full of, having the
  quality of

☐ EXERCISE I

Match each suffix in Column A with its meaning in Column B. Place the letter of the meaning in the blank in front of the suffix it defines.

COLUMN A

1. _____ ory

2. _____ ial

3. _____ ize

4. _____ ance

COLUMN B

a. act of, state of being

b. place where

c. relating to, pertaining to

d. to do or to make

☐ EXERCISE II

Match each prefix in Column A with its meaning in Column B. Place the letter of the meaning in the blank in front of the prefix it defines.

COLUMN A

1. _____ ad
2. _____ trans
3. _____ inter
4. _____ sub
5. _____ post
6. _____ per
7. _____ con
8. _____ uni
9. _____ pro

COLUMN B

a. under

b. through, by means of

c. to, toward

d. together, with

e. between, among

f. before, for, forward, forth

g. one

h. across

i. after, behind

☐ EXERCISE III

A word root and its meaning are listed in each section below. Use your knowledge of prefixes to write the meaning of each word.

A. *-cede* and *-ceed* mean to go

1. exceed _____
2. proceed _____
3. intercede _____
4. recede _____

B. *-mit* means to send

1. permit _____
2. transmit _____
3. admit _____
4. remit _____

C. *-port* means to carry

1. import _____
2. deport _____
3. export _____
4. transport _____

D. *-scribe* means to write

1. transcribe _____
2. subscribe _____
3. inscribe _____
4. prescribe _____

Words That End in *able*

Try to recall each of the following words as a part of the group of words beginning with *able*. If you are uncertain of the meaning or pronunciation of any of these words, refer to your dictionary.

acceptable	Calvin's poor excuse was not accept′a ble.
admirable	The conduct of the large crowd was ad′mi ra ble.
allowable	In this country such actions are not al low′a ble.
applicable	The rules were not ap′pli ca ble.
capable	It will take a ca′pa ble person to fill the position.
chargeable	The purchase was charge′a ble to her account.
charitable	Always be char′i ta ble to the poor and needy.
considerable	It took con sid′er a ble argument to convince her.
desirable	For everyone to be alike is not de sir′a ble.
disagreeable	His sore throat became more dis′a gree′a ble.
durable	This heavy material is very du′ra ble.
excusable	Because of illness, her absence is ex cus′a ble.
favorable	The decision was fa′vor a ble to launch the rocket.
honorable	An hon′or a ble discharge was given to the officer.
miserable	The slaves were mis′er a ble.
movable	Because of snow the trains were not mov′a ble.
notable	The soldiers' return was without doubt a no′ta ble event.
peaceable	They are not peace′a ble.
probable	It is prob′a ble that they will go.
reasonable	The price of the car is not rea′son a ble.
reliable	The lawyer is re li′a ble.
separable	Cream and milk are easily sep′a ra ble.
useable	Even a demolished automobile is use′a ble.

☐ VISUAL DRILL

As you look at each word, try to visualize the whole word with the missing letters in place. Then check yourself by looking at the word as it appears above. Finally, fill in the blanks. Check the spelling again, and make any necessary corrections.

ac __ __ pt __ b __ e	allo __ __ b __ __	fav __ r __ __ le	desi __ __ ble
con __ id __ r __ ble	char __ t __ ble	__ on __ r __ ble	prob __ __ __ __
ap __ l __ c __ b __ __	sep __ r __ ble	p __ __ c __ able	re __ s __ n __ ble
dis __ gre __ __ ble	dur __ __ le	mi __ er __ ble	cap __ b __ __
ex __ us __ b __ __	not __ __ le	mov __ b __ __	charg __ __ ble
rel __ __ b __ __	us __ __ ble	admi __ __ ble	

210

☐ EXERCISE

Write one of the following words in each blank. Study each sentence carefully.

acceptable	capable	desirable	favorable	probable
admirable	charitable	disagreeable	honorable	reasonable
applicable	considerable	excusable	miserable	reliable

1. The developer plans to build new luxury homes in the most

   _____ area of town.

2. It is _____ that the event will occur just as it was originally planned.

3. Martin found that his behavior was so _____ that he was not invited to the next meeting of the group.

4. _____ actions on the part of the officer earned her the respect of the entire battalion.

5. The senator had a reputation as an _____ man.

6. Were you _____ of fulfilling all the qualifications for summer employment at the plant?

7. No more _____ circumstances can be imagined than the abject poverty of the slaves.

8. Mrs. Teng was the most _____ person in the office.

9. The club found that the book was an _____ one and decided to have it reviewed at their next meeting.

10. If the demands of the partisan group are _____ ones, the governor will consider them.

11. Many of the theories you learned in the past are not always _____ to the situations you will meet in the future.

12. Do you think that the business climate is _____ for the expansion of your industry?

13. The drive for funds will be managed by several _____ organizations.

14. Her rude behavior was not _____.

15. Mr. Jordan found that the money had accrued _____ interest since it had been originally deposited.

Words That End in *ible*

As you look at and pronounce the words in this lesson that end in *ible*, place special stress on the letter *i*. Try to recall each word as part of the group of words ending with *ible*. Refer to your dictionary for the pronunciation and meaning of any words of which you are uncertain.

accessible	The mountain stream was not ac ces' si ble.
admissible	The judge ruled the evidence ad mis' si ble.
audible	The feeble words were barely au' di ble.
collectible	The bills were col lect' i ble.
contemptible	Physical aggression against the weak is con tempt' i ble.
convertible	The car had a con vert' i ble top.
corruptible	His morals were cor rupt' i ble.
defensible	Your theory of the explosion is not defen' si ble.
destructible	The baby's new toy was easily de struct' i ble.
dirigible	Another name for an airship is a dir' i gi ble.
divisible	The number is di vis' i ble by three.
eligible	Only adults are el' i gi ble for the contest.
feasible	Which plan is the most fea' si ble?
flexible	The flex' i ble tube was bent into a loop.
incredible	Will's strange story seems in cred' i ble.
indelible	The writing was in in del' i ble ink.
insensible	The blow knocked the boy in sen' si ble.
invisible	The jet fighter plane soon became in vis' i ble.
legible	Good handwriting is always leg' i ble.
permissible	Parking your car at an angle is not per mis' si ble there.
plausible	We believed his plau' si ble story.
responsible	Who was re spon' si ble for the accident?
reversible	Maria purchased a re vers' i ble overcoat.
susceptible	In winter, Jane is particularly sus cep' ti ble to colds.

☐ VISUAL DRILL

As you look at each word, try to visualize the whole word with the missing letters in place. Then check yourself by looking at the word as it appears above. Finally, fill in the blanks. Check the spelling again, and make any necessary corrections.

a __ c __ s __ __ ble	incr __ d __ ble	f __ __ s __ ble	admis __ __ ble
cor __ __ p __ __ ble	defen __ __ ble	fle __ ib __ __	p __ rmis __ __ ble
pl __ __ s __ __ __ __	insen __ __ ble	__ olle __ __ __ ble	a __ d __ b __ __
su __ __ ep __ __ ble	le __ __ ble	dir __ g __ __ le	respon __ __ ble
con __ em __ t __ ble	invi __ __ ble	div __ __ i __ le	indel __ __ __ __
conv __ rt __ b __ __	el __ g __ ble	rever __ __ ble	d __ struc __ __ ble

☐ EXERCISE

In each group of words, cross out any misspelled words. Then write each word correctly in the blank. If there are no misspelled words, write a *C* in the blank.

1. favorable   feasable   flexible   _____

2. enable   excusable   eligable   _____

3. capable   collectible   chargable   _____

4. permisable   plausible   probable   _____

5. acceptable   accessable   audible   _____

6. reliable   reasonable   responsable   _____

7. incredible   indelible   invisible   _____

8. admirable   admissable   applicable   _____

9. contemptable   corruptible   charitable   _____

10. salable   separable   susceptable   _____

11. destructible   defensable   durable   _____

12. dirigible   divisable   disagreeable   _____

13. miserable   indelable   notable   _____

14. peaceable   legible   insensable   _____

15. reversible   honorable   convertable   _____

16. reversable   responsible   indelible   _____

17. collectable   audible   plausible   _____

18. corruptible   insensible   invisable   _____

19. destructible   flexible   incredible   _____

20. plausable   reasonable   admissible   _____

21. dirigible   audable   durable   _____

22. susceptible   honorable   indelable   _____

Some Troublesome Prefixes

Prefixes give much less spelling trouble than do suffixes. Such prefixes as *bene* (well), *co* (together), *dis* (away), *ex* (out of), *il* (not), *in* (not), *ir* (not), *mis* (wrong), and *un* (not) give very little spelling difficulty. Some words beginning with prefixes which are difficult to spell are the following:

arouse	They could not a rouse′ the sleeper.
beneficial	The medicine was ben′ e fi′ cial.
coincide	The two news stories did not co′ in cide′.
disagree	The speakers dis′ a gree′ on the subject.
discovery	The dis cov′ er y of gold was kept secret.
excel	Arturo tried to ex cel′ in all sports.
exile	The prisoners were sent into ex′ ile.
exhibit	Three pictures were placed on ex hib′ it.
expected	Tom is ex pect′ ed to arrive early today.
illiterate	What percentage of the population is il lit′ er ate?
illustrate	Photos were used to il′ lus trate the story.
inability	Her in′ a bil′ i ty to read is unfortunate.
inauguration	There was a delay in the governor's in au′ gu ra′ tion.
irrigation	Much water was distributed by ir′ ri ga′ tion.
irreparable	Fire caused ir rep′ a ra ble damages.
misfortune	His car accident was a great mis for′ tune.
mislay	Where did you mis lay′ your glasses?
mispronounce	Did you mis′ pro nounce′ many words?
mistaken	It was a case of mis tak′ en identity.
unnecessary	There is no un nec′ es sar′ y waste.
unusual	Your conduct is un u′ su al.

☐ VISUAL DRILL

As you look at each word, try to visualize the whole word with the missing letters in place. Check your efforts by looking at the word as it appears earlier in the lesson. Finally, fill in the blanks. Check the spelling again, and make any necessary corrections.

exp __ __ __ ed	aro __ __ __ __	in __ __ g __ ration	dis __ gree
ben __ fi __ __ al	e __ __ ib __ t	ir __ ep __ r __ ble	ex __ el
co __ n __ id __	m __ __ la __	un __ e __ es __ __ ry	mi __ t __ ken
i __ __ __ gation	il __ it __ rate	m __ sfort __ __ __	e __ il __
d __ sc __ v __ ry	il __ __ strate	m __ __ pron __ __ n __ __	
unu __ __ __ l	in __ bil __ ty		

214

☐ EXERCISE

In each sentence, cross out each incorrect word in parentheses. Then write the correct word in the blank.

1. Jim was quite upset over his (enability—inability) to deliver the speech accurately.

   _____

2. The teacher said that you should try not to (mispronounce—misprononce) the words in the lesson. _____

3. Brenda was trying to (excell—excel) as a real estate agent. _____

4. Proper (irigation—irrigation) of the rice fields will bring a larger crop yield.

   _____

5. Roberta felt that additional research would be (unecessary—unnecessary).

   _____

6. Harsh words will (arrouse—arouse) the ire of even the most docile person.

   _____

7. Such an action will cause (irreparable—irrepairable) damage to the community at large. _____

8. Mrs. Wilson was distressed at the number of (iliterate—illiterate) children throughout the state. _____

9. Without hesitating, the jury condemned the man to (exille—exile) from the country.

   _____

10. The Native Americans thought that the waters from the spring were (benneficial—beneficial) to their health. _____

11. The largest crowd that had ever gathered in the capital was at the (inauguration—innauguration) of the governor. _____

12. When (misfortune—missfortune) strikes, it seems to strike with grave results.

    _____

13. That couple tried to collect only the most (unnusual—unusual) lanterns and lamps for their shop. _____

14. The museum has an outstanding (exibit—exhibit) of precious metals this month.

    _____

Words Ending in *el*, *le*, and *al*

There are a number of words ending in *el*, *le*, and *al* which are pronounced with a similar *l* sound. There are no rules which govern the spelling of these endings. Distinct pronunciation is helpful, but for the most part *l*-sounding endings must be visualized carefully. Note the endings of the following words:

acquittal	The jury voted for the prisoner's ac quit' tal.
refusal	A quick re fus' al was given to our offer.
angel	Our dessert was an' gel food cake.
barrel	The bar' rel was full of flour.
label	The la' bel came off the bottle.
novel	This is an interesting nov' el.
parcel	A par' cel came in today's mail.
quarrel	They engaged in a bitter quar' rel.
satchel	Doctor Brown left her satch' el in her office.
tunnel	The train ran through a tun' nel.
vessel	The ves' sel carried cargo.
angle	The an' gle was more than 45 degrees.
axle	The rear ax' le of the car was broken.
humble	The man's manner was hum' ble.
liable	Everyone is li' a ble for personal debts.
meddle	Why med' dle in other people's affairs?
resemble	Twins often re sem' ble each other.
struggle	The strug' gle for existence is unending.
thimble	The needle was easily pushed with a thim' ble.
tremble	The child began to trem' ble with fear.
trifle	The guests were a tri' fle late.
whistle	The train's whis' tle was long and loud.
wrestle	The boys started to wres' tle each other.

☐ VISUAL DRILL

As you look at each word, try to visualize the whole word with the missing letters in place. Then check yourself by looking at the word as it appears earlier in the lesson. Finally, fill in the blanks. Check the spelling again, and make any necessary corrections.

ac __ __ itt __ l	n __ v __ l	ves __ __ l	med __ le	t __ ifl __
ref __ s __ l	par __ __ l	angl __	r __ sembl __	w __ istl __
ang __ l	qu __ __ rel	ax __ __	strug __ l __	wr __ stle
bar __ __ l	s __ __ chel	__ umble	th __ mbl __	
lab __ l	t __ nn __ l	l __ abl __	trem __ __ e	

216

☐ EXERCISE I

Supply *el, le,* or *al* in the following words. In the blank following each word, rewrite the complete word.

1. ax _____   _____   9. strugg _____   _____

2. trif _____   _____   10. whist _____   _____

3. nov _____   _____   11. quarr _____   _____

4. medd _____   _____   12. tremb _____   _____

5. wrest _____   _____   13. lab _____   _____

6. acquitt _____   _____   14. humb _____   _____

7. parc _____   _____   15. tunn _____   _____

8. resemb _____   _____   16. liab _____   _____

☐ EXERCISE II

In each sentence, find any misspelled words. Write each word correctly in the blank. If there are no misspelled words, write a *C* in the blank.

_____   **1.** Are they liabel for the debts that their children have incurred during the last six months?

_____   **2.** I do not think that the jury will bring in a verdict for acquittal in this case.

_____   **3.** The wind caused the cracks to whistel and the timbers to tremble.

_____   **4.** Do you think that the quarrel between the two political parties will lead to a struggel in the election?

_____   **5.** The cargo vessal steamed into port just as the train reached the final tunnel.

_____   **6.** Don't meddel in the case, for only a trifle is concerned.

_____   **7.** The angel of the turn must be straightened before the road is finished.

_____   **8.** Although he came from a humbel background, he reached the top of the legal profession.

_____   **9.** The axel broke while we were in the tunnel.

Words Ending in *ar*, *er*, and *or*

Many persons misspell words which end with an *er* sound. Although the *er* pronunciation is correct for most of these words, it is helpful to give the *ar* endings a slight *a* sound and the *or* endings a slight *o* sound when learning to spell them. Study the following words.

beggar The poor beg′gar was wretched.
cedar They cut down every ce′dar tree.
collar The col′lar was too large.
polar The po′lar bear was white as snow.
vinegar The cider soon turned into very good vin′e gar.
carrier Please call the mail car′ri er back.
consumer The sale benefited each con sum′er.
employer My em ploy′er bought a new typewriter.
jeweler The jew′el er fixed my watch.
laborer John is a la′bor er at the mill.
ledger The entries were posted in the ledg′er.
shoulder The football player injured his shoul′der.
voucher A vouch′er indicated the amount of the sale.
ambassador The foreign am bas′sa dor was present.
author The au′thor of the book was famous.
conductor The con duc′tor collected the tickets.
editor L. C. Smith is ed′i tor of the magazine.
inventor A world-famous in ven′tor was at the conference.
investor She was a heavy in ves′tor in bonds.
rumor The ru′mor spread throughout the city.
senator Carolyn Jones is the new state sen′a tor.
traitor The trai′tor died in exile.
visitor Our vis′i tor stayed a few days.

☐ VISUAL DRILL

As you look at each word, try to visualize the whole word with the missing letters in place. Then check yourself by looking at the word as it appears earlier in the lesson. Finally, fill in the blanks. Check the spelling again, and make any necessary corrections.

begg __ __	jew __ __ __ __	conduct __ __	amba __ s __ d __ __
carri __ __	pol __ __	edit __ __	rum __ r
ced __ __	con __ um __ r	sho __ ld __ __	sen __ t __ __
col __ __ r	labor __ __	v __ __ ch __ r	tra __ t __ __
auth __ __	le __ g __ __	invent __ __	vis __ t __ __
employ __ __	vineg __ __	invest __ __	

Cross out any misspelled words in each group of words. Write each misspelled word correctly in the blank. If there are no misspelled words, write a *C* in the blank.

1. ambassador	consumar	beggar	_____
2. cedar	collar	carriar	_____
3. visitor	traitor	editor	_____
4. inventor	investor	laboror	_____
5. shouldar	polar	vinegar	_____
6. ledger	vouchar	employer	_____
7. visitor	auther	senator	_____
8. rumor	conducter	jeweler	_____

☐ **EXERCISE II**

Match each word in Column A with its meaning in Column B. Place the letter of the meaning in the blank in front of the word it defines.

COLUMN A

1. _____ consumer

2. _____ employer

3. _____ author

4. _____ jeweler

5. _____ conductor

6. _____ editor

7. _____ inventor

8. _____ investor

9. _____ senator

10. _____ traitor

11. _____ visitor

COLUMN B

a. a member of the upper house of a legislative body

b. one who buys products

c. one who betrays his or her country or group

d. one for whom others work

e. one who uses money to make a profit or to draw interest

f. one who sells or makes jewelry

g. one who writes stories, poems, or books

h. one who comes to see a person

i. one who leads an orchestra

j. one who invents

k. one who prepares books or magazines for publication

A. Study each of the following definitions. Choose the one word in the parentheses that most nearly means the same as the definition. Write the correct word in the blank.

1. To underwrite (prescribe, inscribe, subscribe) _____

2. To carry into (deport, import, export) _____

3. To call back (revoke, provoke, invoke) _____

4. To send across (admit, permit, transmit) _____

5. To bring before (infer, prefer, transfer) _____

6. To go beyond (recede, exceed, proceed) _____

Each correct answer is worth 3 points.	Total score: 18 points.

B. Supply *able* or *ible* in each word.

1. prob _ _ _ _

2. allow _ _ _ _

3. elig _ _ _ _

4. aud _ _ _ _

5. honor _ _ _ _

6. access _ _ _ _

7. consider _ _ _ _

8. dur _ _ _ _

9. incred _ _ _ _

10. leg _ _ _ _

11. cap _ _ _ _

12. feas _ _ _ _

13. admir _ _ _ _

14. destruct _ _ _ _

Each correct answer is worth 2 points.	Total score: 28 points.

C. Add prefixes or suffixes as directed.

1. Add a prefix to *lay* to form a word that means to misplace. _____

2. Add a prefix to *ability* to form its opposite. _____

3. Add a suffix to *apply* to form a word that means may apply or can apply.

_____

4. Add a prefix to *agree* to form its opposite. _____

5. Add a prefix to *rouse* to form a word that means to awaken. _____

6. Add a prefix and suffix to *separate* to form a word that means cannot be separated.

_____

7. Add a suffix to *senate* to form a word that means one who is in the senate.

_____

8. Add a prefix to *necessary* to form its opposite. _____

9. Add a suffix to *employ* to form a word that means one who employs.

_____

10. Add a prefix and suffix to *repair* to form a word that means not capable of

being repaired. _____

11. Add a suffix to *consume* to form a word that means one who consumes.

_____

12. Add a prefix to *usual* to form its opposite. _____

13. Add a prefix to *literate* to form its opposite. _____

14. Add a suffix to *move* to form a word that means can be moved. _____

Each correct answer is worth 2 points.　　　　　　　　Total score: 28 points.

D. Insert *el, le, al, ar, er,* or *or* in the spaces in the following words.

1. edit __ __
2. invent __ __
3. pol __ __
4. coll __ __
5. liab __ __
6. rum __ __
7. strugg __ __

8. vess __ __
9. vouch __ __
10. lab __ __
11. trif __ __
12. tunn __ __
13. tremb __ __
14. conduct __ __

15. whist __ __
16. trait __ __
17. ced __ __
18. acquitt __ __
19. vineg __ __
20. visit __ __
21. quarr __ __

22. nov __ __
23. aviat __ __
24. parc __ __
25. humb __ __
26. resemb __ __

Each correct answer is worth 1 point.　　　　　　Total score: 26 points.

Words Ending in *ant* and *ent*

The English language contains many words ending in *ant* and *ent*. Some of them are listed in Part 1 of this text (See Lessons 39 and 49). You can avoid difficulty in spelling these words by pronouncing the endings distinctly. Study the following list of words, paying careful attention to the endings. Try to visualize and pronounce the endings correctly.

abundant	There was an a bun′dant supply of food.
applicant	Are you an ap′pli cant for the position?
defendant	The de fend′ant was set free.
descendant	Mary is a de scend′ant of Thomas Jefferson.
emigrant	His mother was an em′i grant from Germany.
immigrant	Her father was an im′mi grant to America.
important	Your health is an extremely im por′tant matter.
predominant	Industry is the pre dom′i nant activity here.
restaurant	The new res′tau rant serves good food.
significant	It is sig nif′i cant that he arrived early.
tyrant	The mad king became a severe ty′rant.
apparent	It is ap par′ent that the house needs paint.
current	The October magazine is the cur′rent issue.
deficient	Her daily diet was de fi′cient in milk.
dependent	Children are de pend′ent upon their parents.
efficient	Ef fi′cient work is essential to success.
obedient	Mary was o be′di ent.
opponent	He finally overcame his strong op po′nent.
ornament	He hung the or′na ment on the tree.
prevalent	The contagious disease soon became prev′a lent.
resident	The lecturer was not a res′i dent of this city.
violent	A vi′o lent thunderstorm lashed the area.

☐ VISUAL DRILL

As you look at each word, try to visualize the whole word with the missing letters in place. Then check yourself by looking at the word as it appears earlier in the lesson. Finally, fill in the blanks. Check the spelling again, and make any necessary corrections.

abund __ __ t	appl __ c __ __ __ __	cu __ __ __ nt	signif __ c __ nt
ap __ ar __ nt	d __ pend __ __ __	re __ id __ __ t	defi __ __ __ nt
op __ on __ nt	des __ end __ __ __	ef __ ic __ __ nt	import __ __ __
orn __ m __ nt	predom __ n __ __ __ __	obed __ __ nt	
vi __ l __ nt	d __ f __ nd __ __ t	prev __ l __ __ t	
__ mm __ grant	t __ r __ __ t	rest __ __ r __ nt	

In each group of words, cross out any misspelled words. Then write each word correctly in the blank. If there are no misspelled words, write a *C* in the blank.

1. abundant	applicant	apparant	_____
2. dependent	defendent	descendant	_____
3. obedient	opponent	ornament	_____
4. immigrant	emmigrant	important	_____
5. prevalent	deficient	predominent	_____
6. violant	resident	tyrant	_____
7. current	deficiant	efficient	_____
8. tyrent	current	violent	_____

Supply *ant* or *ent* in each word. In the blank following each word, rewrite the complete word.

1. effici _____ _____

2. import _____ _____

3. viol _____ _____

4. signific _____ _____

5. abund _____ _____

6. preval _____ _____

7. restaur _____ _____

8. oppon _____ _____

9. descend _____ _____

10. obedi _____ _____

11. ornam _____ _____

12. emigr _____ _____

13. tyr _____ _____

14. appar _____ _____

15. depend _____ _____

16. resid _____ _____

17. applic _____ _____

18. curr _____ _____

19. defend _____ _____

20. predomin _____ _____

21. immigr _____ _____

22. defici _____ _____

223

Words Ending in *ance* and *ence*

What was said in Lesson 91 about words ending in *ant* and *ent* applies equally to words ending in *ance* and *ence*. Careful pronunciation of the *a* and *e* sounds will help you overcome spelling difficulties with words of this type.

Review the words listed in Lessons 35 and 45. Then study the following words carefully. Mastery of these three sets of words will eliminate most spelling mistakes due to the confusion of *ance* and *ence*.

abundance	Rain caused an a bun′ dance of crops.
admittance	Our tickets gave us ad mit′ tance to the first show.
annoyance	The speaker at the banquet showed an noy′ ance at the interruption.
attendance	The at tend′ ance at the meeting was large.
conveyance	They went in every kind of con vey′ ance that was available to them.
hindrance	Bad roads were a hin′ drance to speed.
ignorance	Lack of study was the cause of such ig′ no rance.
resemblance	The re sem′ blance in looks was remarkable.
resistance	No re sist′ ance seemed too great to overcome.
temperance	Someone advised us to have tem′ per ance in all things.
perseverance	Per′ se ver′ ance will overcome most difficulties.
audience	The au′ di ence cheered for the speaker.
competence	Her com′ pe tence at the task was unquestionable.
excellence	She noted the ex′ cel lence of his manners.
innocence	The accused claimed complete in′ no cence.
intelligence	The child's teachers praised her in tel′ li gence.
interference	The meeting ended without further in′ ter fer′ ence.
negligence	He was fired for neg′ li gence of duty.
inference	Her in′ fer ence was based upon facts.
obedience	Strict o be′ di ence is demanded in the army.
reverence	The memory of heroes is held in rev′ er ence.
violence	The mob continued its acts of vi′ o lence.

☐ VISUAL DRILL

As you look at each word, try to visualize the whole word with the missing letters in place. Then check yourself by looking at the word as it appears earlier in the lesson. Finally, fill in the blanks. Check the spelling again, and make any necessary corrections.

conv _ _ _ _ _ nce	comp _ t _ n _ _	a _ di _ _ ce	per _ ev _ r _ nce
in _ o _ _ nce	ign _ r _ _ c _	negl _ g _ nce	temp _ r _ _ _ ce
hindr _ _ _ _	at _ _ nd _ _ _ e	inf _ r _ nce	admi _ t _ _ ce
an _ oy _ nce	resemb _ _ _ _ _ _	obed _ _ nce	intel _ _ g _ nce
interf _ _ _ nce	res _ _ t _ n _ e	vi _ l _ nce	
rever _ _ _ _	ex _ _ l _ _ nce	abund _ _ _ _	

In each group of words, cross out any misspelled words. Then write each word correctly in the blank. If there are no misspelled words, write a *C* in the blank.

1. perseverence	annoyance	intelligence	_____
2. assistance	residance	assurance	_____
3. resemblance	reverence	resistance	_____
4. audience	abundence	admittance	_____
5. obedience	inferance	appearance	_____
6. resistance	remittance	innocence	_____
7. conveyence	competence	conference	_____
8. nuisance	presence	hindrence	_____
9. preference	reference	temperence	_____
10. maintenance	negligance	confidence	_____

☐ **EXERCISE II**

Supply *ance* or *ence* in each word. In the blank following each word, rewrite the complete word.

1. abund _____ _____

2. innoc _____ _____

3. obedi _____ _____

4. hindr _____ _____

5. interfer _____ _____

6. admitt _____ _____

7. infer _____ _____

8. resist _____ _____

9. annoy _____ _____

10. rever _____ _____

11. temper _____ _____

12. neglig _____ _____

13. attend _____ _____

14. convey _____ _____

15. compet _____ _____

16. resembl _____ _____

17. persever _____ _____

18. excell _____ _____

Words Ending in *ise*, *ize*, and *yze*

The numerous words ending in *ise*, *ize*, and *yze* are frequently misspelled. The best way to learn to spell these words correctly is to memorize them, paying close attention to their endings.

despise	Most persons de spise' lying and cheating in others.
comprise	What items does the new outline com prise'?
devise	We need to de vise' a plan.
disguise	His dis guise' entirely changed his appearance.
enterprise	Robert began another business en' ter prise.
franchise	The city extended the old water fran' chise for a year.
revise	The writer was asked to re vise' the story.
supervise	Who is to su' per vise our work?
antagonize	Let us not an tag' o nize the umpire.
apologize	You should a pol' o gize for your unkind remark.
authorize	Did the manager au' thor ize this change?
baptize	The preacher wanted to bap tize' the baby at once.
economize	Higher labor costs required us to e con' o mize.
emphasize	It is necessary to em' pha size the fact.
equalize	The new plan will e' qual ize the tax burden.
organize	The bowlers decided to or' gan ize a club.
standardize	Dictionaries have helped to stand' ard ize pronunciation.
summarize	The last speaker failed to sum' ma rize her points.
sympathize	We did not sym' pa thize with her views.
utilize	Many machines u' ti lize electricity for power.
visualize	I can vis' u al ize his face.
analyze	This wage problem is difficult to an' a lyze.
paralyze	The blow seemed to par' a lyze his arm.

☐ VISUAL DRILL

As you look at each word, try to visualize the whole word with the missing letters in place. Then check yourself by looking at the word as it appears earlier in the lesson. Finally, fill in the blanks. Check the spelling again, and make any necessary corrections.

franc __ i __ e	eq __ al __ __ __ __	sup __ rv __ __ __ __	bapt __ __ __
revi __ __	org __ ni __ __	enterp __ __ __ __ __	antag __ ni __ e
par __ l __ __ e	a __ th __ ri __ e	apol __ g __ __ __	d __ spi __ __
dev __ __ __	vis __ __ li __ __	e __ on __ mi __ __	ut __ li __ __
d __ sg __ __ se	sum __ ar __ __ e	s __ mp __ th __ __ __	an __ l __ __ e
compr __ __ __	em __ __ asi __ e	stand __ rd __ __ __	

☐ EXERCISE

In each sentence, cross out the incorrect word in parentheses. Then write the correct word in the blank.

1. Will we be able to obtain a (franchise—franchize) for a major league team in the near future? _____

2. Can you (devize—devise) another program that will fit the schedule better?

   _____

3. The union leaders will try to (standardize—standardyze) member regulations by the next meeting. _____

4. The scientists are trying to (analize—analyze) each of the compounds and each of the mixtures. _____

5. The generals felt that the aggressive move would (antagonise—antagonize) the enemy. _____

6. Only the supervisor can (authorize—authorise) the purchase of new equipment.

   _____

7. We found it was necessary to (supervize—supervise) the new employees in our company very carefully. _____

8. (Summarise—Summarize) all the speaker's statements in one good paragraph.

   _____

9. To be a good painter, one must be able to (visualise—visualize) both color and form as it will appear on canvas. _____

10. (Emphasize—Emphasyze) the important points in your outline, and your speech will be an effective one. _____

11. Did the manager feel that she would be able to (utilise—utilize) all the workers in the new plant? _____

12. If Alex would (revize—revise) the story, he might be able to get it published.

    _____

Words Ending in *ary*, *ery*, and *ory*

Words ending in *ary*, *ery*, and *ory* are often misspelled due to the similarity of their endings. In learning these words, pay special attention to the *a*, *e*, or *o* sound in the next-to-last syllable.

boundary	The state bound′ar y on the west is a river.
contrary	Your statement is con′tra ry to the facts.
customary	We followed the cus′tom ar′y procedure.
elementary	The new el′e men′ta ry school has four grades.
literary	We promptly joined the monthly lit′er ar′y society.
ordinary	The trial was just an or′di nar′y affair.
summary	The book sum′ma ry reviewed the main points.
voluntary	Her contribution was entirely vol′un tar′y.
artillery	The parade included a piece of ar til′ler y.
celery	There was too much cel′er y in the salad.
discovery	The dis cov′er y of oil brought prosperity.
recovery	Complete re cov′er y followed the depression.
millinery	This year the women opened a new mil′li ner′y store.
misery	The injured man was in great mis′er y.
mystery	The magazine contained two mys′ter y stories.
accessory	She was an ac ces′so ry in the crime.
depository	The City National Bank is the chief de pos′i to′ry.
directory	His address is in the telephone di rec′to ry.
history	The book contains the his′to ry of slavery.
introductory	Ms. Brown had to make some in′tro duc′to ry remarks.
memory	The old man's mem′o ry for details is remarkable.
preparatory	Last year Alicia went to a college pre′par a to′ry school.
territory	This ter′ri to′ry was first settled by the Indians.

☐ VISUAL DRILL

As you look at each word, try to visualize the whole word with the missing letters in place. Then check yourself by looking at the word as it appears earlier in the lesson. Finally, fill in the blanks. Check the spelling again, and make any necessary corrections.

bo __ nd __ __ y	cust __ m __ __ __	sum __ __ ry	mis __ ry
artil __ __ ry	disc __ v __ ry	hist __ __ __	m __ st __ __ __
cel __ __ y	mil __ __ n __ __ y	mem __ __ __	ord __ n __ ry
intr __ du __ to __ y	re __ ov __ ry	prep __ r __ t __ ry	depos __ t __ __ __
contr __ __ y	elem __ nt __ __	vol __ nt __ ry	dire __ t __ __ __
ac __ es __ __ __ y	lit __ r __ ry	ter __ __ t __ ry	

☐ EXERCISE I

In each sentence, find any misspelled words. Write each word correctly in the blank.
If there are no misspelled words, write a *C* in the blank.

_____ 1. In his introductary remarks, the author asked us to commit a quotation to memory.

_____ 2. At every meeting of the Litarery Society, Mrs. Burnett presents a summary of a new book.

_____ 3. John's actions in helping with the recovery of the missing property were completely voluntery.

_____ 4. It is customery for the volunteers to load each new piece of defense artillery.

_____ 5. You will find a list of college preparratory schools in the current College Directory.

_____ 6. It is a mystery to the jury how such a person could have been an acessory to the crime.

_____ 7. That is the customary treatment for a person with a loss of memry.

_____ 8. I was in misry during my recovery.

_____ 9. Chop the cellery fine, or your sauce will be lumpy.

_____ 10. In one of our geography lessons, we were asked to mark the boundery between France and Italy.

_____ 11. This summary is contrary to an earlier report.

_____ 12. The history of the depository is a great mystry.

☐ EXERCISE II

Supply *ary, ery,* or *ory* in each word. In the blank following each word, rewrite the complete word.

1. discov _____ _____

2. direct _____ _____

3. bound _____ _____

4. deposit _____ _____

5. introduct _____ _____

6. element _____ _____

7. summ _____ _____

8. custom _____ _____

9. mem _____ _____

10. access _____ _____

Words Ending in *cian, cion, sion,* and *tion*

The final group of words with similar endings presented in this text is the group of words ending in *cian, cion, sion,* and *tion.* All these words end with a *shən* sound. When memorizing these words, it is necessary to pay close attention to their endings.
The following words are among the most frequently used words of this group. Study them carefully.

magician (jish′an)	The ma gi′ cian used sleight of hand.
musician (zish′an)	The mu si′ cian played skillfully.
physician (zish′an)	The sick man needs a phy si′ cian.
politician (tish′an)	The pol′ i ti′ cian asked for votes.
suspicion (pish′un)	Our sus pi′ cion required proof.
admission (mish′un)	Ad mis′ sion to the game was free.
conclusion (kloo′zhun)	We came to the same con clu′ sion.
confusion (fu′zhun)	Great con fu′ sion followed the wreck.
division (vizh′un)	The di vi′ sion was simple.
expression (presh′un)	His ex pres′ sion was unchanged.
impression (presh′un)	Elena made a fine im pres′ sion.
permission (mish′un)	Jason had our per mis′ sion.
persuasion (swa′zhun)	He yielded to per sua′ sion.
procession (sesh′un)	We followed the pro ces′ sion.
admiration (ra′shun)	Her act deserved ad′ mi ra′ tion.
ammunition (nish′un)	The soldiers used am′ mu ni′ tion.
collection (lek′shun)	Roberta has a fine col lec′ tion of stamps.
construction (struk′shun)	Con struc′ tion of the roof began.
decoration (ra′shun)	Cut flowers are a beautiful dec′ o ra′ tion.
fiction (fik′shun)	A fable is fic′ tion.
occupation (pa′shun)	Her oc′ cu pa′ tion is dentistry.
retention (ten′shun)	Practice improves re ten′ tion.

☐ VISUAL DRILL

As you look at each word, try to visualize the whole word with the missing letters in place. Then check yourself by looking at the word as it appears earlier in the lesson. Finally, fill in the blanks. Check the spelling again, and make any necessary corrections.

suspi __ __ __ n	confu __ __ __ n	am __ unit __ __ n
magi __ __ __ n	con __ lus __ __ n	o __ cupa __ __ __ n
music __ __ __	pol __ ti __ __ __ n	impre __ __ __ __ n
fic __ __ __ n	adm __ rat __ __ __	dec __ ra __ __ __ n
ph __ si __ __ __ n	expre __ __ __ __ n	persu __ s __ __ __
admis __ __ __ n		

In each group of words, cross out any misspelled words. Then write each word correctly.
If there are no misspelled words, write a *C* in the blank.

1. persuasion	physician	politicion	_____
2. admiration	admiscion	ammunition	_____
3. construcsion	conclusion	confusion	_____
4. occupation	musicion	collection	_____
5. retention	expression	impression	_____
6. fiction	magision	suspicion	_____
7. decorasion	division	procession	_____

□ **EXERCISE II**

Supply *cian, cion, sion,* or *tion* in each word. In the blank following each word, rewrite
the complete word.

1. confu _____ _____

2. occupa _____ _____

3. physi _____ _____

4. ammuni _____ _____

5. persua _____ _____

6. decora _____ _____

7. magi _____ _____

8. admis _____ _____

9. collec _____ _____

10. expres _____ _____

11. musi _____ _____

12. permis _____ _____

13. construc _____ _____

14. impres _____ _____

15. politi _____ _____

16. reten _____ _____

17. proces _____ _____

18. fic _____ _____

19. suspi _____ _____

20. conclu _____ _____

21. divi _____ _____

A. In each sentence, cross out the incorrect word in parentheses. Then write the correct word in the blank.

1. The cherry crop this year is (abundent, abundant). _____

2. The blaring radio was a great (annoyance, annoyence). _____

3. He played to a very appreciative (audiance, audience)._____

4. The patient young man's (perserverance, perseverance) was rewarded.

   _____

5. My answer to that question is highly (dependent, dependant) on the outcome of

   our survey. _____

6. She took vitamins hoping to increase her (resistence, resistance) to disease.

   _____

7. The little puppy was remarkably (obedient, obediant). _____

8. Do you have the (currant, current) issue of that magazine? _____

9. They could not gain (admittence, admittance) until a half hour before the show.

   _____

10. We have had an (abundence, abundance) of rain this spring. _____

11. The (defendant, defendent) rose when the judge entered the courtroom.

   _____

12. He was proud of the fact that he was an (immigrant, immigrunt).

   _____

13. There was no (apparant, apparent) motive for the crime. _____

14. (Attendance, attendence) at the basketball games was better this season.

   _____

15. You could feel the atmosphere of (reverence, reverance) inside the

   Lincoln Memorial. _____

Each correct answer is worth 1 point.	Total score: 15 points.

B. Supply *ise, ize,* or *yze* in each word.

1. author __ __ __
2. equal __ __ __
3. standard __ __ __
4. rev __ __ __
5. antagon __ __ __
6. econom __ __ __

7. compr __ __ __
8. paral __ __ __
9. dev __ __ __
10. superv __ __ __
11. summar __ __ __
12. disgu __ __ __

13. franch __ __ __
14. util __ __ __
15. enterpr __ __ __
16. organ __ __ __
17. emphas __ __ __
18. apolog __ __ __

19. anal __ __ __
20. desp __ __ __
21. bapt __ __ __

Each correct answer is worth 2 points.   Total score: 42 points.

C. In each group of words, cross out any misspelled words. Then write each word correctly in the blank. If there are no misspelled words, write a *C* in the blank.

1. ordinary   summery   occupation   _____
2. decorasion   confusion   contrary   _____
3. mystery   customary   boundery   _____
4. millinary   recovery   permission   _____
5. division   suspicion   celary   _____
6. ammunition   elementary   discovery   _____
7. litarary   admission   construction   _____
8. fiction   retention   voluntery   _____
9. phisician   politician   magician   _____
10. processian   musician   accessory   _____
11. preparatory   memary   collection   _____
12. conclusion   expression   directery   _____
13. introductory   teritory   depository   _____
14. histery   artillery   misery   _____

Each correct answer is worth 3 points.   Total score: 42 points.

POSTTEST

A. In each sentence, find the misspelled words. Write each word correctly in the blank. If there are no misspelled words, write a _C_ in the blank.

_____ 1. The captain made sure all the cargoe was safely aboard the ship.

_____ 2. Dr. Ruiz, an iminent physicist, will speak at the university on Friday.

_____ 3. Which resterant is your favorite?

_____ 4. It is difficult to visuelize the amount of garbage generated by the average American family.

_____ 5. Paula has a penchent for keeping things organized.

_____ 6. The brothers' feelings of affection were mutuel.

_____ 7. Was your house in New Mexico built of adoby?

_____ 8. Joe was surprised by the absense of clutter in his daughter's room.

_____ 9. Try not to arrouse suspicion.

_____ 10. Do you eat at that cafe often?

_____ 11. Is your car a convertable?

_____ 12. Jennifer asked her secretary to duplacate the manuscript.

_____ 13. A college degree is esential to enter that field.

_____ 14. Her grandfather was an imigrent to this country.

_____ 15. Were you able to find enough investers to back your catering company?

_____ 16. His sister works at the libery.

_____ 17. Carlos often plays mischifous pranks.

_____ 18. The price of a haircut at that salon is outragis!

_____ 19. How much is your porcion of the inheritance?

_____ 20. Lt. Sanders will be transfered to a base in Oklahoma.

| Each correct answer is worth 1 point. | Total score: 20 points |

234

B. In each sentence, cross out the incorrect word in parentheses. Then write the correct word in the blank.

1. The boy received an (acolade, accolade) for saving his friend's life.

   _____

2. (Apparantly, apparently) the car swerved to miss the school bus.

   _____

3. Do you know the difference (between, bitween) their ages? _____

4. Clothes made of (coarce, coarse) materials are not usually comfortable.

   _____

5. Have you ever ridden in a (dirigible, derigable)? _____

6. His supervisor gave him a (faverable, favorable) report. _____

7. The child scribbled on the walls with an (indelible, indelable) marker.

   _____

8. Judge Domingues is known for being (just, jest). _____

9. What will my monthly (morgage, mortgage) payments be? _____

10. The Lees expect their children to be (obediant, obedient). _____

11. The attorney tried to (pursuade, persuade) the jury that the defendant was

    innocent. _____

12. Did the American Revolution (precede, preceed) the Russian Revolution?

    _____

13. Are you (quite, quiet) sure you don't want to come? _____

14. I (received, recieved) the package you sent me. _____

15. The doctor (refered, referred) Kristin to a specialist. _____

16. Sean will be a (sophamore, sophomore) this year. _____

17. Are you (using, useing) the toolbox? _____

18. Do you plan to vote (aginst, against) the proposition? _____

Each correct answer is worth 1 point.	Total score: 18 points

C. Each sentence contains one or more spelling errors. Cross out each misspelled word, then write the word correctly above it.

1. Although he is a celebrity, he is actally a humbel person.

2. This country waists a considerible amount of its wealth.

3. As an acolade for your community service, I would like to pressent you with this medal.

4. The kitten climbed the tree easily but was not able to dessend.

5. Is your grandfather loosing his memery altogetther?

6. The park is achally the site of an old battelfield.

7. Threw her kindness, Leticia perssaded the child to trust her.

8. The mayor managed the econamy well.

9. The convertable was stationery when it was struck from behind.

10. He was certan that he would never get over the greif of lossing his brother.

11. The cheif issue that devided Congress was the proposed package of spending cuts.

12. Calvin ecspected to begin work at once.

13. She couldn't deside which door was the main entrence to the building.

14. His behavior seams verry strange to me.

15. Let the games commense!

16. The movie was so frightening, I was completly paralized with fear.

17. He prophecied a plage for the people of that country.

18. Ninteen itims had been stolen from the store.

19. The man at the servise station carefully rinced my windshield.

20. Their parents had stickly forbidden them from rassling in the living room.

Each correct answer is worth 1 point.   Total score: 20 points

D. The following letter contains many spelling errors. Cross out each misspelled word. Then write the word correctly above the misspelled word.

Dear Kim:

The confrence of high school teachers began on Saterday, August twelvth and lasted a hole week. The first speaker was terible. Not a sylable of his speech was audable, and the anoyence of his audience was considerible.

My favorite speaker spoke about an instructer's ability to inspire students to delvip their abilities and exccell in all areas of life. The audience was unamimous in proclaiming her a briliant speaker.

The information I gained was generaly helpful, and will probibly improve my handleing of classroom situations. On the last day, the President of the American Counsel of High School Teachers sumarized the significent points. I can't wait for next year!

Sincerely yours,

Each correct answer is worth 1 point.	Total score: 20 points

E. In each group of words, cross out any misspelled words. Then write each word correctly in the blank. If there are no misspelled words, write a C in the blank.

1. battlefield	nickle	twelfth	_____
2. actually	item	vizualise	_____
3. certain	mischeivus	unanimous	_____
4. anoyence	decide	excel	_____
5. conference	eminent	indelable	_____
6. flexable	mutual	remittance	_____
7. summarize	present	porcion	_____
8. significent	council	brilliant	_____
9. management	penchent	just	_____
10. memory	quite	Saterday	_____

Each correct answer is worth 1 point.	Total score: 10 points

Pretest, P. 6

A: 1. accessible, 2. attendance,
3. because, 4. chocolate,
5. decorations, 6. disagree,
7. forgotten, 8. jealous, 9. C,
10. original, 11. perseverance,
12. practical, 13. quantity,
14. respectively, 15. separate,
16. temporary, 17. tuition, 18. Would,
19. straight, 20. impression

B: 1. advise, 2. authorize, 3. can't,
4. communication, 5. divisible,
6. embarrass, 7. eclairs, 8. faculty,
9. examination, 10. fundamental,
11. horrible, 12. misspelled,
13. lightning, 14. pamphlet, 15. policy,
16. pronounce, 17. recall, 18. recovery

C: The following words are misspelled
in the sentences.
1. whether, warrant; 2. coincide,
biennial; 3. confusion, policy; 4. official,
policy; 5. preparation, patience;
6. ignorant; 7. surprise, shrieked;
8. descendant; 9. devise, gymnasium;
10. Religious, privileges; 11. unusual,
rhythm; 12. Violence;
13. achievements, administration;
14. sugar; 15. chairperson,
standardize; 16. machinery;
17. Maybe, asphalt; 18. Preparations,
buffet; 19. fiery, toward; 20. existence

D: The underlined words are misspelled
in the letter.

Dear Sirs,

I've discovered that some of your
products contain larger <u>quantities</u> of a
hazardous chemical than is <u>allowable</u>.
As the <u>chairperson</u> of <u>Consumers</u> for
the Environment, I'm <u>especially</u>
concerned about the effect large
<u>amounts</u> of this chemical will have
on the environment.

Our <u>country's</u> citizens must use
their <u>influence</u> as <u>consumers</u> to stop
pollution before <u>irreparable</u> harm is
done. Many <u>customers</u> now use their
<u>knowledge</u> of environmental concerns
to choose products.

I am asking for your <u>cooperation</u> in
changing your products to eliminate
hazardous chemicals. I <u>appreciate</u>
<u>anything</u> you can do <u>toward</u> making
your products safer.
Sincerely <u>yours</u>,

E: 1. satchel, 2. bachelor, 3. veil,
4. scissors, 5. carrying, 6. enterprise,
7. height, 8. descendant,
9. drowned, 10. ledger

Lesson 1, P. 10

Exercise I: 1. for, 2. indecision,
3. paying, 4. work, 5. never, 6. to make
uneven, 7. to destroy

Exercise II: 1. account, 2. Just,
3. knew, 4. C, 5. decision, 6. owing,
7. C, 8. financial, 9. vacation,
10. Always

Lesson 2, P. 12

Exercise I: 1. Half, 2. coming, 3. busy,
4. Losing, 5. Saturday, 6. handful,
7. copy, 8. Having, 9. truly, 10. duly

Exercise II: 1. half, having; 2. busy,
copy; 3. losing, handful; 4. coming,
Saturday; 5. duly, bury; 6. truly, buy

Lesson 3, P. 14

Exercise I: The following words are
misspelled in the sentences. 1. It's,
too, there, written; 2. two, right;
3. their, therefore, to; 4. It's, itself;
5. There, write; 6. Two, its; 7. To,
there, right

Exercise II: 1. written, 2. two, 3. To,
4. there, 5. Too, 6. its, 7. itself

Lesson 4, P. 16

Exercise I: 1. flies, 2. until, 3. Either,
4. Whom, 5. style, 6. except, 7. stretch,
8. waist, 9. led, 10. Which, 11. Maybe,
12. whose

Exercise II: 1. waist, 2. want, 3. went,
4. when, 5. where, 6. which, 7. whom,
8. whose

☐ Lesson 5, P. 18

Exercise I: 1. benefited, 2. hoarse,
3. physician, 4. stomach, 5. immediately,
6. C, 7. hospital, 8. medicine

Exercise II: 1. medicine, benefited;
2. accolade; 3. physician, severe;
4. ache, hospital; 5. cough, immediately;
6. hoarse, stomach

☐ Lesson 6, P. 20

Exercise I: 1. break, 2. wait, 3. heard,
4. says, 5. weigh, 6. because, 7. least

Exercise II: 1. enemy, 2. most,
3. wonderful, 4. fine, 5. there,
6. hardly ever

☐ Review 1, Lessons 1–6, P. 22

A: The underlined words are
misspelled in the letter.

Dear Mr. Gray:

I am writing to you in an attempt
to correct the balance in my bank
account. There appears to be an
awful mistake. I am sending you a copy
of the financial statement that I
received last Saturday. It could not
be right because, except for one check
in the amount of $22.95, I have not
written any other checks this month.

I always make sure I at least know
the total amount I have each month,
no matter how busy I am. Maybe your
computer just made an error.

Please check to see if there is an
error, and let me know your decision.
I will be coming downtown next
Monday. Would it help for me to see
you in person?

Sincerely yours,

B: 1. bury, 2. buy, 3. C, 4. truly,
5. losing, 6. Immediately, 7. Weigh,
8. led

C: 1. It's, 2. vacation, 3. too, 4. their,
5. medicine, 6. here, 7. ache,
8. break, 9. coarse, 10. Which,
11. once, 12. physician

D: 1. severe, 2. therefore, 3. cough,
4. stomach, 5. usually, 6. C

☐ Lesson 7, P. 24

Exercise I: The following words are
misspelled in the sentences. 1. parallel;
2. theory; 3. Many, steel, laid;
4. believe, steal, nickel; 5. lose, straight;
6. where; 7. though; 8. parallel; 9. laid;
10. believe; 11. straight

Exercise II: 1. Where, nickel; 2. theory,
parallel; 3. steel, laid; 4. Though;
5. steal, lose; 6. Many, believe

☐ Lesson 8, P. 26

Exercise I: The following words are
misspelled in the sentences. 1. choose,
beautiful, clothes; 2. choose, clothes,
wear; 3. prefer, clothes, color, blue;
4. satisfied, material; 5. beauty;
6. occasionally; 7. women, clothes;
8. woman; 9. satisfied, clothes

Exercise II: 1. clothing, 2. beautiful,
3. women's, 4. chose, 5. preferring,
6. occasionally, 7. satisfied, 8. colored

☐ Lesson 9, P. 28

Exercise I: 1. scenery, autumn;
2. authority, been; 3. sincerity, useful;
4. special, benefit; 5. regard, series;
6. sight, quiet

Exercise II: 1. c, 2. h, 3. b, 4. d, 5. i,
6. g, 7. a, 8. e, 9. f

Lesson 10, P. 30

Exercise I: 1. partially, 2. unsure, 3. creditor, 4. depth, 5. both

Exercise II: 1. junior, 2. merchandise, 3. manufacture, 4. balloon, 5. nineteen, 6. catalog, 7. items, 8. absolutely, 9. neither

Lesson 11, P. 32

Exercise I: 1. entitled, 2. C, 3. affairs, 4. Separate, 5. anxious, 6. salary, 7. using, 8. C

Exercise II: The underlined words are misspelled in the letter.

Dear Representative Bell:

I recently read about your bill to increase the tax on <u>tobacco</u> products. I see two benefits of such legislation. First, it might help discourage young people from <u>using</u> tobacco. Second, it would help pay for services <u>through</u> raising revenue.

It is time we got <u>ready</u> to <u>separate</u> our knowledge about the dangers of smoking from our dislike of government regulation. The Surgeon General has <u>said</u> that smoking is one of the most serious health problems we face in this country. We should all be <u>anxious</u> to help correct the situation.

I feel the American people are <u>entitled</u> to breathe clean air wherever they go. This <u>affair</u> should be one of our top concerns. An <u>absence</u> of this priority among our representatives in Congress does not make them worthy of earning their <u>salary</u>.

Sincerely yours,

Lesson 12, P. 34

Exercise I: 1. is not, 2. do not, 3. could not, 4. would not, 5. does not, 6. cannot

Exercise II: 1. aren't, 2. could've, 3. mustn't, 4. you'd, 5. didn't, 6. should've, 7. let's, 8. weren't, 9. we'd,

10. you're, 11. there's, 12. won't, 13. couldn't, 14. wouldn't, 15. shouldn't, 16. don't

Exercise III: The following words are misspelled in the sentences. 1. doesn't, can't; 2. possessive; 3. sure, period; 4. Wouldn't, would've; 5. couldn't

Review 2, Lessons 7–12, P. 36

A: 1. Choose, 2. sincerity, 3. straight, 4. clothes, 5. steal, 6. sight, 7. balloon, 8. lose, 9. believe, 10. prefer

B: The underlined words are misspelled in the letter.

Dear Gloria,

Rob and I just returned from our trip <u>through</u> New England. We are <u>absolutely</u> certain that the <u>special</u> <u>beauty</u> of the <u>autumn</u> <u>scenery</u> is without <u>parallel</u>. <u>Occasionally</u> we would see a tree of such magnificent <u>height</u> and <u>color</u> that we were <u>certain</u> it <u>couldn't</u> be topped. I <u>can't</u> think of a more <u>quiet</u>, peaceful way to spend a vacation and hope you and Luis are able to go there next year. <u>Don't</u> miss it if you get the chance.

Sincerely,

C: 1. possessive, 2. etc., 3. C, 4. yours, 5. Doesn't, 6. Can't, 7. manufacture, 8. Isn't, 9. believe, 10. benefit, 11. though, 12. material

D: 1. neither, 2. affairs, 3. tobacco, 4. useful, 5. merchandise, 6. theory, 7. C, 8. salary

Lesson 13, P. 38

Exercise I: The underlined words are misspelled in the letter.

Dear Ms. Yancy:

I am writing to apply for a position in your organization. I just left a business where my job required me to act in a courteous, independent manner. The person serving in the capacity of president and chief executive officer of that service-oriented company, found my work to be very satisfactory.

I feel that having a commercial driver's license will also come in handy on this job. If it is your company's policy to grant interviews, I would like to schedule one as soon as possible.

Sincerely yours,

Exercise II: 1. satisfactory, 2. service, 3. courteous, 4. president, 5. capacity, 6. position, 7. commercial, 8. policy, 9. independent, 10. organization

☐ Lesson 14, P. 40

Exercise I: The underlined words are misspelled in the bulletin.

The official weather bulletin from the New Orleans National Weather Service forecasts the possibility of rain Tuesday. Temporary thunderstorms accompanied by lightning are possible for the evening. The weather conditions will be changeable early Wednesday. There is a possibility of the sun shining Wednesday about noon. For further information, please listen to the next weather announcement at four o'clock this afternoon.

Exercise II: 1. g, 2. b, 3. j, 4. c, 5. e, 6. k, 7. h, 8. a, 9. f, 10. i, 11. d, 12. l

☐ Lesson 15, P. 42

Exercise I: 1. advise, 2. traveler, 3. scene, 4. journey, 5. error, 6. length

Exercise II: 1. appreciate, 2. journey, 3. advise, 4. C, 5. circumstances, 6. scene, 7. description, 8. error, 9. length, 10. tired, 11. traveler, 12. proceed

☐ Lesson 16, P. 44

Exercise I: 1. early, 2. expect, 3. naturally, 4. especially, 5. automobile, 6. icicle, 7. rhyme, 8. minute, 9. rhythm, 10. disappear, 11. equipped, 12. hour

Exercise II: 1. C, 2. minute, 3. disappear, 4. equipped, 5. rhythm, 6. hour

☐ Lesson 17, P. 46

Exercise I: 1. origin, 2. occurred, 3. trust, 4. totally, 5. spirit, 6. admit, 7. link

Exercise II: 1. religious, 2. completely, 3. belief, 4. happened, 5. between, 6. source, 7. receipt, 8. shipment, 9. forgotten, 10. soul, 11. Acknowledge, 12. connection

☐ Lesson 18, P. 48

Exercise I: The underlined words are misspelled in the letter.

Dear Mrs. Morrison:

I read your interesting article in this month's *Library Magazine.* I find library science very interesting, and wondered if you could give me some information on how I could become a part-time librarian. I am a sophomore in college, taking courses in literature and in psychology. Our librarian referred me to several pamphlets from the Library Service and to one or two volumes concerning careers in our library. I would like to know even more about various opportunities open to me in this field and to know if you offer part-time jobs at your library.

Thank you in advance for any assistance.

Sincerely yours,

Exercise II: 1. b, 2. e, 3. f, 4. c, 5. d, 6. a

Review 3, Lessons 13–18, P. 50

A: The underlined words are misspelled in the letter.

Dear Mayor Hiller:

I am writing to you in your <u>capacity</u> as head of our city government to ask you not to cut back on a valuable city <u>service</u>. I am referring to your recent <u>announcement</u> of changes in the <u>hours</u> of operation of our city <u>library</u> system. I hope that this new policy of closing the library two hours <u>early</u> on <u>Tuesday</u> and <u>Wednesday</u> will be <u>temporary</u>.

I <u>estimate</u> that I use the <u>library</u> once a week for <u>business</u> reasons. I find the <u>changeable</u> hours confusing and not at all <u>satisfactory</u>.

No other <u>organization</u> in the city is such a complete <u>source</u> of <u>literature</u>, <u>articles</u>, <u>pamphlets</u>, and <u>magazines</u>. Research has shown that there is a <u>connection</u> between the standard of living in a city and the library services it offers. I would <u>appreciate</u> you checking into what I feel is a <u>policy</u> <u>error</u>. I feel that you and the city council have <u>completely</u> <u>forgotten</u> the average citizen by taking the <u>position</u> that you have. If there is any <u>possibility</u> of changing this policy, I would <u>appreciate</u> your doing so.

Yours truly,

B: 1. shining, 2. referred, 3. official, 4. description, 5. disappear, 6. equipped

C: 1. minute, 2. librarian, 3. length, 4. C, 5. proceed, 6. psychology

D: 1. president, 2. independent, 3. weather, 4. courteous, 5. bulletin, 6. bureau, 7. executive, 8. interesting, 9. C, 10. commercial, 11. automobile, 12. C

Lesson 19, P. 52

Exercise I: 1. freight, 2. engineer, 3. toward, 4. passenger, 5. view, 6. occurred

Exercise II: 1. precede, 2. plain, 3. tragedy, 4. imagine, 5. C, 6. toward, 7. engineer, 8. freight

Lesson 20, P. 54

Exercise I: 1. additional, 2. earnest, 3. information, 4. envelope, 5. writing, 6. mentioned, 7. discussion, 8. enclose, 9. speech, 10. invitation, 11. recall, 12. address

Exercise II: 1. C, 2. C, 3. discussion, 4. envelope, 5. Enclose, 6. earnest, 7. additional, 8. mentioned, 9. Writing, 10. discussion, 11. invitation, 12. mentioned

Lesson 21, P. 56

Exercise I: 1. loose, 2. impossible, 3. generally, 4. Could, 5. hear, 6. response, 7. inquiry

Exercise II: 1. inquiry, 2. satisfactorily, 3. trouble, 4. aerial, 5. noticeable, 6. receiving

Lesson 22, P. 58

Exercise I: 1. fiery, 2. field, 3. built, 4. necessity, 5. ascend, 6. waste, 7. fertile, 8. often, 9. column, 10. realize

Exercise II: The following words are misspelled in the sentences. 1. fertile, built, field; 2. field, yield; 3. often, waste, necessity; 4. waste, forest; 5. realize, column; 6. built, forest

☐ Lesson 23, P. 60

Exercise I: 1. studying, 2. professor, 3. sophomore, 4. knowledge, 5. months, 6. college, 7. university, 8. examination, 9. thorough, 10. laboratory

Exercise II: The underlined words are misspelled in the letter.

Dear Marcia,

It seems that I have been in <u>college</u> for years, but actually it has been only a few <u>months</u>. I looked at the <u>calendar</u> today and realized that it is almost time to begin <u>studying</u> for final <u>examinations</u>.

I have really enjoyed living in the <u>dormitory</u> this year, and I am looking forward to my <u>sophomore</u> year. I have really gotten a <u>thorough</u> grounding in English fundamentals, and my French <u>professor</u> says I might be able to take an advanced reading <u>knowledge</u> <u>examination</u> next year. I will also be taking my first biology <u>laboratory</u> course next year.

Sincerely,

☐ Lesson 24, P. 62

Exercise I: 1. since, 2. popular, 3. accept, 4. explanation, 5. Does, 6. very, 7. commission, 8. situation, 9. deceive

Exercise II: 1. conceive, 2. recipient, 3. deceive, 4. receive, 5. either, 6. weird

☐ Review 4, Lessons 19–24, P. 64

A: 1. view, 2. field, 3. receiving, 4. deceive, 5. freight, 6. receive, 7. yield, 8. fiery, 9. conceive, 10. weird

B: The underlined words are misspelled in the letter.

Dear Sir:

I am <u>writing</u> to you since I <u>recall</u> a <u>speech</u> you made on TV that seemed <u>very</u> <u>earnest</u> to me. You said if any of your customers ever had <u>trouble</u> with one of your store's <u>popular</u> brands of dishwashers to let you <u>hear</u> about the <u>situation</u> that has <u>occurred</u>.

I often have <u>trouble</u> with the new dishwasher I recently purchased at your store. I <u>realize</u> that it is almost impossible to <u>imagine</u> that an <u>engineer</u> <u>built</u> a faulty dishwasher in the <u>laboratory</u> of your factory. However, I would appreciate your making an <u>inquiry</u> into the matter so that you can send me <u>thorough</u> <u>information</u> on my <u>loose</u> wires.

I'm sure that the majority of your products are <u>satisfactory</u>, and that you will be anxious to remedy my situation. I realize that no company can achieve perfection all the time. I look forward to your <u>response</u>.

Sincerely,

C: 1. professor, 2. calendar, 3. thorough, 4. dormitory, 5. invitation, 6. necessity, 7. university, 8. tragedy, 9. commission, 10. C

D: 1. sophomore, 2. mentioned, 3. ascend, 4. realize, 5. explanation, 6. C, 7. examination, 8. precede, 9. address

☐ Lesson 25, P. 66

Exercise I: The following words are misspelled in the sentences. 1. sheriff, road; 2. stopped, safety; 3. warrant, cancel; 4. ninety, pursuit; 5. meant, brief; 6. thought, certificate; 7. sheriff, thought; 8. meant

Exercise II: 1. cancel, 2. brief, 3. thought, 4. sheriff, 5. certificate, 6. warrant, 7. road, 8. ninety, 9. pursuit, 10. safety

Lesson 26, P. 68

Exercise I: The underlined words are misspelled in the letter.

Dear Mr. Russo:

We were delighted to receive your recent letter requesting our brochure listing the <u>courses</u> we teach relating to the field of <u>advertising</u>. We are pleased that you <u>chose</u> our school, and our brochure is enclosed.

The <u>latter</u> part of the brochure lists the <u>advertising</u> <u>courses</u> currently being <u>taught</u>. The <u>tuition</u> for each <u>course</u> is also listed. In the <u>past</u> we have also offered <u>courses</u> in the various graphic <u>mediums</u>, and we hope to be able to make them <u>available</u> again in the near <u>future</u>.

We would be delighted to accept your application for registration for the fall semester. Your summer work as a <u>cashier</u> and as a writer on the *Evening Journal* should prove valuable experience for you.

   Sincerely yours,

Exercise II: 1. cashier, 2. medium, 3. journal, 4. chose, 5. taught, 6. latter, 7. tuition, 8. course

Lesson 27, P. 70

Exercise I: 1. much, 2. analyze, 3. essential, 4. know, 5. scheme, 6. assume

Exercise II: 1. analyze, 2. doubtful, 3. certainly, 4. proposition, 5. C, 6. portion, 7. certainly, 8. evident, 9. essential

Lesson 28, P. 72

Exercise I: 1. occasion, 2. economy, 3. Refer, 4. probably, 5. accurate, 6. secretary, 7. solemn, 8. statement

Exercise II: 1. secretary, 2. society, 3. C, 4. C, 5. administration, 6. occasion, 7. accurate

Lesson 29, P. 74

Exercise I: 1. request, 2. wish well, 3. changes, 4. convince, 5. feasible, 6. guiltless, 7. leader, 8. lawyer, 9. very, 10. appears, 11. hold, 12. wishing

Exercise II: The following words are misspelled in the sentences. 1. quite, possible, accommodate; 2. hoping, possible, congratulate; 3. attorney, innocent; 4. accommodate; 5. governor, quite; 6. persuade, innocent; 7. seems; 8. persuade

Lesson 30, P. 76

Exercise I: 1. partner, terms; 2. approval, extension; 3. amount, mortgage; 4. customer, application; 5. concession, remit; 6. quote, security

Exercise II: The underlined words are misspelled in the letter.

Dear Mr. Haynes:

We have received your letter requesting an <u>extension</u> on the <u>terms</u> of your <u>mortgage</u> loan. Our senior <u>partner</u>, Roberta Johnson, submitted your <u>application</u> to our board of directors for their approval.

We are happy to inform you that, since you are a reliable <u>customer</u> of our bank, the board has approved the <u>extension</u> of your <u>mortgage</u> loan. This <u>concession</u> is made in view of your excellent credit rating. Additional <u>security</u> will not be required, and you may <u>remit</u> your payment each month as <u>quoted</u> in your payment book. The total <u>amount</u> of your loan will not change; however, interest charges will be added.

We are happy to have served you and look forward to serving you again in the future.

   Sincerely,

Review 5, Lessons 25–30, P. 78

A: 1. safety, 2. statement, 3. C,
4. governor, 5. proposition,
6. certainly, 7. approval, 8. statement

B: 1. past, 2. road, 3. taught,
4. course, 5. warrant, 6. whole,
7. seems, 8. medium

C: The underlined words are misspelled in the letter.

Dear Sirs:

I am writing to <u>appeal</u> the traffic ticket I received on June 21. When the person from the <u>sheriff's</u> office <u>stopped</u> me on the <u>road</u> after a very <u>brief</u> <u>pursuit</u>, he said I was doing <u>ninety</u> miles an hour in a sixty-five mile-an-hour zone. I <u>assume</u> that it is <u>quite</u> <u>possible</u>, but I think it was <u>certainly</u> <u>doubtful</u> that <u>ninety</u> was my <u>accurate</u> speed. I <u>know</u> I was going <u>much</u> slower—<u>probably</u> more like seventy.

In the <u>past</u>, I have taken a defensive driving <u>course</u> and <u>know</u> the <u>amount</u> of trouble a person who does not obey the traffic laws can get into. I also <u>know</u> traffic laws are an important part of our <u>society</u>.

I am <u>hoping</u> that this statement of my <u>solemn</u> promise to drive more slowly in the <u>future</u> will persuade you to <u>analyze</u> the situation and make a <u>concession</u> this time. While I am not entirely <u>innocent</u> of the speeding charge, I do not believe I was driving as fast as the officer said I was.

Thank you for considering my <u>appeal</u>.

Sincerely,

D: 1. mortgage, 2. meant, 3. C,
4. evident, 5. tomorrow

Lesson 31, P. 80

Exercise I: The following words are misspelled in the sentences.
1. concerning, 2. procedure, 3. wholly,
4. preferred, 5. equipment, 6. instructor

Exercise II: 1. faculty, 2. recommend, 3. C, 4. genius, 5. equipment, 6. preferred, 7. C, 8. genius, 9. gymnasium, 10. committee, 11. brilliant, 12. instructor

Lesson 32, P. 82

Exercise I: 1. suggest, 2. purpose,
3. Pronounce, 4. descend, 5. attacked,
6. desert, 7. practical, 8. courtesy

Exercise II: 1. prior, 2. syllable,
3. desert, 4. practical, 5. C, 6. descend

Lesson 33, P. 84

Exercise I: 1. forty, 2. association,
3. civilization, 4. league, 5. privilege,
6. C

Exercise II: 1. civilization, 2. privilege,
3. quantity, 4. vinegar, 5. Christian,
6. jealous, 7. league, 8. association,
9. ought, 10. alcohol

Lesson 34, P. 86

Exercise I: 1. practical, 2. amateurs,
3. strengthen, 4. bicycling, 5. please,
6. perspiring, 7. exercising,
8. physically, 9. exhaust, 10. athletic

Exercise II: 1. athletics, 2. exercise,
3. athlete, 4. perspiration,
5. tournament, 6. strength

Lesson 35, P. 88

Exercise I: 1. assurance, promise;
2. acquaintance, friend; 3. acceptance, approval; 4. accordance, agreement;
5. appearance, looks; 6. assistance, help; 7. remembrance, recollection;
8. resistance, opposition; 9. remittance, payment; 10. maintenance, upkeep;
11. insurance, guarantee; 12. nuisance, pest

Exercise II: 1. resist, 2. remit,
3. insure, 4. accept, 5. X, 6. accord,
7. remember, 8. acquaint, 9. appear,
10. assure, 11. maintain, 12. assist

Lesson 36, P. 90

Exercise I: 1. council, 2. principal,
3. complement, 4. peace, 5. piece,
6. principle, 7. compliment, 8. counsel

Exercise II: 1. compliment,
2. prophesy, 3. counsel, 4. fourth,
5. complement, 6. prophecy, 7. forth,
8. council

Review 6, Lessons 31–36, P. 92

A: The underlined words are
misspelled in the letter.

Dear Gary,

I am practically exhausted! I have
just returned from a forty-mile bicycle
ride that took all the physical strength
I had. I realize that getting into shape
requires hard work and perspiration.
Still I had hoped that the exercise I
would get from athletics would be a
pleasure. Instead I am finding it to be
a nuisance. I guess I am not a very
good amateur athlete.

My brilliant fitness instructor is a
genius at motivating people, but even
he can't keep me from wanting to give
up sometimes. I'm afraid I much
preferred using the equipment in the
gymnasium at school even though the
faculty there was wholly inferior to my
current instructor. That I continue in
this physical maintenance program is a
compliment to him, I assure you. I
only hope my instructor is not going
to suggest that I enter a tennis
tournament!

I will close for now with a warm
remembrance to you and your family.

Sincerely,

B: 1. procedure, 2. resistance, 3. C,
4. remittance

C: The following words are misspelled in
the sentences. 1. council, principle;
2. acceptance, appearance;
3. insurance, assurance;
4. accordance, committee,
recommends; 5. prophecy,
concerning, marriage; 6. quantity,
alcohol; 7. privilege, acquaintance;
8. Christian, peace; 9. desert,
civilization; 10. fourth, bicycle;
11. principal, assistance;
12. syllable, piece; 13. association,
league; 14. forth; 15. prophesy,
tournament; 16. counsel,
concerning; 17. Descend

Lesson 37, P. 94

Exercise I: 1. invoice, 2. sugar,
3. tariff, 4. passed, 5. supplies,
6. opportunity, 7. potatoes, 8. fulfill,
9. Restaurant, 10. enough

Exercise II: The underlined words are
misspelled in the memo.

Carlos:

The ABC Company's deliveries to our
restaurant have become altogether
unsatisfactory. The situation has passed
the point where we can ignore it. Last
week the invoice on the potatoes and
sugar they delivered included a tariff that
I don't understand.

Please take this opportunity to call them
and tell them enough is enough. If they
don't start to fulfill their promises to
deliver our supplies, tell them it will be
our unanimous decision to cancel service
with their company.

Sincerely,

Lesson 38, P. 96

Exercise I: 1. folks, 2. acknowledgment,
3. terrible, 4. extremely, 5. cemetery,
6. awkward, 7. grateful, 8. grieve,
9. sympathy, 10. later

Exercise II: 1. grateful, 2. sympathy, 3. later, 4. terrible, 5. awkward, 6. extremely, 7. further, 8. forehead

Lesson 39, P. 98

Exercise I: 1. assistance, 2. assistant, 3. attendance, 4. attendant, 5. conscience, 6. conscious, 7. defense, 8. defensive, 9. expense, 10. experience, 11. ignorance, 12. ignorant, 13. inconvenience, 14. inconvenient, 15. nonsense, 16. patience, 17. patient, 18. pleasant, 19. sense, 20. senseless

Exercise II: 1. experience, 2. patience, 3. conscience, 4. pleasant, 5. assistant, 6. inconvenience, 7. ignorant, 8. C, 9. sense, 10. attendant

Lesson 40, P. 100

Exercise I: 1. e, 2. j, 3. h, 4. a, 5. i, 6. b, 7. f, 8. d, 9. g, 10. c

Exercise II: 1. communication, 2. evidence, 3. grammar, 4. judgment, 5. misspell, 6. would

Lesson 41, P. 102

Exercise I: 1. route, 2. Numerous, 3. mutual, 4. community, 5. village, 6. surprise

Exercise II: The underlined words are misspelled in the letter.

Dear Ms. Hernandez:

I'm writing to you in your capacity as transportation director for this community. For numerous years, we've needed a bus route in my area. My neighbors and I are regretting moving to this part of the city.

The original advice not to extend the bus route to our neighborhood was based on an already outdated idea that we could count on the mutual support of our neighbors who all had similar working hours. This is not true. I hope you will expand bus service into our neighborhood before the end of the summer.

Sincerely,

Lesson 42, P. 104

Exercise I: 1. holiday, 2. banquet, 3. barrel, 4. comparatively, 5. shoes, 6. annual, 7. shipped, 8. forward, 9. preliminary, 10. eighth, 11. twelfth, 12. preparation

Exercise II: 1. annual, 2. preparation, 3. comparatively, 4. C, 5. eighth, 6. holiday

Review 7, Lessons 37–42, P. 106

A: 1. supplies, 2. chief, 3. conscience, 4. inconvenience, 5. eighth, 6. experience, 7. grieve, 8. patience

B: 1. restaurant, 2. cemetery, 3. forehead, 4. supplies, 5. unanimous, 6. endeavor, 7. annual, 8. C, 9. communication, 10 comparatively, 11. twelfth, 12. language, 13. fulfill, 14. chief

C: 1. numerous, 2. fulfill, 3. forward, 4. preliminary, 5. barrel, 6. sense, 7. defense, 8. grammar, 9. enough, 10. sympathy, 11. describe, 12. misspell, 13. surprise, 14. similar, 15. mutual, 16. expense, 17. grateful, 18. endeavor, 19. opinion, 20. already

Lesson 43, P. 108

Exercise I: The following words are misspelled in the sentences. 1. succeed; 2. earliest; 3. prompt; 4. cooperation, exception; 5. cordial, holiday; 6. practice, conscientious; 7. suppose; 8. attitude; 9. all right, humorous; 10. prompt; 11. all right; 12. cordial; 13. conscientious; 14. earliest; 15. suppose, humorous

Exercise II: 1. early, est; 2. cooperate, tion; 3. humor, ous; 4. except, tion; 5. conscience, tious

Lesson 44, P. 110

Exercise I: 1. necessity, 2. disciplined, 3. transfer, 4. enemy, 5. conquering, 6. campaigned, 7. necessarily, 8. countries

Exercise II: 1. campaign, 2. conquer, 3. necessary, 4. enemies, 5. transferred, 6. C, 7. Arctic, 8. soldier, 9. lieutenant

Lesson 45, P. 112

Exercise I: 1. influence, 2. occurrence, 3. correspondence, 4. preference, 5. existence, 6. C, 7. conference, 8. consequence, 9. confidence, 10. reference, 11. residence

Exercise II: 1. preference, 2. assurance, 3. sentence, 4. remembrance, 5. confidence, 6. reference, 7. presence, 8. resistance, 9. existence, 10. conscience, 11. insurance, 12. experience, 13. nuisance, 14. occurrence, 15. acquaintance, 16. remittance, 17. residence, 18. influence

Lesson 46, P. 114

Exercise I: 1. agreeable, 2. aggravate, 3. doctor, 4. considerably, 5. rheumatism, 6. every, 7. relieve, 8. leisure

Exercise II: 1. sacrifice, 2. doctor, 3. considerably, 4. C, 5. rheumatism, 6. repetition, 7. formerly, 8. every, 9. minimum, 10. leisure

Lesson 47, P. 116

Exercise I: 1. breakfast, 2. valuable, 3. ascertain, 4. easily, 5. convenient, 6. guess, 7. stationery, 8. dining

Exercise II: The underlined words are misspelled in the letter.

Dear Heather,

You'll never <u>guess</u> where I wound up on vacation! I got on a <u>convenient</u> <u>plane</u> to Hawaii, and here I am. I am <u>positive</u> that I could <u>easily</u> live here for the rest of my life! Each moment is so <u>precious</u> and <u>valuable</u>! Each morning, I go to the hotel <u>dining</u> room for a great <u>breakfast</u> of some type of melon that I've <u>never had</u> before. It is easy to <u>pierce</u> with a knife and is very sweet and <u>juicy</u>. Then I go sun myself on the beach, or swim in the ocean.

I have written so many letters that I ran out of <u>stationery</u>, but I thought you'd like the picture on this postcard. I'll see you soon.

Sincerely yours,

Lesson 48, P. 118

Exercise I: 1. machine, 2. guaranteed, 3. deliver, 4. carry, 5. scheduling, 6. controlled, 7. foreigner, 8. plan

Exercise II: The following words are misspelled in the sentences.
1. government, people; 2. schedule, delivery; 3. advisable, immigration; 4. guarantee, delivery, machinery; 5. planned, control; 6. foreign; 7. people, carrying; 8. advisable; 9. guarantee, schedule

Review 8, Lessons 43–48, P. 120

A: The underlined words are misspelled in the letter.

Dear Sirs:

I find it <u>necessary</u> to initiate this <u>correspondence</u> in <u>reference</u> to the <u>attitude</u> of Joe Parker, one of your employees, who was rude while making his most recent <u>delivery</u>. He was also not on <u>schedule</u>.

Up to now, I have counted on the <u>cooperation</u> of all of your <u>people</u>. They have been <u>conscientious</u>, <u>prompt</u>, <u>cordial</u>, <u>positive</u>, and <u>agreeable</u>. This is <u>considerably</u> different from Joe's <u>attitude</u> last Monday.

I <u>guess</u> everyone makes mistakes. I also think it is <u>advisable</u> to call this <u>exception</u> to the usual <u>practice</u> of your employees to your attention. That way you can <u>maintain</u> <u>control</u> so there won't be a <u>repetition</u> of this problem. I have <u>every</u> <u>confidence</u> that you will be able to <u>influence</u> Joe's behavior <u>easily</u> and <u>guarantee</u> me the <u>excellent</u> service that I had <u>formerly</u> come to expect.

Sincerely,

B: 1. C, 2. arctic, 3. campaign, 4. lieutenant, 5. conference

C: 1. foreign, 2. consequence, 3. humorous, 4. residence, 5. pierce, 6. ascertain, 7. aggravate, 8. leisure, 9. conscientious, 10. relieve, 11. rheumatism, 12. machinery, 13. transferred, 14. colonel, 15. convenient, 16. precious, 17. occurrence, 18. positive

Lesson 49, P. 122

Exercise I: 1. competent, 2. confident, 3. prominent, 4. intelligent, 5. superintendent, 6. C, 7. excellent, 8. recent, 9. magnificent

Exercise II: 1. judgment, 2. accident, 3. ignorant, 4. excellent, 5. government, 6. competent, 7. assistant, 8. magnificent, 9. president, 10. confident

Lesson 50, P. 124

Exercise I: 1. tries, 2. capital, 3. difficult, 4. continually, 5. license, 6. partial, 7. paragraph, 8. exceed, 9. sufficient, 10. success

Exercise II: The following words are misspelled in the sentences. 1. partial, success; 2. exceed, license; 3. beginning, paragraph, capital; 4. difficult, tries; 5. continually, success; 6. achievement; 7. sufficient; 8. exceed; 9. success, achievement

Lesson 51, P. 126

Exercise I: 1. across, 2. variety, 3. Spirits, 4. February, 5. effect, 6. site

Exercise II: 1. disappoint, 2. accidentally, 3. brought, 4. beautiful, 5. particular, 6. raise

Lesson 52, P. 128

Exercise I: 1. picture, 2. familiar, 3. interest, 4. ghost, 5. genuine, 6. ancient, 7. seize, 8. great

Exercise II: 1. duplicate, 2. seize, 3. great, 4. determine, 5. whether, 6. although, 7. picture, 8. familiar, 9. genuine, 10. C

Lesson 53, P. 130

Exercise I: 1. taking care of, 2. caretaker, 3. vocation, 4. one who lives nearby, 5. recognition, 6. to influence, 7. presentation

Exercise II: 1. perform, 2. criticize, 3. die, 4. grieve, 5. dispose, 6. responsibility, 7. effect

Lesson 54, P. 132

Exercise: 1. mountain, 2. compelled, 3. getting, 4. kerosene, 5. mileage, 6. climb, 7. carriage, 8. scarcely, 9. carburetor, 10. chauffeur, 11. gasoline, 12. finally

Review 9, Lessons 49–54, P. 134

A: 1. capital, 2. site, 3. accidentally, 4. February, 5. effect, 6. raise, 7. great, 8. whether, 9. seize, 10. affect, 11. dying, 12. finally

B: 1. tries, 2. achievement, 3. sufficient, 4. seize, 5. neighbor, 6. variety, 7. ancient, 8. grievous

C: The underlined words are misspelled in the letter.

Dear Mr. Lyle:

I feel <u>compelled</u> to write you after my <u>recent</u> experience. I hired one of your limousines to take me to my hotel. I am <u>confident</u> that we avoided an <u>accident</u> because of the <u>excellent</u> driving <u>performance</u> of the <u>chauffeur</u>, Mr. Ed Smith.

We were driving <u>across</u> town when a car <u>tried</u> to cut our limousine off. It was a <u>difficult</u> <u>achievement</u> to avoid an accident. Mr. Smith had <u>success</u> in doing so because he was <u>competent</u> and <u>responsible</u> in <u>handling</u> the problem.

Because the other driver tried to <u>exceed</u> the speed limit and, in <u>particular</u>, because he tried to cut in front of us, he should lose his driver's <u>license</u>.

Usually, letters bring <u>criticism</u> and not <u>appreciation</u>. I want to express my <u>genuine</u> appreciation to the <u>management</u> of your company and to Mr. Smith for being a <u>guardian</u> of my safety. Mr. Smith certainly sets a <u>magnificent</u> example for his <u>profession</u>.

D: 1. superintendent, 2. disappoint, 3. familiar, 4. C, 5. disposition, 6. carburetor, 7. gasoline

Lesson 55, P. 136

Exercise I: 1. decide, 2. possession, 3. allowance, 4. arrangement, 5. C, 6. principally, 7. niece, 8. Mysterious, 9. character, 10. C

Exercise II: The underlined words are misspelled in the letter.

Dear Latonia,

I am having a great time here in Buffalo. I am <u>principally</u> just relaxing. Last night I couldn't <u>decide</u> what I wanted to do, so my little eight-year-old <u>niece</u> spent her <u>allowance</u> and took me downtown to the <u>American</u> Theater to see a melodrama.

The <u>arrangement</u> of the seats was wonderful, and I could see everything. I especially enjoyed watching the <u>character</u> of the <u>mysterious</u> villain. He was able to <u>establish</u> such dislike among the audience that the <u>majority</u> of us who were in the <u>possession</u> of popcorn used it to toss at him! It was a fun evening.

Sincerely,

☐ Lesson 56, P. 138

Exercise I: 1. criticize, reproach; 2. volunteer, offer; 3. different, unusual; 4. argument, debate; 5. allowed, permitted; 6. basis, foundation; 7. prejudice, intolerance; 8. captain, leader; 9. apartment, place to live; 10. definite, distinct; 11. personal, private; 12. convenience, ease

Exercise II: The following words are misspelled in the sentences. 1. captain, allowed, personal; 2. volunteer, basis; 3. apartment, convenience; 4. argument, criticize, prejudice; 5. different, definite; 6. captain, volunteered; 7. convenience

☐ Lesson 57, P. 140

Exercise I: The following words are misspelled in the sentences.
1. argument, fundamental; 2. volunteer, disease; 3. stating, basis; 4. opposite, criticize; 5. divided, personal; 6. captain, extraordinary; 7. recognize, apartment; 8. allowed, merely; 9. definite, pressure

Exercise II: The underlined words are misspelled in the letter.

Dear Silvia,
This letter of commendation is to recognize your <u>extraordinary</u> community service work over the past five years. When you began, you <u>stated</u> that combatting a dread <u>disease</u> among neighbors in your immediate <u>vicinity</u> was your <u>fundamental</u> goal, and you really have made a big <u>difference</u>.
Before your effort, the community's awareness of the <u>disease</u> was <u>merely</u> superficial. Now it is just the <u>opposite</u>. There is <u>pressure</u> to take a more <u>sensible</u> approach and not be so <u>divided</u> on the issue of the disease's cause.
Congratulations on your caring attitude, hard work, and dedication!
Sincerely,

☐ Lesson 58, P. 142

Exercise I: 1. attended, 2. sincere, 3. respect, 4. affection, 5. real, 6. character

Exercise II: 1. comparison, 2. relative, 3. competition, 4. representative, 5. C, 6. individual, 7. characteristic

☐ Lesson 59, P. 144

Exercise I: 1. Treasurer, 2. vacuum, 3. purchase, 4. propeller, 5. shepherd, 6. forfeit, 7. piano, 8. guest, 9. embarrass

Exercise II: 1. apparently, 2. C, 3. orchestra, 4. superstitious, 5. piano

☐ Lesson 60, P. 146

Exercise I: 1. substitute, 2. C, 3. current, 4. siege, 5. stationary, 6. concrete, 7. desirable, 8. destroy, 9. instead, 10. apparatus, 11. building, 12. irresistible, 13. current, 14. destroy, 15. siege, 16. concrete, 17. substitute, 18. desirable, 19. anything, 20. auxiliary

☐ Review 10, Lessons 55–60, P. 148

A: 1. divided, 2. apparently, 3. merely, 4. possession, 5. sensible, 6. irresistible, 7. convenience, 8. principally, 9. propeller, 10. majority

B: The underlined words are misspelled in the note.

Dear Jeff,
I <u>sincerely</u> appreciate the <u>really</u> <u>extraordinary</u> tie you sent me for my birthday. I <u>recognize</u> your <u>personal</u> <u>attention</u> in selecting it. I have never seen <u>anything</u> so <u>irresistible</u>. It is perfect for the <u>current</u> style. The thoughtfulness you showed is so

characteristic of you. The tie is so different and individual that it has already become a favorite possession of mine. I will wear it for my piano solo in the orchestra next month.

Affectionately,

C: The following words are misspelled in the sentences. 1. character, villain; 2. orchestra, decided, purchase, piano; 3. seige; 4. volunteer, basis; 5. criticize, captain; 6. Stating, respectfully; 7. niece, allowed, allowance; 8. apartment, opposite, vicinity; 9. substitute, current, treasurer; 10. pressure, mysterious, disease; 11. definite, prejudice, American; 12. argument, arrangement; 13. desirable, establish; 14. decide, competition; 15. fundamental, difference, vacuum; 16. apparatus, stationary; 17. auxiliary, Representative; 18. destroy, concrete; 19. guest, instead, relative; 20. comparison, embarrass; 21. conscious, superstitious; 22. shepherd, forfeit

☐ Lesson 61, P. 152

Exercise: Definitions will vary. Suggested:

1. noun, One of many successive payments to settle a debt
2. noun, Incomplete or inadequate adaptation
3. adjective, Of or about the temperature scale that registers the freezing point of water at 32°F and the boiling point as 212°F under the standard atmospheric pressure
4. noun, The group of people employed by an organization, business, or service
5. noun, A school of economic thought that opposes government regulation
6. noun, One that copies, esp. a machine for copying printed matter
7. adjective, Of or used in a sound reproduction system that uses two or more separate channels

8. adjective, Moving away from the center or axis
9. verb, To think carefully about
10. adjective, Intersecting so as to form a right angle
11. verb, To move in a smooth motion like a wave
12. noun, Containing mercury
13. noun, An accomplished deed or fact which cannot be undone
14. adjective, Relating to atheism or atheists
15. adverb, Containing errors in reasoning and logic
16. noun, The act of indicting or state of being indicted
17. noun, The state of being perpetual
18. adjective, Of the same kind or type
19. noun, The act of committing or having committed
20. noun, Sleight of hand
21. noun, Medical treatment using chemical agents
22. noun, A small piece of fabric

☐ Lesson 62, P. 154

Exercise I: 1. illustrate, il-lus-trate, ĭl′ ə strāt′, 2. horticulture, hor-ti-cul-ture, hôr′ tĭ kŭl′ chər, 3. lingerie, lin-ge-rie, län′ zhə rā′, 4. metabolism, me-tab-o-lism, mə tăb′ ə lĭz′ əm, 5. combustion, com-bus-tion, kəm bŭs′ chən, 6. transaction, trans-ac-tion, trăn săk′ shən, 7. qualification, qual-i-fi-ca-tion, kwŏl′ ə fĭ kā′ shən, 8. illiteracy, il-lit-er-a-cy, ĭ lĭt′ ər ə sē, 9. exotic, ex-ot-ic, ĭg zŏt′ ĭk, 10. upholstery, up-hol-ster-y, ŭp hōl′ stə rē, 11. pedagogy, ped-a-go-gy, pĕd′ ə gō′ jē, 12. retractable, re-tract-a-ble, rĭ trăkt′ ə bəl, 13. calculator, cal-cu-la-tor, kăl′ kyə lā′ tər, 14. fuselage, fu-se-lage, fyōō′ sə läzh′, 15. archipelago, ar-chi-pel-a-go, är′ kə pĕl′ ə gō′, 16. judicial, ju-di-cial, jōō dĭsh′ əl, 17. penicillin, pen-i-cil-lin, pĕn′ ĭ sĭl′ ĭn,

Exercise II: 1. wrench, 2. penicillin, 3. illiteracy, 4. qualification, 5. exotic

Lesson 63, P. 156

Exercise I: Definitions will vary. Suggested: 1. elicit—To bring or call out, illicit—Forbidden by custom or law, 2. envelop—To cover entirely, envelope—Something that covers entirely, 3. expansive—Having a tendency to expand, expensive—Costing a great deal of money, 4. extant—Existing, extent—The quantity of space or time over which a thing extends, 5. formally—Relating to form, formerly—In a former time

Exercise II: 1. eminent, 2. imminent, 3. eligible, 4. illegible, 5. morale, 6. moral

Lesson 64, P. 158

Exercise I: Definitions will vary. Suggested: 1. appraise—To determine the worth of, apprise—To tell or inform, 2. immigrate—To travel to and make one's home in a country other than the one in which one is born, emigrate—To leave a country and go to live elsewhere, 3. liable—Having a legal obligation, libel—A published defamatory statement, 4. persecute—To persistently and purposefully mistreat, prosecute—To pursue or bring criminal action against, 5. perspective—A technique used to represent three-dimensional objects on a two-dimensional surface, prospective—Likely to happen

Exercise II: Answers will vary.

Lesson 65, P. 160

Exercise: 1. actually, ac-tu-al-ly, ăk′ choo əl ē, 2. bachelor, bach-e-lor, băch′ ə lər, 3. chocolate, choc-o-late, chô′ kə lĭt, 4. diamond, di-a-mond, dī′ ə mənd, 5. history, his-to-ry, hĭs′ tə rē, 6. hungry, hun-gry, hŭng′ grē, 7. interrupt, in-ter-rupt, ĭn′ tə rŭpt′, 8. omelet, om-e-let, ŏm′ ə lĭt, 9. slippery, slip-per-y, slĭp′ ə rē, 10. temperature, tem-per-a-ture,

těm′ pər ə chŏŏr′, 11. botany, bot-a-ny, bŏt′ n ē, 12. granary, gran-a-ry, grăn′ ə rē 13. sentinel, sen-ti-nel, sĕn′ tə nəl, 14. ticklish, tick-lish, tĭk′ lĭsh, 15. medieval, me-di-e-val, mē′ dē ē vəl, 16. ruffian, ruf-fi-an, rŭf′ ē ən, 17. preposition, prep-o-si-tion, prĕp′ ə zĭsh′ ən, 18. legislature, leg-is-la-ture, lĕj′ ĭ slā′ chər, 19. liable, li-a-ble, lī′ ə bəl, 20. bibliography, bib-li-og-ra-phy, bĭb′ lē ŏg′ rə fē

Lesson 66, P. 162

Exercise: Answers will vary.

Review 11, Lessons 61–66, P. 164

A: 1. noun, 2. noun, 3. verb, 4. adverb, 5. adjective, 6. verb, 7. noun, 8. adjective, 9. noun, 10. verb or noun 11. adverb, 12. noun

B: 1. in sult′, 2. pro gress′, 3. pre sent′, 4. rec′ ord, 5. con vict′, 6. en′ trance, 7. in crease′, 8. pres′ ent, 9. de sert′, 10. ab′ stract

C: 1. illegible, 2. continuous, 3. biennial, 4. eligible, 5. healthy, 6. stature, 7. biannual, 8. continual, 9. healthful, 10. statute, 11. adapt, 12. complement, 13. prescribe, 14. adopt, 15. counsel, 16. council, 17. respectively, 18. compliment, 19. proscribe, 20. respectfully

Lesson 67, P. 166

Exercise I: Definitions will vary. Suggested: 1. rĕp′ ər twär′; The collection of songs, plays, etc. that a player or company is able to perform 2. sə pē′ nə; A legal instrument requiring a person to testify in court. 3. kwôr′ əm; The number of members of an elected body who must be present for the valid transaction of business 4. dĭ zûrt′; A sweet food served after a meal 5. strā′ tə; pl. of stratum; 6. ə lŭm′ nē′; Female graduates of a school, college, or university

7. kə mēl′ yən; A tropical Old World lizard having the ability to change color
8. mā′ lā′; Confused scuffling or violence
9. rän′ dā vōō′; An agreed-upon time or place to meet

Exercise II: Answers will vary.

☐ Lesson 68, P. 168

Exercise I: 1. ə chēv′, 2. kə mens′, 3. kōō′ pŏn′, 4. dē′ pō, 5. ĕn′ trēz, 6. grēf, 7. ĭn dīt′, 8. ĭr′ ĭ gāt′, 9. lĕj′ ər, 10. ə fĕns′, 11. plāg, 12. nŏŏ mŏn′ yə, 13. sĭz′ ərz, 14. thēf, 15. tŭng, 16. vĕn′ jəns, 17. rĕnch, 18. yät

Exercise II: 1. achievement, 2. commencing, 3. entry, 4. indictment, 5. irrigation, 6. offensive, 7. scissors, 9. thieves

Exercise III: 1. thief, 2. achieve, 3. entries, 4. grief

☐ Lesson 69, P. 170

Exercise I: Definitions will vary. Suggested: 1. ĕk′ wĭ tē; The quality of being fair to all 2. vou′ chər; A document which gives proof of something 3. ĭl′ ə strāt′; To make clear by using examples or comparisons 4. fə säd′; The front of a building 5. mə lĭsh′ ə; A military force called for service only in an emergency 6. fûr′ lō; A leave of absence granted to military personnel 7. mō tēf′; A theme or element that recurs throughout an artistic or literary work. 8. sĭn thĕt′ ĭk; About or involving synthesis 9. rĕk′ lə mā′ shən; The act of reclaiming 10. sŭf′ rĭj; The right to vote 11. ĭs′ məs; A narrow land mass which connects two larger land masses 12. mə trĭk′ yə lāt′; To enroll in a college or university

Exercise II: 1. boulder, 2. honorable, 3. dangerous, 4. readily, 5. drowned, 6. weighed, 7. equity, 8. voucher, 9. illustrate, 10. militia, 11. furlough,

12. synthetic, 13. reclamation, 14. suffrage, 15. isthmus, 16. matriculate

☐ Lesson 70, P. 172

Exercise: Definitions will vary. Suggested: 1. săk ər ĭn; A manmade powder with a taste much sweeter than cane sugar 2. swē′ băk′; A kind of bread baked as a loaf and then cut into slices and toasted 3. bĭ tōō′ mə nəs; Containing bitumin 4. ĭ lōō′ mə nāt′; To focus light on 5. hĕm′ ə rĭj; Loss of blood 6. kăl′ ə pərz; Instruments used for measurement of internal and external dimensions 7. nŏŏ răl′ jə; Pain occurring along a nerve 8. pûr′ pĭ tōō′ ĭ tē; The state of being perpetual 9. tŏŏr′ mə lĭn; A kind of gemstone 10. krŏn′ ĭ kəl; A historical record of events 11. ĭn jŭngk′ shən; A court order forbidding someone to take a particular action 12. sə pē′ nə; A legal instrument requiring a person to testify in court 13. īd′ l; A short work of literature which describes country life 14. sə lĭl′ ə kwē; Literary or dramatic device in which a character talks to himself or herself without addressing another character 15. kə rō′ zhən; The process or result of corroding 16. kwō′ shənt; The number which results when one number is divided by another 17. pôr′ trĭ chŏŏr′; The making of portraits 18. kō hē′ zhən; The state of cohering 19. stăt′ ĭk; Not moving 20. ĭn′ hə bĭsh′ ən; The state of being inhibited 21. sī′ kĭk; Relating to special mental powers

☐ Lesson 71, P. 174

Exercise I: 1. ŏ; 2. ô; 3. ō, ŏ; 4. ō; 5. ŏ; 6. ŏ; 7. ō; 8. ō; 9. ō; 10. ō; 11. ō; 12. ŏ, ō; 13. ô; 14. ô; 15. ô; 16. ŏ; 17. ō; 18. ô; 19. ō, ŏ; 20. ō, ŏ

Exercise II: 1. cellō, 2. comptrōller, 3. fôrk, 4. sōōn, 5. ŏccupation, 6. swôrd, 7. hŏnorable, 8. sōōt

Lesson 72, P. 176

Exercise I: 1. suite, 2. horrible, 3. evening, 4. strictly, 5. C, 6. library, 7. foreign, 8. C, 9. arctic, 10. C, 11. honorable, 12. deficit, 13. forehead, 14. secretary, 15. C, 16. attacked, 17. overalls, 18. parliament, 19. deteriorate, 20. heroine, 21. experiment, 22. genuine

Exercise II: 1. parliament, 2. library, 3. diptheria, 4. suede, 5. C, 6. recognized

Review 12, Lessons 67–72, P. 178

A: The underlined words are misspelled in the letter.

Dear Dora:

Despite any nasty <u>rumor</u> you may hear to the contrary from Ted, he and I are having a wonderful time in Paris. Our hotel <u>suite</u> is beautiful. Just this afternoon, we had a delightful luncheon <u>buffet</u> in a <u>cafe</u> <u>across</u> from a museum. I especially enjoyed the seafood <u>crepe</u> I had. We were entertained by <u>cello</u> music as we dined.

After lunch, Ted and I explored an old bookstore where we bought an <u>antique</u> book covered in <u>genuine</u> <u>suede</u>.

Sincerely,

B: 1. achieve, 2. yacht, 3. vengeance, 4. C, 5. scissors, 6. pneumonia, 7. ledger, 8. irrigate, 9. indict, 10. C

C: 1. author, 2. collar, 3. comptroller, 4. subpoena, 5. commence, 6. mortar, 7. ego, 8. across, 9. motif, 10. experiment, 11. rinse, 12. chronicle

D: 1. debris, 2. editor, 3. sphere, 4. forehead, 5. library, 6. dangerous, 7. horrible, 8. secretary, 9. coupon, 10. genuine, 11. Italian, 12. plague, 13. illustrate

Lesson 73, P. 180

Exercise I: Answers will vary.

Exercise II: 1. h, 2. a, 3. c, 4. e, 5. b, 6. d, 7. f, 8. g

Lesson 74, P. 182

Exercise: Answers will vary.

Lesson 75, P. 184

Exercise I: 1. plan, 2. com-mu-ni-ty, 3. among, 4. with-in, 5. hap-py, 6. pray-ed, 7. event-ful, 8. com-mand, 9. cam-er-a, 10. dem-on-strate, 11. snow-bound, 12. em-ploy-ee, 13. whole-sale, 14. caf-e-te-ri-a, 15. four-foot-ed, 16. mus-cle, 17. am-mu-ni-tion, 18. fresh-wa-ter, 19. qual-i-ty

Exercise II: 1. math-e-mat-ics, 2. kin-der-gar-ten, 3. rhyme, 4. o-mis-sion, 5. quar-ter, 6. cal-cu-la-tor, 7. diet, 8. four-teen, 9. mar-ry, 10. coun-sel-or

Exercise III: 1. among, 2. pray-ed, 3. four-foot-ed, 4. sit-uation, 5. diet, 6. math-ematics

Lesson 76, P. 186

Exercise I: 1. door-to-door salesperson, 2. five-year-old child, 3. a meeting after school, 4. a do-gooder, 5. great-great-grandmother, 6. twenty-five-barrel load, 7. Governor-elect Milburn, 8. commander-in-chief, 9. one-half of the students, 10. up-to-date model, 11. one hundred dollars and seventy-six cents

Exercise II: 1. C, 2. two-year-old, 3. northeast, 4. C, 5. C, 6. up-to-date, 7. one-half, 8. C, 9. eager-beaver, 10. high-tail

Lesson 77, P. 188

Exercise I: 1. are not, 2. it were, 3. cannot, 4. do not, 5. could not, 6. we are, 7. is not, 8. they are, 9. of the clock, 10. I have, 11. let us, 12. must not, 13. she would or she had, 14. what is, 15. will not, 16. it would, 17. who is, 18. does not, 19. had not, 20. has not

Exercise II: 1. he'd, 2. didn't, 3. she's, 4. they've, 5. shouldn't, 6. should've, 7. there's, 8. you've, 9. you're, 10. you'll, 11. they'd, 12. we're, 13. it's, 14. what's, 15. it'd, 16. I'll, 17. could've, 18. would've

Exercise III: The following words are misspelled in the sentences. 1. *i's, s's, p's;* 2. They're, their; 3. It's, its; 4. Don't, *x's, y's;* 5. Your, you're, your; 6. I'll, ours, theirs; 7. Let's, hers, yours, 8. There are, 8's; 9. I'm, doesn't; 10. he's, hers

Lesson 78, P. 190

Exercise I: 1. Brown and Sanders's, 2. woman's, 3. spectacles', 4. Amalgamated Motors', 5. everyone's, 6. authors', 7. firm's, 8. its, 9. oxen's, 10. brother-in-law's, 11. children's, 12. James's, 13. U.S.A.'s, 14. notebooks', 15. ladies', 16. everyone else's, 17. employees', 18. telephones', 19. editor-in-chief's, 20. gentlemen's, 21. month's, 22. committee's, 23. week's, 24. days', 25. attorney general's, 26. half an hour's, 27. process's, 28. travelers', 29. actors', 30. manager's

Exercise II: 1. tonight's, Amy's; 2. son-in-law's; 3. Smiths'; 4. somebody else's; 5. university's; 6. Jim and Rob's; 7. buildings; 8. restaurant's; 9. John's, Heather's; 10. jury's; 11. parents', houses; 12. Jennifer's; T-shirts; 13. wife's, brownies; 14. athlete's

Review 13, Lessons 73–78, P. 192

A: Sentences will vary. 1. pro′duce, 2. trans port′, 3. re′fuse, 4. pro′ject, 5. con fine′, 6. sub′ject, 7. con trast′

B: Sentences will vary. 1. sau te′, 2. men′u, 3. es prit′ de corps′, 4. e clair′, 5. lin′ge rie, 6. ad in fi ni′tum, 7. au′ re voir′

Lesson 79, P. 194

Exercise: 1. Mountains, 2. Avenue, 3. north, 4. Uncle, 5. university, 6. Tuesday, 7. North, 8. uncle, 9. February, 10. University, 11. Capitol, 12. mountains, 13. avenue, 14. capital, 15. Venus, 16. earth

Lesson 80, P. 196

Exercise I: 1. disadvantage, 2. advantageous, 3. unnoticeable, 4. outrageous, 5. argument, arguable; 6. judgment, judgeship, judgmatic; 7. awesome, awful; 8. useful, useless, useable, usage; 9. careful, careless; 10. wholesome, wholly

Exercise II: 1. weird, 2. height, 3. ancient, 4. neither, 5. foreign, 6. species, 7. counterfeit

Lesson 81, P. 198

Exercise I: 1. conceit, 2. perceive, 3. achieve, 4. twentieth, 5. received, 6. fiend, 7. shriek, 8. C

Exercise II: 1. achieve, 2. ceiling, 3. conceit, 4. conceived, 5. fiend, 6. fierce, 7. fortieth, 8. grievance, 9. perceive, 10. receipts, 11. received, 12. shriek, 13. veil, 14. weighed, 15. wield

Lesson 82, P. 200

Exercise: 1. tallies, 2. flies, 3. desires, 4. loaves, 5. data, 6. cargoes, 7. neighbors, 8. stimuli, 9. attorneys, 10. ponies, 11. stitches, 12. children, 13. heroes, 14. passes, 15. solos, 16. faces, 17. men, 18. masses, 19. parties, 20. debts, 21. receipts, 22. babies, 23. businesses, 24. valleys, 25. secretaries, 26. duties, 27. pieces, 28. geese, 29. allies, 30. taxes, 31. mice, 32. typists, 33. acts, 34. houses, 35. axes, 36. ladies, 37. cotton, 38. economies, 39. apparatus, 40. moose, 41. clothes, 42. consortia

Lesson 83, P. 202

Exercise I: 1. Ph.D., 2. i.e., 3. e.g., 4. B.A., 5. mgr., 6. asst., 7. No., 8. lb., 9. A.M., 10. B.S., 11. oz., 12. Sept., 13. P.S., 14. vs., 15. ft., 16. capt., 17. Co., 18. dept., 19. M.D., 20. Apr., 21. supt., 22. R.S.V.P., 23. P.O., 24. B.C.

Exercise II: 1. in the year of the Lord, 2. Master of Arts, 3. Reverend, 4. collect or cash on delivery, 5. afternoon, 6. dozen, 7. attorney, 8. Junior, 9. pages, 10. and so forth or et cetera, 11. Senior, 12. volume, 13. inches, 14. Mister, 15. Avenue, 16. memorandum, 17. Street, 18. December, 19. November, 20. miles per hour, 21. Doctor, 22. August

Lesson 84, P. 204

Exercise I: 1. NJ, 2. WY, 3. DC, 4. ME, 5. MA, 6. MS, 7. OK, 8. AZ, 9. SD, 10. PA, 11. GA, 12. AK, 13. PR, 14. WV, 15. TX, 16. IL, 17. KY, 18. MT, 19. LA, 20. UT, 21. IA, 22. NV, 23. VA, 24. OH

Exercise II: 1. Kansas, 2. Michigan, 3. California, 4. Missouri, 5. Minnesota, 6. Guam, 7. Colorado, 8. Nevada, 9. Oregon, 10. Rhode Island, 11. Connecticut, 12. New York, 13. Indiana, 14. Maryland, 15. Florida, 16. Nebraska, 17. Hawaii, 18. Ohio, 19. Washington, 20. Wisconsin, 21. Texas, 22. Alabama, 23. Louisiana, 24. Iowa

Review 14, Lessons 79–84, P. 206

A: 1. Mountains, mountains; 2. January, July; 3. capitol, capital; 4. Avenue, avenue; 5. universities, University; 6. superintendent, Superintendent; 7. professor, Professor; 8. Uncle, uncle; 9. north; 10. North, South, Civil; 11. uncle, February; 12. winter, Avenue

B: The following words are misspelled in the sentences. 1. counterfeit, advantageous, neither; 2. science, ancient, species; 3. awful, noticeable; 4. mileage, wholly; 5. outrageous, argument, judgment

C: 1. ceiling, 2. receipts, 3. apiece, 4. conceived, 5. grievance, 6. achieve, 7. wield, 8. received, 9. priest, 10. deceit, 11. fierce, 12. perceive, 13. twentieth, 14. fiend, 15. pier, 16. vein, 17. ancient, 18. height, 19. species, 20. leisure, 21. conceit, 22. diet, 23. weird, 24. foreign, 25. counterfeit, 26. forfeit, 27. science, 28. either, 29. heir, 30. perceive

Lesson 85, P. 208

Exercise I: 1. b, 2. c, 3. d, 4. a
Exercise II: 1. c, 2. h, 3. e, 4. a, 5. i, 6. b, 7. d, 8. g, 9. f

Exercise III: A. 1. go away from, 2. go forward, 3. to go between, 4. to go back
B. 1. send through, 2. send across, 3. send to, 4. send back
C. 1. carry in, 2. carry away, 3. carry out, 4. carry across
D. 1. write across, 2. write under, 3. write in, 4. write before

☐ Lesson 86, P. 210

Exercise: 1. desirable, 2. probable, 3. disagreeable, 4. Admirable, 5. honorable, 6. capable, 7. miserable, 8. reliable, 9. acceptable, 10. reasonable, 11. applicable, 12. favorable, 13. charitable, 14. excusable, 15. considerable

☐ Lesson 87, P. 212

Exercise: 1. feasible, 2. eligible, 3. chargeable, 4. permissible, 5. accessible, 6. responsible, 7. C, 8. admissible, 9. contemptible, 10. susceptible, 11. defensible, 12. divisible, 13. indelible, 14. insensible, 15. convertible, 16. reversible, 17. collectible, 18. invisible, 19. C, 20. plausible, 21. audible, 22. indelible

☐ Lesson 88, P. 214

Exercise: 1. inability, 2. mispronounce, 3. excel, 4. irrigation, 5. unnecessary, 6. arouse, 7. irreparable, 8. illiterate, 9. exile, 10. beneficial, 11. inauguration, 12. misfortune, 13. unusual, 14. exhibit

☐ Lesson 89, P. 216

Exercise I: 1. axle, 2. trifle, 3. novel, 4. meddle, 5. wrestle, 6. acquittal, 7. parcel, 8. resemble, 9. struggle, 10. whistle, 11. quarrel, 12. tremble, 13. label, 14. humble, 15. tunnel, 16. liable
Exercise II: 1. liable, 2. C, 3. whistle, 4. struggle, 5. vessel, 6. meddle, 7. angle, 8. humble, 9. axle

☐ Lesson 90, P. 218

Exercise I: 1. consumer, 2. carrier, 3. C, 4. laborer, 5. shoulder, 6. voucher, 7. author, 8. conductor
Exercise II: 1. b, 2. d, 3. g, 4. f, 5. i, 6. k, 7. j, 8. e, 9. a, 10. c, 11. h

☐ Review 15, Lessons 85–90, P. 220

A: 1. subscribe, 2. import, 3. revoke, 4. transmit, 5. prefer, 6. exceed
B: 1. probable, 2. allowable, 3. eligible, 4. audible, 5. honorable, 6. accessible, 7. considerable, 8. durable, 9. incredible, 10. legible, 11. capable, 12. feasible, 13. admirable, 14. destructible
C: 1. mislay, 2. disability, 3. applicable, 4. disagree, 5. arouse, 6. inseparable, 7. senator, 8. unnecessary, 9. employer, 10. irreparable, 11. consumer, 12. unusual, 13. illiterate, 14. moveable
D: 1. editor, 2. inventor, 3. polar, 4. collar, 5. liable, 6. rumor, 7. struggle, 8. vessel, 9. voucher, 10. label, 11. trifle, 12. tunnel, 13. tremble, 14. conductor, 15. whistle, 16. traitor, 17. cedar, 18. acquittal, 19. vinegar, 20. visitor, 21. quarrel, 22. novel, 23. aviator, 24. parcel, 25. humble, 26. resemble

Lesson 91, P. 222

Exercise I: 1. apparent, 2. defendant, 3. C, 4. emigrant, 5. predominant, 6. violent, 7. deficient, 8. tyrant

Exercise II: 1. efficient, 2. important, 3. violent, 4. significant, 5. abundant, 6. prevalent, 7. restaurant, 8. opponent, 9. descendant, 10. obedient, 11. ornament, 12. emigrant, 13. tyrant, 14. apparent, 15. dependent, 16. resident, 17. applicant, 18. current, 19. defendant, 20. predominant, 21. immigrant, 22. deficient

Lesson 92, P. 224

Exercise I: 1. perseverance, 2. residence, 3. C, 4. abundance, 5. inference, 6. C, 7. conveyance, 8. hindrance, 9. temperance, 10. negligence

Exercise II: 1. abundance, 2. innocence, 3. obedience, 4. hindrance, 5. interference, 6. admittance, 7. inference, 8. resistance, 9. annoyance, 10. reverence, 11. temperance, 12. negligence, 13. attendance, 14. conveyance, 15. competence, 16. resemblance, 17. perseverance, 18. excellence

Lesson 93, P. 226

Exercise: 1. franchise, 2. devise, 3. standardize, 4. analyze, 5. antagonize, 6. authorize, 7. supervise, 8. Summarize, 9. visualize, 10. Emphasize, 11. utilize, 12. revise

Lesson 94, P. 228

Exercise I: 1. introductory, 2. Literary, 3. voluntary, 4. customary, 5. preparatory, 6. accessory, 7. memory, 8. misery, 9. celery, 10. boundary, 11. C, 12. mystery

Exercise II: 1. discovery, 2. directory, 3. boundary, 4. depository, 5. introductory, 6. elementary, 7. summary, 8. customary, 9. memory, 10. accessory

Lesson 95, P. 230

Exercise I: 1. politician, 2. admission, 3. construction, 4. musician, 5. C, 6. magician, 7. decoration

Exercise II: 1. confusion, 2. occupation, 3. physician, 4. ammunition, 5. persuasion, 6. decoration, 7. magician, 8. admission, 9. collection, 10. expression, 11. musician, 12. permission, 13. construction, 14. impression, 15. politician, 16. retention, 17. procession, 18. fiction, 19. suspicion, 20. conclusion, 21. division

Review 16, Lessons 91–95, P. 232

A: 1. abundant, 2. annoyance, 3. audience, 4. perseverance, 5. dependent, 6. resistance, 7. obedient, 8. current, 9. admittance, 10. abundance, 11. defendant, 12. immigrant, 13. apparent, 14. Attendance, 15. reverence

B: 1. authorize, 2. equalize, 3. standardize, 4. revise, 5. antagonize, 6. economize, 7. comprise, 8. paralyze, 9. devise, 10. supervise, 11. summarize, 12. disguise, 13. franchise, 14. utilize, 15. enterprise, 16. organize, 17. emphasize, 18. apologize, 19. analyze, 20. despise, 21. baptize

C: 1. summary, 2. decoration,
3. boundary, 4. millinery, 5. celery,
6. C, 7. literary, 8. voluntary,
9. physician, 10. procession,
11. memory, 12. directory,
13. territory, 14. history

☐ Posttest, P. 234

A: 1. cargo, 2. eminent, 3. restaurant,
4. visualize, 5. penchant, 6. mutual,
7. adobe, 8. absence, 9. arouse, 10. C,
11. convertible, 12. duplicate,
13. essential, 14. immigrant,
15. investors, 16. library,
17. mischievous, 18. outrageous,
19. portion, 20. transferred

B: 1. accolade, 2. Apparently, 3. between,
4. coarse, 5. dirigible, 6. favorable,
7. indelible, 8. just, 9. mortgage,
10. obedient, 11. persuade,
12. precede, 13. quite, 14. received,
15. referred, 16. sophomore,
17. using, 18. against

C: The following words are misspelled
in the sentences.
1. actually, humble; 2. wastes,
considerable; 3. accolade, present;
4. descend; 5. losing, memory,
altogether; 6. actually, battlefield;
7. Through, persuaded; 8. economy;
9. convertible, stationary; 10. certain,
grief, losing; 11. chief, divided;
12. expected; 13. decide, entrance;
14. seems, very; 15. commence;
16. completely, paralyzed;
17. prophesied, plague; 18. Nineteen,
items; 19. service, rinsed;
20. strictly, wrestling

D: The underlined words are misspelled
in the letter.

Dear Kim:

The conference of high school
teachers began on Saturday, August
twelfth and lasted a whole week.
The first speaker was terrible. Not a
syllable of his speech was audible,
and the annoyance of his audience
was considerable.

My favorite speaker spoke about an
instructor's ability to inspire students
to develop their abilities and excel in
all areas of life. The audience was
unanimous in proclaiming her a
brilliant speaker.

The information I gained was
generally helpful, and will probably
improve my handling of classroom
situations. On the last day, the
President of the American Council of
High School Teachers summarized the
significant points. I can't wait for next
year!

Sincerely yours,

E: 1. latter, 2. visualize, 3. mischievous,
4. annoyance, 5. indelible,
6. flexible, 7. portion, 8. significant,
9. penchant, 10. Saturday